Everyday Mathematics®

The University of Chicago School Mathematics Project

Assessment Handbook

Grade 6

McGraw Hill Education

Chicago, IL • Columbus, OH • New York, NY

The University of Chicago School Mathematics Project (UCSMP)

Max Bell, Director, UCSMP Elementary Materials Component; Director, *Everyday Mathematics* First Edition; James McBride, Director, *Everyday Mathematics* Second Edition; Andy Isaacs, Director, *Everyday Mathematics* Third Edition; Amy Dillard, Associate Director, *Everyday Mathematics* Third Edition; Rachel Malpass McCall, Associate Director, *Everyday Mathematics* Common Core State Standards Edition

Authors
Jean Bell, William M. Carroll, Amy Dillard, Kathleen Pitvorec

Common Core State Standards Edition
Sarah R. Burns, Mary Ellen Dairyko, Rachel Malpass McCall, Cheryl G. Moran, Lila K. Schwartz

Technical Art
Diana Barrie

Teacher in Residence
Soundarya Radhakrishnan

Contributors
Tracy Bougher, Jennifer Jacobson, Carol Maliza, Sharon Draznin, Nancy Hanvey, Laurie Leff, Denise Porter, Herb Price, Joyce Timmons, Lisa Winters

Acknowledgements
We gratefully acknowledge the work of the following classroom teachers who provided input and suggestions as we designed this handbook: Huong Banh, Fran Moore, Jenny Waters, and Lana Winnet.

Photo Credits
Cover (l)Stuart Westmoreland/CORBIS, (r)Kelly Kalhoefer/Botanica/Getty Images, (bkgd)Digital Vision/Getty Images; **Back Cover Spine** Kelly Kalhoefer/Botanica/Getty Images.

Permissions
The quotes on pages 4, 5, 8, and 35 are reprinted with permission from *Knowing What Students Know: The Science and Design of Educational Assessment* © 2001 by the National Academy of Sciences, courtesy of the National Academies Press, Washington, D.C.

 This material is based upon work supported by the National Science Foundation under Grant No. ESI-9252984. Any opinions, findings, conclusions, or recommendations expressed in this material are those of the authors and do not necessarily reflect the views of the National Science Foundation.

everyday**math**.com

 **Education**

Send all inquiries to:
McGraw-Hill Education
STEM Learning Solutions Center
P.O. Box 812960
Chicago, IL 60681

ISBN: 978-0-07-657704-0
MHID: 0-07-657704-X

Printed in the United States of America.

1 2 3 4 5 6 7 8 9 QDB 17 16 15 14 13 12 11

McGraw-Hill is committed to providing instructional materials in Science, Technology, Engineering, and Mathematics (STEM) that give all students a solid foundation, one that prepares them for college and careers in the 21st century.

The *McGraw-Hill* Companies

Contents

Philosophy of Assessment in *Everyday Mathematics*®

Introduction

Too often, school assessment tends to provide only scattered snapshots of student achievement rather than continuous records of growth. In *Everyday Mathematics*, assessment is like a motion picture, revealing the development of each student's mathematical understanding over time while also giving the teacher useful feedback about the instructional needs of individual students and the class.

For assessment to be useful to teachers, students, parents, and others, the *Everyday Mathematics* authors believe that ...

◆ Teachers need to have a variety of assessment tools and techniques to choose from so students can demonstrate what they know in a variety of ways and teachers can have reliable information from multiple sources.

◆ Students should be included in the assessment process. Self assessment and reflection are skills students will develop over time if they are encouraged.

◆ Assessment and instruction should be closely aligned. Assessment should assist teachers in making instructional decisions concerning individual students and the class.

◆ Assessment should focus on all important outcomes, not only on outcomes that are easy to measure.

◆ A good assessment program makes instruction easier.

◆ The best assessment plans are developed by teachers working collaboratively within schools and districts.

Everyday Mathematics offers many opportunities for assessing students' knowledge and skills. This handbook describes the *Everyday Mathematics* assessment resources and serves as a guide for navigating through those resources and helping you design and implement a balanced classroom assessment plan.

Balanced Assessment

When planning a balanced assessment, begin by asking several basic questions:

◆ *What are the purposes of assessment?*

◆ *What are the contexts for assessment?*

◆ *What are the sources of evidence for assessment?*

◆ *What content is assessed?*

What Are the Purposes of Assessment?

The purposes of assessment serve three main functions: to support learning, to measure achievement, and to evaluate programs. Each purpose is integral to achieving a balanced assessment plan.

Formative assessment supports learning by providing information about students' current knowledge and abilities so you can plan future instruction more effectively. Formative assessment encourages students to identify their areas of weakness or strength so they can focus their efforts more precisely.

Summative assessment measures student growth and achievement. A summative assessment might be designed, for example, to determine whether students have learned certain material by the end of a fixed period of study.

Program evaluation means judging how well a program is working. A school district, for example, may want to identify schools with especially strong mathematics programs so their successes can be replicated in other schools with weaker programs. Program evaluation makes this possible.

Assessment tools and techniques often serve more than one purpose. Assessments built into a curriculum might give teachers information they can use to plan future instruction more effectively or prepare progress reports. District administrators might use this information to allocate professional development resources.

Purposes of Assessment

Formative Assessment	Summative Assessment	Program Evaluation
◆ Used to plan instruction ◆ Helps students to reflect on their progress	◆ Used to measure student growth and achievement ◆ Helps determine if students have learned content	◆ Used to evaluate overall success of the math program

What Are the Contexts for Assessment?

Assessment occurs in a variety of contexts.

◆ **Ongoing assessment** involves gathering information from students' everyday work. These assessments can take place at the same time as regular classroom instruction.

◆ **Periodic assessment** consists of formal assessments that are built in to a curriculum, such as an end-of-unit Progress Check.

◆ **External assessment** is independent of the curriculum. An example of an external assessment is a standardized test.

Everyday Mathematics supports all three contexts for assessment, and it provides tools and materials for ongoing and periodic assessments that you can use to create a balanced assessment plan.

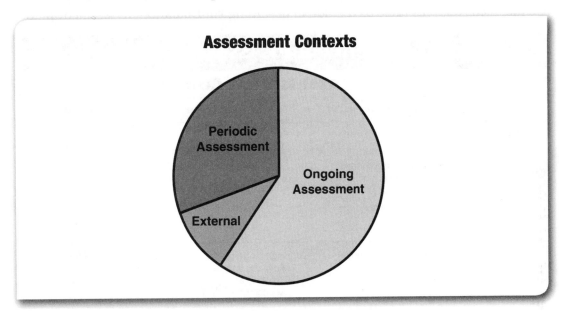

The sizes of the sections of the circle in the figure above are meant to be suggestive, but the exact proportions of ongoing, periodic, and external assessments will vary depending on your grade level, the time of year, state and district mandates, and many other factors.

For all *Everyday Mathematics* assessments, provide students with tools that may be helpful in completing the assessment. Such tools include, but are not limited to, number lines, number grids, scratch paper, base-10 blocks, coins and bills, counters, blank situation diagrams, Pattern Blocks, and Geometry Templates.

What Are the Sources of Evidence for Assessment?

> *Assessment is a process of reasoning from evidence.*
>
> (Pellegrino, Chudowsky, and Glaser 2001, 36)

The evidence for assessing what students know is indirect because we cannot know exactly what they are thinking. Evidence about students' knowledge and capabilities comes from observing students while they are actively engaged and from analyzing the products of their work. Whatever conclusions we may make about students' thinking must be based on **observations** or **products.**

The table below shows the different contexts for assessment and the sources of evidence used for each context. Specific assessment tasks in *Everyday Mathematics* are included. Use this table as a guide in designing your balanced assessment plan.

Sources of Evidence and Assessment Contexts

		Assessment Contexts		
		Ongoing Assessment	**Periodic Assessment**	**External Assessment**
Sources of Evidence	**Observation**	◆ Informing Instruction notes ◆ Recognizing Student Achievement notes for • Mental Math and Reflexes ◆ "Kid watching"	◆ Progress Check Oral/Slate Assessments	◆ Classroom observations by resource teachers or other outside experts
	Product	◆ Recognizing Student Achievement notes for • Journal pages • Exit Slips • Games record sheets • Math Boxes ◆ Writing/Reasoning prompts ◆ Portfolio opportunities	◆ Beginning-of-Year, Mid-Year, and End-of-Year assessments ◆ Progress Check Written Assessments ◆ Student Self Assessments ◆ Open Response problems	◆ Standardized tests mandated by the school district or the state

Each context for assessment (ongoing, periodic, or external) can yield evidence through observations or products.

◆ Observing students as they are doing their daily work can provide a great deal of information about their understandings, skills, and dispositions; this kind of ongoing observational assessment may be considered "kid watching."

◆ A written assessment that is included as part of a curriculum is an example of a periodic product assessment.

◆ A classroom visit by an outside expert who will observe particular students is an example of an external assessment using observational evidence.

What Content Is Assessed?

Assessment does not exist in isolation, but must be closely aligned with the goals of curriculum and instruction.

(Pellegrino, Chudowsky, and Glaser 2001, 36)

In recent years, national organizations and most states have issued detailed sets of learning goals and standards, which provide useful guidance about what content is important to learn and, therefore, important to assess. Aligning assessment, curriculum, and instruction with standards and goals increases coherence in the system and produces better outcomes. To help teachers understand the structure of *Everyday Mathematics* and therefore better understand what to assess, the authors developed Program Goals, which are organized by content strand and carefully articulated across the grades. Below are the six content strands and their related Program Goals:

Everyday Mathematics Program Goals

Number and Numeration
- Understand the meanings, uses, and representations of numbers
- Understand equivalent names for numbers
- Understand common numerical relations

Operations and Computation
- Compute accurately
- Make reasonable estimates
- Understand meanings of operations

Data and Chance
- Select and create appropriate graphical representations of collected or given data
- Analyze and interpret data
- Understand and apply basic concepts of probability

Measurement and Reference Frames
- Understand the systems and processes of measurement; use appropriate techniques, tools, units, and formulas in making measurements
- Use and understand reference frames

Geometry
- Investigate characteristics and properties of two- and three-dimensional geometric shapes
- Apply transformations and symmetry in geometric situations

Patterns, Functions, and Algebra
- Understand patterns and functions
- Use algebraic notation to represent and analyze situations and structures

Program Goals are threads that weave the curriculum together across grades. "Compute accurately," for example, is a Program Goal. Students in *Everyday Mathematics* are expected to compute accurately. The expectations for a student achieving this goal in Grade 2 are obviously different from what is expected from a student in Grade 6. For this reason, the Program Goals are further refined through Grade-Level Goals.

Grade-Level Goals are guideposts along trajectories of learning that span multiple years. They are the big ideas at each grade level; they do not capture all of the content covered. The Grade-Level Goals describe how *Everyday Mathematics* builds mastery over time—first through informal exposure, later through more formal instruction, and finally through application. Because the Grade-Level Goals are cumulative, it is essential for students to experience the complete curriculum at each grade level. The example below shows the development of Grade-Level Goals for models for the operations.

Grade K	Identify join and take-away situations.
Grade 1	Identify change-to-more, change-to-less, comparison, and parts-and-total situations.
Grade 2	Identify and describe change, comparison, and parts-and-total situations; use repeated addition, arrays, and skip counting to model multiplication; use equal sharing and equal grouping to model division.
Grade 3	Recognize and describe change, comparison, and parts-and-total situations; use repeated addition, arrays, and skip counting to model multiplication; use equal sharing and equal grouping to model division.
Grade 4	Use repeated addition, skip counting, arrays, area, and scaling to model multiplication and division.
Grade 5	Use repeated addition, arrays, area, and scaling to model multiplication and division; use ratios expressed as words, fractions, percents, and with colons; solve problems involving ratios of parts of a set to the whole set.
Grade 6	Use ratios and scaling to model size changes and to solve size-change problems; represent ratios as fractions, percents, and decimals, and using a colon; model and solve problems involving part-to-whole and part-to-part ratios; model rate and ratio number stories with proportions; use and explain cross multiplication and other strategies to solve proportions.

All assessment opportunities in *Everyday Mathematics* are linked to specific Grade-Level Goals. The curriculum is designed so that the vast majority of students will reach the Grade-Level Goals for a given grade upon completion of that grade and as a result will be well prepared to succeed in higher levels of mathematics. The complete list of Program Goals and Grade-Level Goals begins on page 37 of this handbook.

Creating a Balanced Assessment Plan

In *Everyday Mathematics,* assessment is primarily designed to help you

◆ learn about students' current knowledge and abilities so you can plan future instruction more effectively—formative assessment; and

◆ measure students' progress toward and achievement of Grade-Level Goals—summative assessment.

Although there is no one right assessment plan for all classrooms, all assessment plans should provide a balance of assessment sources from different contexts. See the chart on page 4 of this handbook for specific assessment tasks in *Everyday Mathematics* that support the different sources and contexts.

Planning Tips

Do not try to use all the assessment resources at once. Instead, devise a manageable, balanced plan. Choose those tools and techniques that best match your teaching style and your students' needs.

Consider the following guidelines:

◆ Start small.
◆ Incorporate assessment into your daily class routine.
◆ Set up an easy and efficient record-keeping system.
◆ Personalize and adapt the plan as the year progresses.

Your assessment plan should be designed to answer these questions:

◆ How is the class doing?
◆ How are individual students doing?
◆ How do I need to adjust instruction to meet students' needs?
◆ How can I communicate to students, parents, and others about the progress being made?

The following sections of this handbook provide further details about the tools and techniques you can use to develop a balanced assessment plan. Using these tools, you can support student learning, improve your instruction, measure student growth and achievement, and make the most of your experience with *Everyday Mathematics.*

Ongoing Assessment

No single test score can be considered a definitive measure of a student's competence. Multiple measures enhance the validity and fairness of the inferences drawn by giving students various ways and opportunities to demonstrate their competence.

(Pellegrino, Chudowsky, and Glaser 2001, 253)

An integral part of a balanced assessment plan involves gathering information from student's everyday work. Opportunities for collecting ongoing assessment in the form of observations and products are highlighted in *Everyday Mathematics* through Informing Instruction and Recognizing Student Achievement notes.

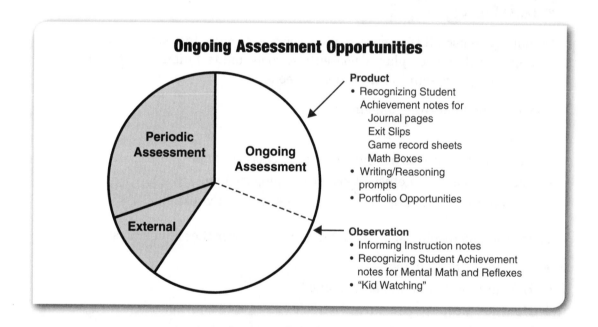

Ongoing Assessment Opportunities

Product
- Recognizing Student Achievement notes for
  - Journal pages
  - Exit Slips
  - Game record sheets
  - Math Boxes
- Writing/Reasoning prompts
- Portfolio Opportunities

Observation
- Informing Instruction notes
- Recognizing Student Achievement notes for Mental Math and Reflexes
- "Kid Watching"

Ongoing Assessment— Informing Instruction

Informing Instruction notes are designed to help you anticipate and recognize common errors and misconceptions in students' thinking and alert you to multiple solution strategies or unique insights that students may offer. These notes suggest how to use observations of students' work to effectively adapt instruction.

 Sample 1 Informing Instruction

 Ongoing Assessment: Informing Instruction

Watch for students who assume that adding or subtracting the same nonzero number to the numerator and the denominator will yield an equivalent fraction. Give them examples, such as $\frac{1}{2} + \frac{2}{2} = \frac{3}{2}$ and $\frac{1}{2} * \frac{2}{2} = \frac{2}{4}$. Compare each answer to $\frac{1}{2}$.

 Sample 2 Informing Instruction

 Ongoing Assessment: Informing Instruction

Watch for students who do not recognize that they can write any whole number with a decimal point following the last digit. Suggest that they rewrite whole numbers to include the decimal, for example, rewrite 8 as 8.0.

Ongoing Assessment—
Recognizing Student Achievement

Each lesson in *Everyday Mathematics* contains a Recognizing Student Achievement note. These notes highlight specific tasks that teachers can use for assessment to monitor students' progress toward Grade-Level Goals.

These tasks include:

◆ Journal pages (written problems—sometimes including explanations)
◆ Mental Math and Reflexes (oral or slate)
◆ Exit Slips (explanations of strategies and understanding)
◆ *Everyday Mathematics* games (record sheets or follow-up sheets)
◆ Math Boxes (written practice problems)

Each Recognizing Student Achievement note identifies the task to gather information from, the concept or skill to be assessed, and the expectations for a student who is *making adequate progress* toward meeting the specific Grade-Level Goal.

Sample 1 **Recognizing Student Achievement**
Math Journal 1

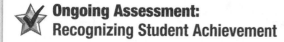

Ongoing Assessment:
Recognizing Student Achievement

Journal
Page 11
Problems a–d

Use **journal page 11, Problems a–d** to assess students' ability to find the minimum, maximum, range, and mode of data displayed in a stem-and-leaf plot. Students are making adequate progress if they accurately calculate these landmarks from their constructed plots. Some students may be able to navigate the double stems to find the median (near the 24th and 25th values).

[Data and Chance Goal 2]

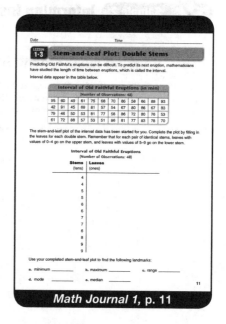

Math Journal 1, p. 11

Sample 2 Recognizing Student Achievement
Mental Math and Reflexes

 Ongoing Assessment:
Recognizing Student Achievement

Mental Math and Reflexes

Use **Mental Math and Reflexes** to assess students' ability to solve open number sentences involving signed numbers. Students are making adequate progress if they can calculate the missing sums. Some students may be able to solve the problems involving missing addends.

[Operations and Computation Goal 1]

Mental Math and Reflexes

Students find the missing sums or addends.

Suggestions:

●○○ $-6 + 5 = s$ $s = -1$

●●○ $5 + (-2) + 3 = s$ $s = 6$

●●● $-3 + (-5) + 4 + (-6) = s$ $s = -10$

$5 + a = -2$ $a = -7$

$-4 + 6 + a = -3$ $a = -5$

$6 + a + (-6) + (-3) = 1$ $a = 4$

 Sample 3 Recognizing Student Achievement
Exit Slip

 Ongoing Assessment:
Recognizing Student Achievement

Exit Slip

Use an **Exit Slip** (*Math Masters,* p. 404) to assess students' understanding of median and mean. Students are making adequate progress if they can acknowledge that the median is less affected by outliers than the mean is.

Pose the following informal assessment item to students: In 2004, baseball player Derek Jeter earned about $25 million in salary, bonuses, and endorsements. If you were to report the typical annual earnings for baseball players, would it be more accurate to report the mean or median earnings? Why?

[Data and Chance Goal 2]

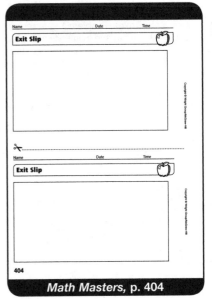

Math Masters, p. 404

Ongoing Assessment:
Recognizing Student Achievement

Math Masters
Page 455

Use *Math Masters,* **page 455** to assess students' ability to compare decimals through thousandths. Students are making adequate progress if they are able to identify the larger number. Some students may not need a calculator to find the difference between scores.

[Number and Numeration Goal 6]

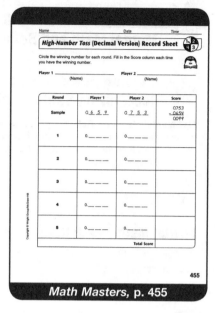

Math Masters, p. 455

 Sample 5 **Recognizing Student Achievement**
Math Boxes

 Ongoing Assessment:
Recognizing Student Achievement

Math Boxes
Problem 1

Use **Math Boxes, Problem 1** to assess students' abilities to name a spreadsheet cell (Problem 1a) and to identify a spreadsheet formula for calculating a total (Problem 1b). Students are making adequate progress if they can correctly complete Problems 1a and 1b. Some students may be able to write a spreadsheet formula for calculating the total earnings for Monday (Problem 1c).

[Patterns, Functions, and Algebra Goal 1]

1. Darin charges $5 an hour to baby-sit on weekdays and $7 an hour on weekends. The spreadsheet is a record of the baby-sitting Darin did during one week. Complete the spreadsheet.

	A	B	C
1	Day of the Week	Number of Hours	Earnings ($)
2	Monday	4	
3	Wednesday	2	
4	Saturday	5	
5	**Total**		

a. Which cell contains the number of hours Darin worked on Saturday? _____

b. Circle the formula Darin should NOT use to calculate his total earnings.

   $C5 = C2 + C3 + C4$ $C5 = 6 * B5$ $C5 = (5 * B2) + (5 * B3) + (7 * B4)$

c. Write a formula that Darin can use to calculate his earnings for Monday.

The Recognizing Student Achievement tasks were chosen with the expectation that the majority of students will be successful with them. Students who are *making adequate progress* as defined by a Recognizing Student Achievement task are on a trajectory to meet the corresponding Grade-Level Goal. Based on student progress toward Grade-Level Goals, you may choose to use Readiness activities or Enrichment activities to modify your instructional plan to meet an individual student's needs. See the chart on the next page for how to understand and use the results of the Recognizing Student Achievement tasks.

Using the Results of Recognizing Student Achievement Tasks

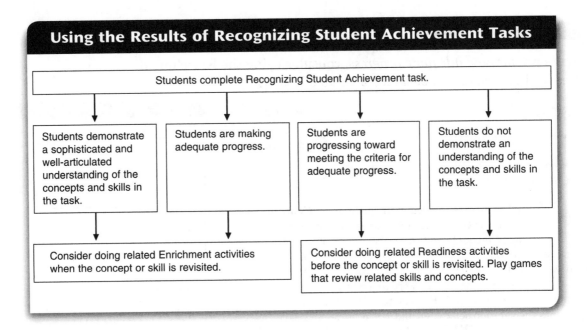

Students complete Recognizing Student Achievement task.

| Students demonstrate a sophisticated and well-articulated understanding of the concepts and skills in the task. | Students are making adequate progress. | Students are progressing toward meeting the criteria for adequate progress. | Students do not demonstrate an understanding of the concepts and skills in the task. |

Consider doing related Enrichment activities when the concept or skill is revisited.

Consider doing related Readiness activities before the concept or skill is revisited. Play games that review related skills and concepts.

 **Sample**   **Recognizing Student Achievement**

The following example illustrates how to implement further Enrichment or Readiness for a given Recognizing Student Achievement task.

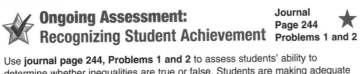

Ongoing Assessment:
Recognizing Student Achievement

Journal
Page 244
Problems 1 and 2

Use **journal page 244, Problems 1 and 2** to assess students' ability to determine whether inequalities are true or false. Students are making adequate progress if they are able to complete Problems 1 and 2. Some students may be able to describe the solution sets in Problem 3.

[Patterns, Functions, and Algebra Goal 2]

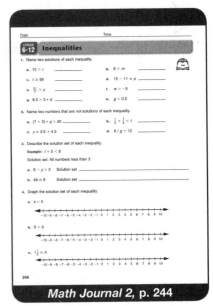

Math Journal 2, p. 244

If students are *making adequate progress,* consider using the Enrichment activities in this lesson, if applicable, or related lessons.

ENRICHMENT

▶ Graphing Compound Inequalities

(*Math Masters*, p. 212)

 To further explore compound inequalities, students graph the solution sets of compound inequalities and write compound inequalities to describe graphs. For Problem 4, remind students that all square roots have a positive and a negative value; that is, $\sqrt{9} = 3$ or -3, because $3 * 3 = 9$ and $-3 * -3 = 9$. Students can use the word *and* when writing the inequalities for Problems 5–7. For example, the graph in Problem 5 represents the solution set $x \geq -8$ and $x \leq 5$.

INDEPENDENT ACTIVITY

15–30 Min

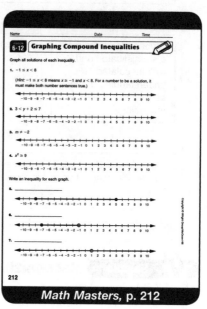

Math Masters, p. 212

 **Sample** **Readiness**

If students are *not making adequate progress,* consider using the Readiness activities before teaching related lessons.

READINESS

▶ Reviewing Relation Symbols and Inequalities

(*Math Masters*, p. 211)

To provide experience with identifying relation symbols and properties of number sentences, have students work with a partner to complete *Math Masters,* page 211. This activity is preparation for finding and graphing solution sets of inequalities.

PARTNER ACTIVITY

5–15 Min

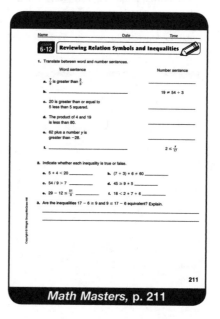

Math Masters, p. 211

Writing/Reasoning Prompts for Math Boxes

Every unit contains suggestions for prompts to use with Math Boxes problems. Use these prompts in a number of ways: (1) Collect student responses to these prompts on Exit Slips. (2) Request that students keep a math notebook where they record their answers to Math Message problems, Exit Slip prompts, and Writing/Reasoning prompts for Math Boxes problems. (3) Have students record responses on Math Log or Exit Slip masters and then add them to their portfolio collections.

✓ Sample 1 Writing/Reasoning Prompt

Portfolio Ideas **Writing/Reasoning** Have students write a response to the following: *Explain how you might find the sum of the interior angle measures in Problem 1 without using a protractor.* Sample answer: Use diagonals to divide the hexagon into 4 triangles. Multiply the number of triangles by the sum of the interior angle measures of each triangle ($4 * 180° = 720°$).

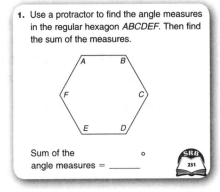

1. Use a protractor to find the angle measures in the regular hexagon *ABCDEF*. Then find the sum of the measures.

Sum of the
angle measures = _____ °

SRB
231

✓ Sample 2 Writing/Reasoning Prompt

Writing/Reasoning Have students write a response to the following: *Explain how you know where to place the decimal point in the quotient of Problem 4.* Sample answer: I estimated. 90 divided by 6 is 15, so 93.6 divided by 6 is about 15.

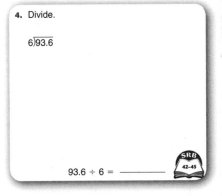

4. Divide.

6)93.6

93.6 ÷ 6 = _____

SRB
42–45

Portfolios

Portfolios are a versatile tool for student assessment. They help students reflect on their mathematical growth and help you understand and document that growth. Portfolios are part of a balanced assessment plan in that they:

◆ emphasize progress over time;

◆ involve students more directly in the assessment process as they participate in selecting work and explaining what the work demonstrates; and

◆ document strengths and weaknesses in a student's mathematical development.

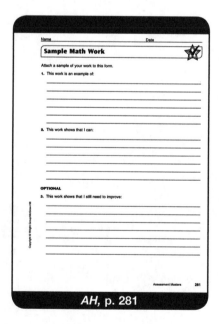 is the symbol used to indicate opportunities to collect students' work for portfolios. Several portfolio opportunities are highlighted in each unit but in addition to highlighted opportunities, you and your students can choose from the variety of work in daily lessons to add to student's portfolios.

Consider asking students to write about their selected works. Two optional masters, Sample Math Work and Discussion of My Math Work, are provided for this.

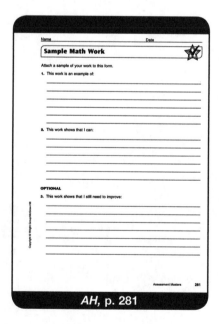

AH, p. 281

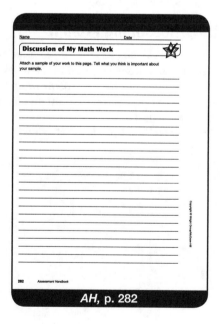

AH, p. 282

See pages 276–283 in this book for additional masters that you might ask students to complete periodically and incorporate into their portfolios.
For example:

- ◆ Evaluating My Math Class
- ◆ My Math Class
- ◆ Weekly Math Log
- ◆ Number-Story Math Log

You may also ask parents to complete a Parent Reflections page (*Assessment Handbook*, page 284) for inclusion in student portfolios.

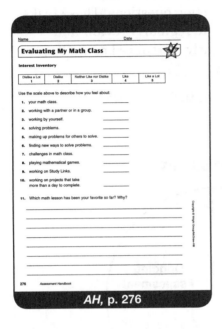

AH, p. 276

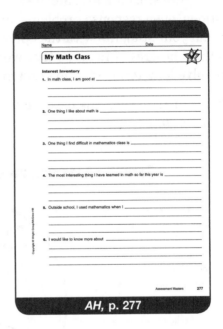

AH, p. 277

AH, p. 278

AH, p. 280

Periodic Assessment

Periodic assessments are another key component of a balanced assessment plan. Progress Check lessons and Beginning-of-Year, Mid-Year, and End-of-Year assessments require students to complete a variety of tasks, including short answer questions, open response problems, and reflection questions. These tasks provide you and your students with the opportunity to regularly review and reflect upon their progress—in areas that were recently introduced as well as in areas that involve long-term retention and mastery.

The figure below lists the various periodic assessment tasks provided in *Everyday Mathematics*.

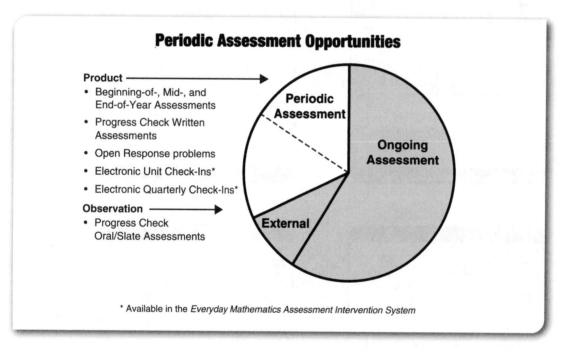

Periodic Assessment Opportunities

Product
- Beginning-of-, Mid-, and End-of-Year Assessments
- Progress Check Written Assessments
- Open Response problems
- Electronic Unit Check-Ins*
- Electronic Quarterly Check-Ins*

Observation
- Progress Check Oral/Slate Assessments

Periodic Assessment

Ongoing Assessment

External

* Available in the *Everyday Mathematics Assessment Intervention System*

Progress Check Written Assessments

Each Progress Check lesson includes a Written Assessment incorporating tasks that address content from lessons in the current and previous units. The Grade-Level Goals addressed in the Written Assessment are listed at the beginning of the lesson. These assessments provide information for evaluating student progress and planning for future instruction.

Written Assessments are one way students demonstrate what they know. Maximize opportunities for students to show the breadth of their knowledge on these assessments by adapting questions as appropriate. Beginning on page 51 in the unit-specific section of this handbook, there are suggested modifications for the Written Assessments that will allow you to tailor questions and get a more accurate picture of what students know.

Experts in assessment distinguish between summative and formative purposes of assessment. Summative assessment measures student growth and achievement so you can determine whether students have learned certain material. Formative assessment provides information about students' current knowledge and abilities so you can plan future instruction more effectively.

Accordingly, all *Everyday Mathematics* Progress Check written assessments include two parts:

◆ Part A is designed for summative purposes. The questions provide teachers with information on how students are progressing toward Grade-Level Goals. The questions can be used in the same way as Recognizing Student Achievement notes. Students *making adequate progress* toward Grade-Level Goals should do fairly well on this section.

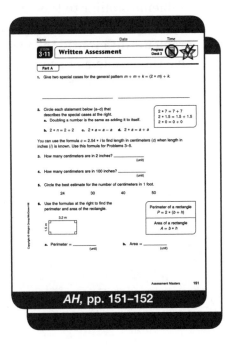

AH, pp. 151–152

◆ Part B is designed for formative purposes. The questions can be used to establish baselines for documenting student growth over time. The questions also assist teachers in their long-term planning in the same way as Informing Instruction notes help teachers in planning lessons.

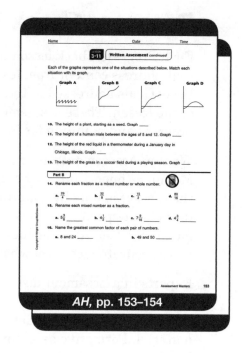

AH, pp. 153–154

Oral and Slate Assessment

Each Progress Check lesson features an Oral and Slate Assessment that includes problems similar to those in Mental Math and Reflexes, which appears in each lesson. You may choose to manage the collection of information from these problems differently than you do with the daily practice. For example, you may give the problems to small groups of students at a time or have students record their answers on paper rather than on slates.

Student Self Assessment

Each Progress Check lesson includes a Self Assessment master that students complete. These Self Assessments are part of a balanced assessment plan as they allow:

◆ students to reflect on their progress, strengths, and weaknesses;
◆ teachers to gain insights into how students perceive their progress; and
◆ teachers and students to plan how to address weaknesses.

The Self Assessment engages students in evaluating their competency with the concepts and skills addressed in the unit. For each skill or concept, students check a box to indicate one of the following:

◆ I can do this on my own and explain how to do it.
◆ I can do this on my own.
◆ I can do this if I get help or look at an example.

If students feel as though they need help or do not understand, consider talking with them about how they may learn more about the concept or skill. Look to related Readiness activities in Part 3 of lessons and to games for ideas about further developing students' understanding.

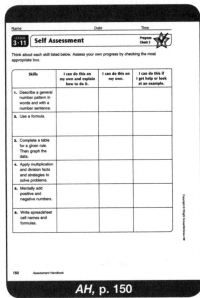

AH, p. 150

Open Response Tasks

Each Progress Check lesson includes an Open Response task linked to one or more Grade-Level Goals emphasized in the unit. These Open Response assessment tasks can provide additional balance in an assessment plan as they allow students to:

◆ become more aware of their problem-solving processes as they communicate their understanding, for example, through words, pictures, or diagrams;
◆ apply a variety of strategies to solve the longer tasks;
◆ further demonstrate their knowledge and understanding through application of skills and concepts in meaningful contexts; and
◆ be successful on a variety of levels.

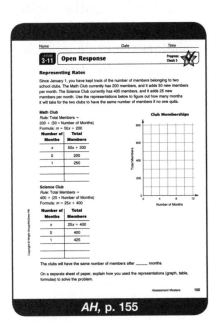

AH, p. 155

The Open Response tasks have been selected with the following points in mind:

◆ The problem context makes sense to students.

◆ The skill level of the problem is appropriate for students.

◆ The problem involves mathematics in which students have a foundation.

◆ The mathematics of the problem is important to the grade level. The problem addresses one or more Grade-Level Goals for the grade.

◆ The problem has connections to the real world that students have experience with.

◆ The problem may not be a multistep problem, but the solution strategy involves several steps.

◆ The problem may have more than one correct solution.

In the unit-specific section of this handbook that begins on page 51, each Open Response task has suggested implementation strategies, a sample task-specific rubric, and annotated student samples demonstrating the expectations described in the rubric. The unit-specific section also includes suggestions for adapting the Open Response task to meet the needs of a diverse group of students.

The sample rubrics are on a 4-point scale. The top two scores (4 points and 3 points) are designated for student work that demonstrates success with the task. The bottom two scores (2 points and 1 point) are designated for student work that does not demonstrate success with the task; 0 points are reserved for situations where students have made no effort to understand or solve the problem.

In general, the sample rubrics focus on assessing the following items:

◆ whether the mathematics students use is correct;

◆ whether the solution strategy makes sense, is reasonable, addresses the problem, and may lead to a successful solution;

◆ whether the explanation of the strategy is clear and easy to follow; and

◆ whether the solution is correct (or correct except for minor errors).

A Rate Problem Rubric

4	Completes the tables and plots ordered pairs correctly. Connects plotted points and indicates the graphed lines intersect at the correct coordinates. Clearly explains all of the steps for how a representation (formula, table, graph) is used to solve the problem.
3	Completes the tables and plots ordered pairs correctly. Connects plotted points and indicates the graphed lines intersect at the correct coordinates. Explains some steps for how a representation (formula, table, graph) is used, but the steps might require clarification or additional information.
2	Completes the tables and plots some ordered pairs, but not all are plotted correctly. Might or might not connect the plotted points. Attempts to use the rules, the table patterns, or the graph to solve the problem, but the strategy used is unclear or might have errors.
1	Attempts to complete the table and plot the ordered pairs, but there might be errors. The explanation describes a strategy that might be incorrect or make no sense in the context of the problem.
0	Does not attempt to solve the problem.

You may want to work with other teachers from your grade level to apply the *Everyday Mathematics* rubric to your students' work or to create rubrics for scoring these tasks. Consider the expectations of standardized tests in your area when creating or applying a rubric and modify this sample rubric as appropriate. For more student involvement, consider having students participate in developing a list of expectations for a Level-4 paper

Beginning-of-Year, Mid-Year, and End-of-Year Assessments

To provide a snapshot of how students are progressing toward a broader range of Grade-Level Goals, the program includes three assessments at each grade level—Beginning-of-Year, Mid-Year, and End-of-Year. These assessments cover important concepts and skills presented throughout the year. The Beginning-of-Year, Mid-Year, and End-of-Year assessments provide additional information that you may wish to include in developing your balanced assessment plan.

External Assessment

Outside tests, which are one example of external assessment, are generally tests given at the school, district, or state level, or are nationally standardized tests. Most teachers are familiar with the standardized tests that have multiple-choice responses. The frustrating aspect of this type of test is that it analyzes a narrow range of mathematical thinking and does not assess the depth and breadth of the mathematical knowledge that should be attained in a well-implemented *Everyday Mathematics* classroom.

Everyday Mathematics can help your students function more effectively in testing environments. For example, some Math Boxes problems have been tailored to help prepare students for the formats of an outside test. Even without such preparation, *Everyday Mathematics* students generally do just as well on the computation sections of standardized tests. However, they do much better on concepts and problem-solving sections than students in traditional programs.

More recently, some district and state tests have included performance assessments or open-ended components. *Everyday Mathematics* presents varied mathematics tasks that prepare students for these testing situations: problems requiring students to explain their thinking, writing prompts designed to help students explore content more deeply, and richer Open Response tasks that may require an entire class period for students to solve. If you have a choice in your district, encourage the use of these performance-based or open-ended assessments. They better depict the depth of your students' understandings, as well as their abilities to communicate mathematically, solve problems, and reason.

Performance-based assessments developed at the school or district level probably provide the best opportunities to gather information about student achievement in local classrooms. Teams of teachers and administrators can develop assessments and rubrics that enhance the learning process rather than focus on narrow thinking used only in a small portion of mathematical activities. At some grade levels, these assessments can be used exclusively. When standardized testing is mandatory at a certain grade level, performance-based assessments can provide a better picture of the mathematical education occurring in the classroom than other types of standardized tests.

Record Keeping

If you teach *Everyday Mathematics* as intended and use the techniques described in this book, you will soon have a vast amount of information about students' mathematical skills and understanding. This section of the handbook offers several tools to help you organize and record this information.

Class Checklists and Individual Profiles of Progress

Each lesson in *Everyday Mathematics* identifies a suggested ongoing assessment opportunity in the form of a Recognizing Student Achievement note. These notes highlight specific tasks from which teachers can collect student performance data to monitor and document students' progress toward meeting specific Grade-Level Goals. Each unit in *Everyday Mathematics* contains a Progress Check lesson with suggested periodic assessment tasks. A wealth of assessment information can be collected from these and other sources.

To help you keep track of students' progress in areas that are important to your school and district, checklists for individuals and for the class are provided beginning on page 226 of this handbook. There are Class Checklists for each unit and for each quarter. There are Individual Profiles of Progress for each unit. These checklists provide an organizational system for recording the information you collect to assess student progress on Grade-Level Goals.

The unit checklists include places to record information gathered from the Recognizing Student Achievement notes and from the Progress Check lesson in the unit. The checklists identify the related Grade-Level Goal for each Recognizing Student Achievement task. There is an additional column in which you can add your comments or other notes. To simplify data entry, these checklists are organized according to lesson number.

The quarterly checklists include places to record information gathered throughout the quarter from the Recognizing Student Achievement tasks. To simplify the process of aggregating data in meaningful ways, these checklists are organized according to mathematical strand.

You may prefer using the Class Checklists (on the right) to gather and organize information, transferring selected information to the Individual Profiles of Progress sheet for each student's portfolio or for use during parent conferences.

AH, p. 228

Checklist Flow Chart

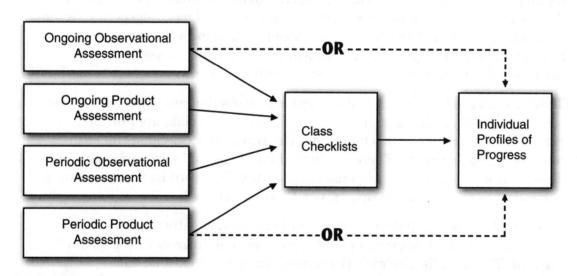

The Individual Profiles of Progress, Class Checklists, and Quarterly Checklists can be found in the Assessment Masters beginning on page 226 of this handbook. Blank checklists have been provided as well. Assessment checklists are also available online at www.everydaymathonline.com.

Options for Recording Data on Checklists

There are several different record-keeping schemes for checklists. Two such schemes are described below.

Option 1

Because Recognizing Student Achievement suggestions include descriptions of the expectations for *making adequate progress,* consider recording this information on a checklist using the following:

A	Student is making adequate progress toward Grade-Level Goal.
N	Student is not making adequate progress toward Grade-Level Goal.

or

✓	Student is making adequate progress toward Grade-Level Goal.
–	Student is not making adequate progress toward Grade-Level Goal.

Option 2

As the teacher, you can decide how you define what is *making adequate progress* and what is not. For example, if you use a 4-point rubric like the sample below, you may decide to define 3 or 4 points as *making adequate progress* and 1 or 2 points as *not making adequate progress.*

4 points	Student is making adequate progress. Student solves the problem correctly and demonstrates a sophisticated and well-articulated understanding of the concept or skill being assessed.
3 points	Student is making adequate progress. Student solves the problem correctly with only minor errors and demonstrates a developmentally appropriate understanding of the concept or skill being assessed.
2 points	Student is not making adequate progress. Student appears to understand some components of the problem and attempts to solve the problem. Student demonstrates an understanding of the concept or skill being assessed that is marginally short of what is expected.
1 point	Student is not making adequate progress. Student appears to not understand the problem but makes some attempt to solve it. Student demonstrates an understanding of the concept or skill being assessed that is significantly short of what is expected.
0 points	Student does not attempt to solve the problem.

Assessment Management Spreadsheets

Introduction

The digital *Everyday Mathematics Assessment Management Spreadsheets* are designed to help you track and record information about student progress towards the *Everyday Mathematics* Grade-Level Goals and the Common Core State Standards. This application contains digital versions of all of the Class Checklists and Individual Profiles of Progress located at the back of this book and can be found at www.everydaymathonline.com.

Everyday Mathematics: Common Core State Standards Edition was designed so the vast majority of students will be successful in mastering the Common Core State Standards and the *Everyday Mathematics* Grade-Level Goals for a given grade upon completion of that grade. Each assessment task provides a snapshot of a student's progress toward the corresponding Grade-Level Goal(s). Taken together, these snapshots form a moving picture that can help you assess whether a student is on a trajectory, or path, to meet the Grade-Level Goal.

Record Keeping

You can use the digital *Everyday Mathematics Assessment Management Spreadsheets* to enter student performance information for the following assessment types:

◆ Ongoing Assessment: Recognizing Student Achievement
◆ Progress Check: Oral and Slate
◆ Progress Check: Written Assessment Parts A and B
◆ Progress Check: Open Response
◆ Beginning-of-Year Assessment
◆ Mid-Year Assessment
◆ End-of-Year Assessment

You can also easily complement the assessments provided in *Everyday Mathematics* by adding student performance data from tasks you design or from the many other tasks in the *Everyday Mathematics* curriculum.

Grading Assistance

While grading is not the primary goal of the *Everyday Mathematics Assessment Management Spreadsheets,* the tool can assist you in assigning grades and creating report cards. You can use it to record student progress on many types of assessment tasks, including those that you create, so your evidence for assessment is based on multiple sources. These records of student performance, combined with the careful observations you make about your students' work, will help you assign fair and accurate grades.

Using the Digital *Assessment Management Spreadsheets*

The digital *Assessment Management Spreadsheets* include many features for supporting your balanced assessment plan. *For example:*

◆ All the suggested *Everyday Mathematics* assessment tasks are built into the system. Selecting a unit number will bring you to a screen that mirrors the Class Checklist masters, which list all the assessment tasks in a given unit.

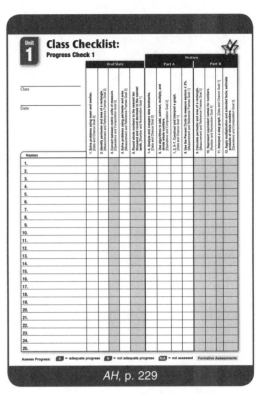

Digital versions of these checklists for all units are available through the Assessment Management Spreadsheets, *found at www.everydaymathonline.com.*

◆ A digital version of the Individual Profile of Progress can be automatically generated from the digital class checklists. You can add text comments for individual students on the digital Individual Profile of Progress.

◆ Teacher-created tasks can be added to the digital spreadsheets.

◆ In addition to classifying students' performance as "making adequate progress" or "not making adequate progress," there is a 0- to 4-point (detailed) scoring option. The detailed scoring option can be used for all assessments or just for open-response items. You can determine the level of specificity that best suits your assessment needs.

For assistance with the *Assessment Management Spreadsheets* and specific feature instructions, click the Help link at the top of any screen within the tool.

Frequently Asked Questions

1. **Do the Grade-Level Goals summarize all the concepts and skills that are covered each year?**

   No; Although the Grade-Level Goals reflect the core of the curriculum at each grade level, they are not comprehensive. They do not capture all the content that is addressed each year. Nor are they a list of activities that are completed each year. Some grade-level content supports future Grade-Level Goals that are not articulated at the given grade level.

2. **With all these Grade-Level Goals, how will I know when I'm simply exposing students to a concept or skill?**

   The *Everyday Mathematics* curriculum aims for student proficiency with concepts and skills through repeated exposures over several years. The *Teacher's Lesson Guide* alerts teachers to content that is being introduced for the first time through Links to the Future notes. These notes provide specific references to future Grade-Level Goals and help teachers understand introductory activities at their grade level in the context of the entire K–6 curriculum.

   All the content in *Everyday Mathematics* is important, whether it's being experienced for the first or the fifth time. The *Everyday Mathematics* curriculum is similar to an intricately woven rug, with many threads that appear and reappear to form complex patterns. Different students will progress at different rates, so multiple exposures to important content are critical for accommodating individual differences. The program was created so it is consistent with how students learn mathematics. It builds understanding over a period of time, first through informal exposure and later through more formal and directed instruction. For students to succeed, they need the opportunity to experience all that the curriculum has to offer in every grade.

3. **There are a lot of lessons in my grade-level materials. Do I have to finish all of them? For example, I teach second grade. Automaticity with multiplication facts is not a Grade-Level Goal until third grade. Can't I just skip all of the second-grade lessons that cover multiplication facts?**

Everyday Mathematics was created to be consistent with how students actually learn mathematics, building understanding over time, first through informal exposure and later through more formal instruction. Because the Grade-Level Goals are cumulative, it is essential for students to experience the complete curriculum at each grade level. Children in *Second Grade Everyday Mathematics,* for example, participate in many hands-on activities designed to develop an understanding of multiplication. This makes it possible for students to achieve multiplication goals in third grade.

4. **Do I need to keep track of progress on Program Goals?**

Program Goals are the threads that weave the content together across grade levels and form the skeleton of the curriculum. The Program Goals are further refined through the Grade-Level Goals. *Everyday Mathematics* provides a variety of tools you can use to assess student progress on the Grade-Level Goals throughout the year. Because every Grade-Level Goal is related to a Program Goal, you are gathering information at this less-specific level as well. This allows great flexibility in reporting to parents. Depending on how your district requires you to aggregate data, you can look broadly at content strands, more closely at Program Goals, or specifically at Grade-Level Goals using the suggested assessments in *Everyday Mathematics*.

5. **What do the authors mean by "adequate progress"?**

Students who are making adequate progress as defined by a Recognizing Student Achievement note are on a trajectory to meet the Grade-Level Goal. Such students have successfully accomplished what is expected up to that point in the curriculum. If students continue to progress as expected, then they will demonstrate proficiency with the Grade-Level Goal upon completion of the year.

The performance expectations described in the Recognizing Student Achievement notes for any given Grade-Level Goal progress developmentally throughout the year. The level of performance that is expected in October is not the same as what is expected in April. The term *adequate progress* describes the level of competency that the majority of students can be expected to have at a particular time. The authors of *Everyday Mathematics* chose the Recognizing Student Achievement tasks with the expectation that the majority of students would be successful with them, which is in line with the expectation that the vast majority of students will successfully reach the Grade-Level Goals for their grade level.

6. **Do students have to complete all of the Recognizing Student Achievement tasks before I can know whether they are making adequate progress?**

Each lesson in *Everyday Mathematics* contains a Recognizing Student Achievement note. These notes highlight specific tasks from which teachers can collect student performance data to monitor and document students' progress toward meeting specific Grade-Level Goals. Each Recognizing Student Achievement note addresses part of a Grade-Level Goal. The suggested assessment tasks build a complete picture over time for each Grade-Level Goal. If students perform well on one or two Recognizing Student Achievement tasks for a goal, that may not provide enough information about the goal in its entirety. Teachers are the experts in their classrooms. If you choose to not do some of the Recognizing Student Achievement tasks, consider collecting similar information from tasks you designate to assemble a complete picture for each Grade-Level Goal.

7. **Can I use only Math Boxes to collect assessment information? They seem to have all the skills in them.**

Everyday Mathematics includes a variety of assessment tasks to ensure that all students have sufficient opportunities to demonstrate what they know. Some students best demonstrate their knowledge through pencil-and-paper tasks, some through performance tasks, and some through explanations and demonstrations. The assessment tasks in the program have been chosen to accommodate a range of learners. Using only one tool might limit what you are able to learn about your students.

8. **I understand that *Everyday Mathematics* provides a Recognizing Student Achievement task for every lesson. May I choose my own instead of or in addition to the ones designated by the curriculum? If I don't think the results of a particular Recognizing Student Achievement task accurately reflect what a student knows, what should I do?**

The Recognizing Student Achievement tasks and Progress Check questions occur at carefully chosen points, based on the opportunities for distributed practice that occur throughout the program. Assessment tasks were also designed to vary the ways in which students are assessed for each Grade-Level Goal.

The *Everyday Mathematics* authors respect teachers as professionals and expect that teachers will use their professional judgment when assessing students. If a particular Recognizing Student Achievement task does not adequately assess student achievement, the teacher may choose to disregard it. The *Everyday Mathematics* authors also anticipate that students' performances on tasks that are not identified in Recognizing Student Achievement notes will often provide useful information regarding their progress toward a particular Grade-Level Goal. Teachers should feel free to link such tasks to appropriate Grade-Level Goals and include them in their assessment stories.

9. **I understand the different record-keeping options that were presented in this handbook. My district, however, evaluates students by assigning traditional letter grades. How should I evaluate student performance?**

Because local assessment systems are based on local norms and values, it would be impossible to design a system that would apply universally. But the authors of *Everyday Mathematics* recognize that many teachers are required by their districts to give traditional grades. And although it is impossible to design a single grading system that will work for everyone, there are some broad principles to follow:

◆ Grades should be fair and based on evidence that can be documented.
◆ Evidence for grading should come from multiple sources.
◆ Grades should be based on content that is important. They should not be based only on the content that is most easily assessed.
◆ The grading system should be aligned with both state and local standards and with the curriculum.

10. **Suppose a student makes adequate progress on the majority of Recognizing Student Achievement tasks and Progress Check questions for a given Grade-Level Goal throughout the year. At the end of the year how likely is it that the student will have achieved the Grade-Level Goal?**

The Recognizing Student Achievement and Progress Check tasks supply a great deal of data on which teachers can base inferences about students' achievement of Grade-Level Goals. In the case of a consistent pattern of adequate progress on assessment tasks for a given Grade-Level Goal, one can reasonably conclude that the student has in fact achieved the given goal. As with any assessment, however, inferences based on positive performance are more straightforward than those based on negative performance. That is, if a student performs well, the most straightforward conclusion is that the student has probably mastered the material; whereas if a student performs poorly, there are many possible explanations, only one of which is a lack of mastery.

Teachers should also recognize that inferences about what students know should always be considered provisional, because the inferences are fallible, based as they are on incomplete information, and because students are constantly growing and changing.

According to *Knowing What Students Know*:

> *. . . by its very nature, assessment is imprecise to some degree. Assessment results are estimates, based on samples of knowledge and performance drawn from the much larger universe of everything a person knows and can do. . . . Assessment is a process of reasoning from evidence. Because one cannot directly perceive students' mental processes, one must rely on less direct methods to make judgments about what they know*
>
> (Pellegrino, Chudowsky, and Glaser 2001, 36)
>
> *An assessment is a tool designed to observe students' behavior and produce data that can be used to draw reasonable inferences about what students know.*
>
> (Pellegrino, Chudowsky, and Glaser 2001, 42)

11. What about a student who normally performs well in class but does poorly on the electronic Quarterly Check-Ins?

Electronic Quarterly Check-Ins are just one piece of the *Everyday Mathematics* assessment story; they are not meant to stand alone and do not provide a complete picture of student progress toward any one goal. Because they can be administered and scored electronically, they provide teachers with some relatively easy data collection. However, because the Quarterly Check-Ins were written in multiple-choice format, they are limited in the information they can provide about what a student knows.

The pencil-and-paper Mid-Year and End-of-Year Assessments are the "best" assessments we offer in *Everyday Mathematics*. They are more comprehensive in their coverage of what students should be responsible for knowing at the time they are given. Students are able to show what they know in a variety of ways, and teachers can gather more information about a student by reviewing the work produced during one of these assessments.

We recommend that teachers administer both the Quarterly Check-Ins and the Mid- and End-of-Year Assessments. However, teachers worried about over-testing may choose to skip the review portion of the Quarter 2 Check-In, as the questions related to those goals are assessed in a more comprehensive manner on the Mid-Year Assessment.

Recommended Reading

Black, Paul, and Dylan Wiliam. "Assessment and Classroom Learning." *Assessment in Education* (March, 1998): 7–74.

———. "Inside the Black Box: Raising Standards Through Classroom Assessment." *Phi Delta Kappan* 80, no. 2 (October, 1998): 139–149.

Bryant, Brian R., and Teddy Maddox. "Using Alternative Assessment Techniques to Plan and Evaluate Mathematics." *LD Forum 21,* no. 2 (winter, 1996): 24–33.

Eisner, Elliot W. "The Uses and Limits of Performance Assessment." *Phi Delta Kappan* 80, no. 9 (May, 1999): 658–661.

Kulm, Gerald. *Mathematics Assessment: What Works in the Classroom.* San Francisco: Jossey-Bass Publishers, 1994.

National Council of Teachers of Mathematics (NCTM). *Curriculum and Evaluation Standards for School Mathematics.* Reston, Va.: NCTM, 1989.

———. *Assessment Standards for School Mathematics.* Reston, Va.: NCTM, 1995.

———. *Principles and Standards for School Mathematics.* Reston, Va.: NCTM, 2000.

National Research Council. Committee on the Foundations of Assessment. Pellegrino, James W., Naomi Chudowsky, and Robert Glaser, eds. *Knowing What Students Know: The Science and Design of Educational Assessment.* Washington, D.C.: National Academy Press, 2001.

National Research Council, Mathematical Sciences Education Board. *Measuring What Counts: A Conceptual Guide for Mathematics Assessment.* Washington, D.C.: National Academy Press, 1993.

Pearson, Bethyl, and Cathy Berghoff. "London Bridge Is Not Falling Down: It's Supporting Alternative Assessment." *TESOL Journal* 5, no. 4 (summer, 1996): 28–31.

Shepard, Lorrie A. "Using Assessment to Improve Learning." *Educational Leadership* 52, no. 5 (February, 1995): 38–43.

Stenmark, Jean Kerr, ed. *Mathematics Assessment: Myths, Models, Good Questions, and Practical Suggestions.* Reston, Va.: National Council of Teachers of Mathematics, 1991.

Stiggens, Richard J. *Student-Centered Classroom Assessment.* Englewood Cliffs, N.J.: Prentice-Hall, 1997.

Webb, N. L., and A. F. Coxford, eds. *Assessment in the Mathematics Classroom: 1993 Yearbook.* Reston, Va.: National Council of Teachers of Mathematics, 1993.

http://everydaymath.uchicago.edu/

Everyday Mathematics GOALS

The following tables list the Grade-Level Goals organized by Content Strand and Program Goal.

Everyday Mathematics®

Content Strand: NUMBER AND NUMERATION

Program Goal: Understand the Meanings, Uses, and Representations of Numbers

Content	Kindergarten	First Grade	Second Grade	Third Grade	Fourth Grade	Fifth Grade	Sixth Grade
Rote counting	**Goal 1.** Count on by 1s to 100; count on by 2s, 5s, and 10s and count back by 1s with number grids, number lines, and calculators.	**Goal 1.** Count on by 1s, 2s, 5s, and 10s past 100 and back by 1s from any number less than 100 with and without number grids, number lines, and calculators.	**Goal 1.** Count on by 1s, 2s, 5s, 10s, 25s, and 100s past 1,000 and back by 1s, 10s, and 100s from any number less than 1,000 with and without number grids, number lines, and calculators.				
Rational counting	**Goal 2.** Count 20 or more objects; estimate the number of objects in a collection.	**Goal 2.** Count collections of objects accurately and reliably; estimate the number of objects in a collection.					
Place value and notation	**Goal 3.** Model numbers with manipulatives; use manipulatives to exchange 1s for 10s and 10s for 100s; recognize that digits can be used and combined to read and write numbers; read numbers up to 30.	**Goal 3.** Read, write, and model with manipulatives whole numbers up to 1,000; identify places in such numbers and the values of the digits in those places.	**Goal 2.** Read, write, and model with manipulatives whole numbers up to 10,000; identify places in such numbers and the values of the digits in those places; read and write money amounts in dollars-and-cents notation.	**Goal 1.** Read and write whole numbers up to 1,000,000; read, write, and model with manipulatives decimals through hundredths; identify places in such numbers and the values of the digits in those places; translate between whole numbers and decimals represented in words, in base-10 notation, and with manipulatives.	**Goal 1.** Read and write whole numbers up to 1,000,000,000 and decimals through thousandths; identify places in such numbers and the values of the digits in those places; translate between whole numbers and decimals represented in words and in base-10 notation.	**Goal 1.** Read and write whole numbers and decimals; identify places in such numbers and the values of the digits in those places; use expanded notation to represent whole numbers and decimals.	**Goal 1.** Read and write whole numbers and decimals; identify places in such numbers and the values of the digits in those places; use expanded notation, number-and-word notation, exponential notation, and scientific notation to represent whole numbers and decimals.

Everyday Mathematics

Content Strand: NUMBER AND NUMERATION *cont.*

Program Goal: Understand the Meanings, Uses, and Representations of Numbers *cont.*

Content	Kindergarten	First Grade	Second Grade	Third Grade	Fourth Grade	Fifth Grade	Sixth Grade
Meanings and uses of fractions	**Goal 4.** Use manipulatives to model half of a region or a collection; describe the model.	**Goal 4.** Use manipulatives and drawings to model halves, thirds, and fourths as equal parts of a region or a collection; describe the model.	**Goal 3.** Use manipulatives and drawings to model fractions as equal parts of a region or a collection; describe the models and name the fractions.	**Goal 2.** Read, write, and model fractions; solve problems involving fractional parts of a region or a collection; describe strategies used.	**Goal 2.** Read, write, and model fractions; solve problems involving fractional parts of a region or a collection; describe and explain strategies used; given a fractional part of a region or a collection, identify the unit whole.	**Goal 2.** Solve problems involving percents and discounts; describe and explain strategies used; identify the unit whole in situations involving fractions.	**Goal 2.** Solve problems involving percents and discounts; explain strategies used; identify the unit whole in situations involving fractions, decimals, and percents.
Number theory		**Goal 5.** Use manipulatives to identify and model odd and even numbers.	**Goal 4.** Recognize numbers as odd or even.	**Goal 3.** Find multiples of 2, 5, and 10.	**Goal 3.** Find multiples of whole numbers less than 10; identify prime and composite numbers; find whole-number factors of numbers.	**Goal 3.** Identify prime and composite numbers; factor numbers; find prime factorizations.	**Goal 3.** Use GCFs, LCMs, and divisibility rules to manipulate fractions.

Program Goal: Understand Equivalent Names for Numbers

Content	Kindergarten	First Grade	Second Grade	Third Grade	Fourth Grade	Fifth Grade	Sixth Grade
Equivalent names for whole numbers	**Goal 5.** Use manipulatives, drawings, and numerical expressions involving addition and subtraction of 1-digit numbers to give equivalent names for whole numbers up to 20.	**Goal 6.** Use manipulatives, drawings, tally marks, and numerical expressions involving addition and subtraction of 1- or 2-digit numbers to give equivalent names for whole numbers up to 100.	**Goal 5.** Use tally marks, arrays, and numerical expressions involving addition and subtraction to give equivalent names for whole numbers.	**Goal 4.** Use numerical expressions involving one or more of the basic four arithmetic operations to give equivalent names for whole numbers.	**Goal 4.** Use numerical expressions involving one or more of the basic four arithmetic operations and grouping symbols to give equivalent names for whole numbers.	**Goal 4.** Use numerical expressions involving one or more of the basic four arithmetic operations, grouping symbols, and exponents to give equivalent names for whole numbers; convert between base-10, exponential, and repeated-factor notations.	**Goal 4.** Apply the order of operations to numerical expressions to give equivalent names for rational numbers.

Everyday Mathematics

Content Strand: NUMBER AND NUMERATION *cont.*

Program Goal: Understand Equivalent Names for Numbers *cont.*

Content	Kindergarten	First Grade	Second Grade	Third Grade	Fourth Grade	Fifth Grade	Sixth Grade
Equivalent names for fractions, decimals, and percents			**Goal 6.** Use manipulatives and drawings to model equivalent names for $\frac{1}{2}$.	**Goal 5.** Use manipulatives and drawings to find and represent equivalent names for fractions; use manipulatives to generate equivalent fractions.	**Goal 5.** Use numerical expressions to find and represent equivalent names for fractions and decimals; use and explain a multiplication rule to find equivalent fractions; rename fourths, fifths, tenths, and hundredths as decimals and percents.	**Goal 5.** Use numerical expressions to find and represent equivalent names for fractions, decimals, and percents; use and explain multiplication and division rules to find equivalent fractions and fractions in simplest form; convert between fractions and mixed numbers; convert between fractions, decimals, and percents.	**Goal 5.** Find equivalent fractions and fractions in simplest form by applying multiplication and division rules and concepts from number theory; convert between fractions, mixed numbers, decimals, and percents.

Program Goal: Understand Common Numerical Relations

Content	Kindergarten	First Grade	Second Grade	Third Grade	Fourth Grade	Fifth Grade	Sixth Grade
Comparing and ordering numbers	**Goal 6.** Compare and order whole numbers up to 20.	**Goal 7.** Compare and order whole numbers up to 1,000.	**Goal 7.** Compare and order whole numbers up to 10,000; use area models to compare fractions.	**Goal 6.** Compare and order whole numbers up to 1,000,000; use manipulatives to order decimals through hundredths; use area models and benchmark fractions to compare and order fractions.	**Goal 6.** Compare and order whole numbers up to 1,000,000,000 and decimals through thousandths; compare and order integers between −100 and 0; use area models, benchmark fractions, and analyses of numerators and denominators to compare and order fractions.	**Goal 6.** Compare and order rational numbers; use area models, benchmark fractions, and analyses of numerators and denominators to compare and order fractions and mixed numbers; describe strategies used to compare fractions and mixed numbers.	**Goal 6.** Choose and apply strategies for comparing and ordering rational numbers; explain those choices and strategies.

Everyday Mathematics

Content Strand: OPERATIONS AND COMPUTATION

Program Goal: Compute Accurately

Content	Kindergarten	First Grade	Second Grade	Third Grade	Fourth Grade	Fifth Grade	Sixth Grade
Addition and subtraction facts	**Goal 1.** Use manipulatives, number lines, and mental arithmetic to solve problems involving the addition and subtraction of single-digit whole numbers; demonstrate appropriate fluency with addition and subtraction facts within 5.	**Goal 1.** Demonstrate appropriate fluency with addition and subtraction facts through 10 + 10.	**Goal 1.** Demonstrate automaticity with all addition facts through 10 + 10 and fluency with the related subtraction facts.	**Goal 1.** Demonstrate automaticity with all addition and subtraction facts through 10 + 10; use basic facts to compute fact extensions such as 80 + 70.	**Goal 1.** Demonstrate automaticity with addition and subtraction fact extensions.		
Addition and subtraction procedures		**Goal 2.** Use manipulatives, number grids, tally marks, mental arithmetic, and calculators to solve problems involving the addition and subtraction of 1-digit whole numbers with 2-digit whole numbers; calculate and compare the values of combinations of coins.	**Goal 2.** Use manipulatives, number grids, tally marks, mental arithmetic, paper & pencil, and calculators to solve problems involving the addition and subtraction of multidigit whole numbers; describe the strategies used; calculate and compare values of coin and bill combinations.	**Goal 2.** Use manipulatives, mental arithmetic, paper-and-pencil algorithms and models, and calculators to solve problems involving the addition and subtraction of whole numbers and decimals in a money context; describe the strategies used and explain how they work.	**Goal 2.** Use manipulatives, mental arithmetic, paper-and-pencil algorithms and models, and calculators to solve problems involving the addition and subtraction of whole numbers and decimals through hundredths; describe the strategies used and explain how they work.	**Goal 1.** Use manipulatives, mental arithmetic, paper-and-pencil algorithms and models, and calculators to solve problems involving the addition and subtraction of whole numbers, decimals, and signed numbers; describe the strategies used and explain how they work.	**Goal 1.** Use mental arithmetic, paper-and-pencil algorithms and models, and calculators to solve problems involving the addition and subtraction of whole numbers, decimals, and signed numbers; describe the strategies used and explain how they work.

Everyday Mathematics

Content Strand: OPERATIONS AND COMPUTATION *cont.*

Program Goal: Compute Accurately *cont.*

Content	Kindergarten	First Grade	Second Grade	Third Grade	Fourth Grade	Fifth Grade	Sixth Grade
Multiplication and division facts				**Goal 3.** Demonstrate automaticity with multiplication facts through 10 × 10.	**Goal 3.** Demonstrate automaticity with multiplication facts through 10 * 10 and proficiency with related division facts; use basic facts to compute fact extensions such as 30 * 60.	**Goal 2.** Demonstrate automaticity with multiplication and division fact extensions.	
Multiplication and division procedures				**Goal 4.** Use arrays, mental arithmetic, paper-and-pencil algorithms and models, and calculators to solve problems involving the multiplication of 2- and 3-digit whole numbers by 1-digit whole numbers; describe the strategies used.	**Goal 4.** Use manipulatives, mental arithmetic, paper-and-pencil algorithms and models, and calculators to solve problems involving the multiplication of multidigit whole numbers by 2-digit whole numbers and the division of multidigit whole numbers by 1-digit whole numbers; describe the strategies used and explain how they work.	**Goal 3.** Use manipulatives, mental arithmetic, paper-and-pencil algorithms and models, and calculators to solve problems involving the multiplication of whole numbers and decimals and the division of multidigit whole numbers and decimals by whole numbers; express remainders as whole numbers or fractions as appropriate; describe the strategies used and explain how they work.	**Goal 2.** Use mental arithmetic, paper-and-pencil algorithms and models, and calculators to solve problems involving the multiplication and division of whole numbers, decimals, and signed numbers; describe the strategies used and explain how they work.

Everyday Mathematics

Content Strand: OPERATIONS AND COMPUTATION *cont.*

Program Goal: Compute Accurately *cont.*

Content	Kindergarten	First Grade	Second Grade	Third Grade	Fourth Grade	Fifth Grade	Sixth Grade
Procedures for addition and subtraction of fractions					**Goal 5.** Use manipulatives, mental arithmetic, and calculators to solve problems involving the addition and subtraction of fractions and mixed numbers; describe the strategies used.	**Goal 4.** Use mental arithmetic, paper-and-pencil algorithms and models, and calculators to solve problems involving the addition and subtraction of fractions and mixed numbers; describe the strategies used and explain how they work.	**Goal 3.** Use mental arithmetic, paper-and-pencil algorithms and models, and calculators to solve problems involving the addition and subtraction of fractions and mixed numbers; describe the strategies used and explain how they work.
Procedures for multiplication and division of fractions						**Goal 5.** Use area models, mental arithmetic, paper-and-pencil algorithms and models, and calculators to solve problems involving the multiplication of fractions and mixed numbers; use visual models, paper-and-pencil methods, and calculators to solve problems involving the division of fractions; describe the strategies used.	**Goal 4.** Use mental arithmetic, paper-and-pencil algorithms and models, and calculators to solve problems involving the multiplication and division of fractions and mixed numbers; describe the strategies used and explain how they work.

Everyday Mathematics

Content Strand: OPERATIONS AND COMPUTATION *cont.*

Program Goal: Make Reasonable Estimates

Content	Kindergarten	First Grade	Second Grade	Third Grade	Fourth Grade	Fifth Grade	Sixth Grade
Computational estimation		**Goal 3.** Estimate reasonableness of answers to basic fact problems (e.g., Will 7 + 8 be more or less than 10?).	**Goal 3.** Make reasonable estimates for whole number addition and subtraction problems; explain how the estimates were obtained.	**Goal 5.** Make reasonable estimates for whole number addition, subtraction, multiplication, and division problems; explain how the estimates were obtained.	**Goal 6.** Make reasonable estimates for whole number and decimal addition and subtraction problems and whole number multiplication and division problems; explain how the estimates were obtained.	**Goal 6.** Make reasonable estimates for whole number and decimal addition, subtraction, multiplication, and division problems and fraction and mixed number addition and subtraction problems; explain how the estimates were obtained.	**Goal 5.** Make reasonable estimates for whole number, decimal, fraction, and mixed number addition, subtraction, multiplication, and division problems; explain how the estimates were obtained.

Program Goal: Understand Meanings of Operations

Content	Kindergarten	First Grade	Second Grade	Third Grade	Fourth Grade	Fifth Grade	Sixth Grade
Models for the operations	**Goal 2.** Identify join and take-away situations.	**Goal 4.** Identify change-to-more, change-to-less, comparison, and parts-and-total situations.	**Goal 4.** Identify and describe change, comparison, and parts-and-total situations; use repeated addition, arrays, and skip counting to model multiplication; use equal sharing and equal grouping to model division.	**Goal 6.** Recognize and describe change, comparison, and parts-and-total situations; use repeated addition, arrays, and skip counting to model multiplication; use equal sharing and equal grouping to model division.	**Goal 7.** Use repeated addition, skip counting, arrays, area, and scaling to model multiplication and division.	**Goal 7.** Use repeated addition, arrays, area, and scaling to model multiplication and division; use ratios expressed as words, fractions, percents, and with colons; solve problems involving ratios of parts of a set to the whole set.	**Goal 6.** Use ratios and scaling to model size changes and to solve size-change problems; represent ratios as fractions, percents, and decimals, and using a colon; model and solve problems involving part-to-whole and part-to-part ratios; model rate and ratio number stories with proportions; use and explain cross multiplication and other strategies to solve proportions.

Everyday Mathematics

Content Strand: DATA AND CHANCE

Program Goal: Select and Create Appropriate Graphical Representations of Collected or Given Data

Content	Kindergarten	First Grade	Second Grade	Third Grade	Fourth Grade	Fifth Grade	Sixth Grade
Data collection and representation	**Goal 1.** Collect and organize data to create class-constructed tally charts, tables, and bar graphs.	**Goal 1.** Collect and organize data to create tally charts, tables, bar graphs, and line plots.	**Goal 1.** Collect and organize data or use given data to create tally charts, tables, graphs, and line plots.	**Goal 1.** Collect and organize data or use given data to create charts, tables, graphs, and line plots.	**Goal 1.** Collect and organize data or use given data to create charts, tables, graphs, and line plots.	**Goal 1.** Collect and organize data or use given data to create graphic displays with reasonable titles, labels, keys, and intervals.	**Goal 1.** Collect and organize data or use given data to create graphic displays with reasonable titles, labels, keys, and intervals.

Program Goal: Analyze and Interpret Data

Content	Kindergarten	First Grade	Second Grade	Third Grade	Fourth Grade	Fifth Grade	Sixth Grade
Data analysis	**Goal 2.** Use graphs to answer simple questions.	**Goal 2.** Use graphs to answer simple questions and draw conclusions; find the maximum and minimum of a data set.	**Goal 2.** Use graphs to ask and answer simple questions and draw conclusions; find the maximum, minimum, mode, and median of a data set.	**Goal 2.** Use graphs to ask and answer simple questions and draw conclusions; find the maximum, minimum, range, mode, and median of a data set.	**Goal 2.** Use the maximum, minimum, range, median, mode, and graphs to ask and answer questions, draw conclusions, and make predictions.	**Goal 2.** Use the maximum, minimum, range, median, mode, and mean and graphs to ask and answer questions, draw conclusions, and make predictions.	**Goal 2.** Use data landmarks, measures of spread, and graphs to ask and answer questions, draw conclusions, and make predictions; compare and contrast the median and mean of a data set.

Program Goal: Understand and Apply Basic Concepts of Probability

Content	Kindergarten	First Grade	Second Grade	Third Grade	Fourth Grade	Fifth Grade	Sixth Grade
Qualitative probability	**Goal 3.** Describe events using *certain, possible, impossible,* and other basic probability terms.	**Goal 3.** Describe events using *certain, likely, unlikely, impossible,* and other basic probability terms.	**Goal 3.** Describe events using *certain, likely, unlikely, impossible,* and other basic probability terms; explain the choice of language.	**Goal 3.** Describe events using *certain, very likely, likely, unlikely, very unlikely, impossible,* and other basic probability terms; explain the choice of language.	**Goal 3.** Describe events using *certain, very likely, likely, unlikely, very unlikely, impossible,* and other basic probability terms; use *more likely, equally likely, same chance, 50–50, less likely,* and other basic probability terms to compare events; explain the choice of language.	**Goal 3.** Describe events using *certain, very likely, likely, unlikely, very unlikely, impossible,* and other basic probability terms; use *more likely, equally likely, same chance, 50–50, less likely,* and other basic probability terms to compare events; explain the choice of language.	

Everyday Mathematics

Content Strand: DATA AND CHANCE *cont.*

Program Goal: Understand and Apply Basic Concepts of Probability *cont.*

Content	Kindergarten	First Grade	Second Grade	Third Grade	Fourth Grade	Fifth Grade	Sixth Grade
Quantitative probability				**Goal 4.** Predict the outcomes of simple experiments and test the predictions using manipulatives; express the probability of an event by using "___ out of ___" language.	**Goal 4.** Predict the outcomes of experiments and test the predictions using manipulatives; summarize the results and use them to predict future events; express the probability of an event as a fraction.	**Goal 4.** Predict the outcomes of experiments, test the predictions using manipulatives, and summarize the results; compare predictions based on theoretical probability with experimental results; use summaries and comparisons to predict future events; express the probability of an event as a fraction, decimal, or percent.	**Goal 3.** Use the Multiplication Counting Principle, tree diagrams, and other counting strategies to identify all possible outcomes for a situation; predict results of experiments, test the predictions using manipulatives, and summarize the findings; compare predictions based on theoretical probability with experimental results; calculate probabilities and express them as fractions, decimals, and percents; explain how sample size affects results; use the results to predict future events.

Everyday Mathematics

Content Strand: MEASUREMENT AND REFERENCE FRAMES

Program Goal: Understand the Systems and Processes of Measurement; Use Appropriate Techniques, Tools, Units, and Formulas in Making Measurements

Content	Kindergarten	First Grade	Second Grade	Third Grade	Fourth Grade	Fifth Grade	Sixth Grade
Length, weight, and angles	**Goal 1.** Use nonstandard tools and techniques to estimate and compare weight and length; identify standard measuring tools.	**Goal 1.** Use nonstandard tools and techniques to estimate and compare weight and length; measure length with standard measuring tools.	**Goal 1.** Estimate length with and without tools; measure length to the nearest inch and centimeter; use standard and nonstandard tools to measure and estimate weight.	**Goal 1.** Estimate length with and without tools; measure length to the nearest $\frac{1}{2}$ inch and $\frac{1}{2}$ centimeter; draw and describe angles as records of rotations.	**Goal 1.** Estimate length with and without tools; measure length to the nearest $\frac{1}{4}$ inch and $\frac{1}{2}$ centimeter; use tools to measure and draw angles; estimate the size of angles without tools.	**Goal 1.** Estimate length with and without tools; measure length with tools to the nearest $\frac{1}{8}$ inch and millimeter; estimate the measure of angles with and without tools; use tools to draw angles with given measures.	**Goal 1.** Estimate length with and without tools; measure length with tools to the nearest $\frac{1}{16}$ inch and millimeter; estimate the measure of angles with and without tools; use tools to draw angles with given measures.
Area, perimeter, volume, and capacity			**Goal 2.** Partition rectangles into unit squares and count unit squares to find areas.	**Goal 2.** Describe and use strategies to measure the perimeter of polygons; find the areas of rectangles.	**Goal 2.** Describe and use strategies to measure the perimeter and area of polygons, to estimate the area of irregular shapes, and to find the volume of rectangular prisms.	**Goal 2.** Describe and use strategies to find the perimeter of polygons and the area of circles; choose and use appropriate methods, including formulas, to find the areas of rectangles, parallelograms, and triangles, and the volume of a prism; define *pi* as the ratio of a circle's circumference to its diameter.	**Goal 2.** Choose and use appropriate formulas to calculate the circumference of circles and to solve area, perimeter, and volume problems.
Units and systems of measurement			**Goal 3.** Describe relationships between days in a week and hours in a day.	**Goal 3.** Describe relationships among inches, feet, and yards; describe relationships between minutes in an hour, hours in a day, days in a week.	**Goal 3.** Describe relationships among U.S. customary units of measure and among metric units of measure.	**Goal 3.** Describe relationships among U.S. customary units of measure and among metric units of measure.	**Goal 3.** Describe relationships among U.S. customary units of measure and among metric units of measure.

Everyday Mathematics

Content Strand: MEASUREMENT AND REFERENCE FRAMES *cont.*

Program Goal: Understand the Systems and Processes of Measurement; Use Appropriate Techniques, Tools, Units, and Formulas in Making Measurements *cont.*

Content	Kindergarten	First Grade	Second Grade	Third Grade	Fourth Grade	Fifth Grade	Sixth Grade
Money	**Goal 2.** Identify pennies, nickels, dimes, quarters, and dollar bills.	**Goal 2.** Know and compare the value of pennies, nickels, dimes, quarters, and dollar bills; make exchanges between coins.	**Goal 4.** Make exchanges between coins and bills.				

Program Goal: Use and Understand Reference Frames

Content	Kindergarten	First Grade	Second Grade	Third Grade	Fourth Grade	Fifth Grade	Sixth Grade
Temperature	**Goal 3.** Describe temperature using appropriate vocabulary, such as *hot, warm,* and *cold;* identify a thermometer as a tool for measuring temperature.	**Goal 3.** Identify a thermometer as a tool for measuring temperature; read temperatures on Fahrenheit and Celsius thermometers to the nearest 10°.	**Goal 5.** Read temperature on both the Fahrenheit and Celsius scales.				
Time	**Goal 4.** Describe and use measures of time periods relative to a day and week; identify tools that measure time.	**Goal 4.** Use a calendar to identify days, weeks, months, and dates; tell and show time to the nearest half and quarter hour on an analog clock.	**Goal 6.** Tell and show time to the nearest five minutes on an analog clock; tell and write time in digital notation.	**Goal 4.** Tell and show time to the nearest minute on an analog clock; tell and write time in digital notation.			
Coordinate systems					**Goal 4.** Use ordered pairs of numbers to name, locate, and plot points in the first quadrant of a coordinate grid.	**Goal 4.** Use ordered pairs of numbers to name, locate, and plot points in all four quadrants of a coordinate grid.	**Goal 3.** Use ordered pairs of numbers to name, locate, and plot points in all four quadrants of a coordinate grid.

Everyday Mathematics

Content Strand: GEOMETRY

Program Goal: Investigate Characteristics and Properties of Two- and Three-Dimensional Geometric Shapes

Content	Kindergarten	First Grade	Second Grade	Third Grade	Fourth Grade	Fifth Grade	Sixth Grade
Lines and angles			**Goal 1.** Draw line segments and identify parallel line segments.	**Goal 1.** Identify and draw points, intersecting and parallel line segments and lines, rays, and right angles.	**Goal 1.** Identify, draw, and describe points, intersecting and parallel line segments and lines, rays, and right, acute, and obtuse angles.	**Goal 1.** Identify, describe, compare, name, and draw right, acute, obtuse, straight, and reflex angles; determine angle measures in vertical and supplementary angles and by applying properties of sums of angle measures in triangles and quadrangles.	**Goal 1.** Identify, describe, classify, name, and draw angles; determine angle measures by applying properties of orientations of angles and of sums of angle measures in triangles and quadrangles.
Plane and solid figures	**Goal 1.** Identify and describe plane and solid figures including circles, triangles, squares, rectangles, spheres, and cubes.	**Goal 1.** Identify and describe plane and solid figures including circles, triangles, squares, rectangles, spheres, cylinders, rectangular prisms, pyramids, cones, and cubes.	**Goal 2.** Identify, describe, and model plane and solid figures including circles, triangles, squares, rectangles, hexagons, trapezoids, rhombuses, spheres, cylinders, rectangular prisms, pyramids, cones, and cubes.	**Goal 2.** Identify, describe, model, and compare plane and solid figures including circles, polygons, spheres, cylinders, rectangular prisms, pyramids, cones, and cubes using appropriate geometric terms including the terms *face, edge, vertex,* and *base.*	**Goal 2.** Describe, compare, and classify plane and solid figures, including polygons, circles, spheres, cylinders, rectangular prisms, cones, cubes, and pyramids, using appropriate geometric terms including *vertex, base, face, edge,* and *congruent.*	**Goal 2.** Describe, compare, and classify plane and solid figures using appropriate geometric terms; identify congruent figures and describe their properties.	**Goal 2.** Identify and describe similar and congruent figures and describe their properties; construct a figure that is congruent to another figure using a compass and straightedge.

Program Goal: Apply Transformations and Symmetry in Geometric Situations

Content	Kindergarten	First Grade	Second Grade	Third Grade	Fourth Grade	Fifth Grade	Sixth Grade
Transformations and symmetry	**Goal 2.** Identify shapes having line symmetry.	**Goal 2.** Identify shapes having line symmetry; complete line-symmetric shapes or designs.	**Goal 3.** Create and complete two-dimensional symmetric shapes or designs.	**Goal 3.** Create and complete two-dimensional symmetric shapes or designs; locate multiple lines of symmetry in a two-dimensional shape.	**Goal 3.** Identify, describe, and sketch examples of reflections; identify and describe examples of translations and rotations.	**Goal 3.** Identify, describe, and sketch examples of reflections, translations, and rotations.	**Goal 3.** Identify, describe, and sketch (including plotting on the coordinate plane) instances of reflections, translations, and rotations.

Everyday Mathematics

Content Strand: PATTERNS, FUNCTIONS, AND ALGEBRA

Program Goal: Understand Patterns and Functions

Content	Kindergarten	First Grade	Second Grade	Third Grade	Fourth Grade	Fifth Grade	Sixth Grade
Patterns and functions	**Goal 1.** Extend, describe, and create visual, rhythmic, and movement patterns; use rules, which will lead to functions, to sort, make patterns, and play "What's My Rule?" and other games.	**Goal 1.** Extend, describe, and create numeric, visual, and concrete patterns; solve problems involving function machines, "What's My Rule?" tables, and Frames-and-Arrows diagrams.	**Goal 1.** Extend, describe, and create numeric, visual, and concrete patterns; describe rules for patterns and use them to solve problems; use words and symbols to describe and write rules for functions involving addition and subtraction and use those rules to solve problems.	**Goal 1.** Extend, describe, and create numeric patterns; describe rules for patterns and use them to solve problems; use words and symbols to describe and write rules for functions involving addition, subtraction, and multiplication and use those rules to solve problems.	**Goal 1.** Extend, describe, and create numeric patterns; describe rules for patterns and use them to solve problems; use words and symbols to describe and write rules for functions that involve the four basic arithmetic operations and use those rules to solve problems.	**Goal 1.** Extend, describe, and create numeric patterns; describe rules for patterns and use them to solve problems; write rules for functions involving the four basic arithmetic operations; represent functions using words, symbols, tables, and graphs and use those representations to solve problems.	**Goal 1.** Extend, describe, and create numeric patterns; describe rules for patterns and use them to solve problems; represent patterns and rules using algebraic notation; represent functions using words, algebraic notation, tables, and graphs; translate from one representation to another and use representations to solve problems involving functions.

Program Goal: Use Algebraic Notation to Represent and Analyze Situations and Structures

Content	Kindergarten	First Grade	Second Grade	Third Grade	Fourth Grade	Fifth Grade	Sixth Grade
Algebraic notation and solving number sentences	**Goal 2.** Read and write expressions and number sentences using the symbols $+$, $-$, and $=$.	**Goal 2.** Read, write, and explain expressions and number sentences using the symbols $+$, $-$, and $=$ and the symbols $>$ and $<$ with cues; solve equations involving addition and subtraction.	**Goal 2.** Read, write, and explain expressions and number sentences using the symbols $+$, $-$, $=$, $>$, and $<$; solve number sentences involving addition and subtraction; write expressions and number sentences to model number stories.	**Goal 2.** Read, write, and explain number sentences using the symbols $+$, $-$, $\times$, $\div$, $=$, $>$, and $<$; solve number sentences; write expressions and number sentences to model number stories.	**Goal 2.** Use conventional notation to write expressions and number sentences using the four basic arithmetic operations; determine whether number sentences are true or false; solve open sentences and explain the solutions; write expressions and number sentences to model number stories.	**Goal 2.** Determine whether number sentences are true or false; solve open number sentences and explain the solutions; use a letter variable to write an open sentence to model a number story; use a pan-balance model to solve linear equations in one unknown.	**Goal 2.** Determine whether equalities and inequalities are true or false; solve open number sentences and explain the solutions; use a pan-balance model to solve linear equations in one or two unknowns; use trial-and-error and equivalent equations strategies to solve linear equations in one unknown.

Everyday Mathematics

Program Goal: Use Algebraic Notation to Represent and Analyze Situations and Structures *cont.*

Content	Kindergarten	First Grade	Second Grade	Third Grade	Fourth Grade	Fifth Grade	Sixth Grade
Order of operations				**Goal 3.** Recognize that numeric expressions can have different values depending on the order in which operations are carried out; understand that grouping symbols can be used to affect the order in which operations are carried out.	**Goal 3.** Evaluate numeric expressions containing grouping symbols; insert grouping symbols to make number sentences true.	**Goal 3.** Evaluate numeric expressions containing grouping symbols and nested grouping symbols; insert grouping symbols and nested grouping symbols to make number sentences true; describe and use the precedence of multiplication and division over addition and subtraction.	**Goal 3.** Describe and apply the conventional order of operations.
Properties of the arithmetic operations		**Goal 3.** Apply the Commutative and Associative Properties of Addition and the Additive Identity to basic addition fact problems.	**Goal 3.** Describe the Commutative and Associative Properties of Addition and the Additive Identity and apply them to mental arithmetic problems.	**Goal 4.** Describe and apply the Commutative and Associative Properties of Addition and Multiplication and the Multiplicative Identity; apply the Distributive Property of Multiplication over Addition.	**Goal 4.** Describe and apply the Distributive Property of Multiplication over Addition.	**Goal 4.** Describe and apply properties of arithmetic.	**Goal 4.** Describe and apply properties of arithmetic and multiplicative and additive inverses.

Assessment Overviews

This section summarizes the assessment opportunities in each unit. Ongoing assessments, such as the Informing Instruction and Recognizing Student Achievement notes, are listed by lesson. Portfolio opportunities, paired or linked Math Boxes, and Writing/Reasoning prompts are also highlighted. You will find information on periodic assessments as well. Modifications for each unit's Progress Check Written Assessment, tips for implementing Open Response tasks (including rubrics for each task), and sample student responses for each rubric level are provided.

Contents

Beginning-of-Year Assessment Goals

The Beginning-of-Year Assessment (pages 202A–D) can be used to gauge students' readiness for the content they will encounter early in sixth grade. This allows you to plan your instruction accordingly. The following table provides the goals for all the problems in the Beginning-of-Year Assessment.

Problem(s)	Grade-Level Goal
1, 2, 6, 9, 12	**Number and Numeration 1:** Read and write whole numbers and decimals; identify places in such numbers and the values of the digits in those places; use expanded notation, number-and-word notation, exponential notation, and scientific notation to represent whole numbers and decimals.
3, 4, 7, 10, 11	**Operations and Computation 2:** Use mental arithmetic, paper-and-pencil algorithms and models, and calculators to solve problems involving the multiplication and division of whole numbers, decimals, and signed numbers; describe the strategies used and explain how they work.
5, 8, 13	**Patterns, Functions, and Algebra 1:** Extend, describe, and create numeric patterns; describe rules for patterns and use them to solve problems; represent patterns and rules using algebraic notation; represent functions using words, algebraic notation, tables, and graphs; translate from one representation to another and use representations to solve problems involving functions.

Assessment Overview

In this unit, students expand on their work with data from previous years including a review of bar graphs, line plots, and data landmarks. Use the information in this section to develop your assessment plan for Unit 1.

Ongoing Assessment

Opportunities for using and collecting ongoing assessment information are highlighted in Informing Instruction and Recognizing Student Achievement notes. Student products, along with observations and suggested writing prompts, provide a range of useful assessment information.

Informing Instruction

The Informing Instruction notes highlight students' thinking and point out common misconceptions. Informing Instruction in Unit 1: Lessons 1-3, 1-6, 1-7, 1-8, 1-10, and 1-11.

Recognizing Student Achievement

The Recognizing Student Achievement notes highlight specific tasks from which teachers can collect assessment data to monitor and document student progress toward meeting Grade-Level Goals.

Lesson	Content Assessed	Where to Find It
1◆1	**Multiply 2-digit whole numbers.** [Operations and Computation Goal 2]	*TLG*, p. 20
1◆2	**Demonstrate knowledge of landmark terms.** [Data and Chance Goal 2]	*TLG*, p. 25
1◆3	**Find the minimum, maximum, range, and mode of data displayed in a stem-and-leaf plot.** [Data and Chance Goal 2]	*TLG*, p. 30
1◆4	**Acknowledge the difference between median and mean.** [Data and Chance Goal 2]	*TLG*, p. 36
1◆5	**Construct a line plot and calculate the mean of a data set.** [Data and Chance Goals 1 and 2]	*TLG*, p. 41
1◆5a	**Calculate the interquartile range of a data set.** [Data and Chance Goal 2]	*TLG*, p. 42D
1◆6	**Read data values from a broken-line graph.** [Data and Chance Goal 1]	*TLG*, p. 46
1◆7	**Construct a bar graph from a description of data.** [Data and Chance Goal 1]	*TLG*, p. 50
1◆8	**Draw a broken-line graph from a table of data values.** [Data and Chance Goal 1]	*TLG*, p. 57
1◆9	**Estimate and measure sector sizes using the Percent Circle.** [Measurement and Reference Frames Goal 1]	*TLG*, p. 63
1◆10	**Explain how data landmarks change as data values change.** [Data and Chance Goal 2]	*TLG*, p. 69
1◆11	**Read and interpret a broken-line graph.** [Data and Chance Goal 2]	*TLG*, p. 74
1◆12	**Read and interpret side-by-side bar graphs.** [Data and Chance Goal 2]	*TLG*, p. 79

Math Boxes

Math Boxes, one of several types of tasks highlighted in the Recognizing Student Achievement notes, have an additional useful feature. Math Boxes in most lessons are paired or linked with Math Boxes in one or two other lessons that have similar problems. Paired or linked Math Boxes in Unit 1: 1-1 and 1-3; 1-2, 1-4, and 1-5a; 1-5 and 1-7; 1-6 and 1-8; 1-9 and 1-11; and 1-10 and 1-12.

Writing/Reasoning Prompts

In Unit 1, a variety of writing prompts encourage students to explain their strategies and thinking, to reflect on their learning, and to make connections to other mathematics or life experiences. Here are some of the Unit 1 suggestions:

Lesson	Writing/Reasoning Prompts	Where to Find It
1◆1	Explain how you could check your answer to a subtraction problem.	*TLG*, p. 20
1◆2	Explain how you can check your answer to a division problem without using a calculator.	*TLG*, p. 25
1◆5	Explain the strategy you used to convert between centimeters and meters.	*TLG*, p. 41
1◆6	Explain why your estimate of a product could be greater or less than the exact answer.	*TLG*, p. 46
1◆9	Explain what would happen to the median if the number of people for Tour 3 changed from 40 to 22.	*TLG*, p. 63

Portfolio Opportunities

Portfolios are a versatile tool for assessment. They help students reflect on their mathematical growth and help teachers understand and document that growth. Each unit identifies several student products that can be selected and stored in a portfolio. Here are some of the Unit 1 suggestions:

Lesson	Portfolio Opportunities	Where to Find It
1◆3	Students construct a back-to-back stem-and-leaf plot that has 2-digit stems.	*TLG*, p. 32
1◆8	Students complete a table and construct and interpret a step graph.	*TLG*, p. 58
1◆9	Students use computer software to generate a circle graph.	*TLG*, p. 64
1◆10	Students draw rectangles with given perimeters and determine perimeters.	*TLG*, p. 69
1◆10	Students calculate the areas of rectangular regions.	*TLG*, p. 70

Periodic Assessment

Every Progress Check lesson includes opportunities to observe student progress and to collect student products in a variety of ways—Self Assessment, Oral and Slate Assessment, Written Assessment, and an Open Response task. For more details, see the first page of Progress Check 1, Lesson 1-13 on page 82, of the *Teacher's Lesson Guide*.

Progress Check Modifications

Written Assessments are one way students demonstrate what they know. The table below shows modifications for the Written Assessment in this unit. Use these to maximize opportunities for students to demonstrate what they know. Modifications can be given individually or written on the board for the class.

Problem(s)	Modifications for Written Assessment
1, 2	For Problems 1 and 2, first put the numbers of the data set in order; then cross off each number as you enter it into your plot.
3	For Problem 3, write each student's age on a stick-on note and organize the stick-on notes from least to greatest.
7c	For Problem 7c, redraw the graph on centimeter grid paper. Draw the graph so that the axis for "Dollar Amounts" starts at 0. Use the same interval (5 thousand) to label the "Dollar Amounts" axis.
11	For Problem 11, explain why a step graph is a useful way to represent the information about Canoe Rental Prices.

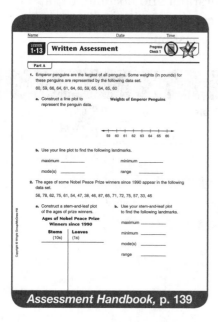

Assessment Handbook, p. 139

The Written Assessment for the Unit 1 Progress Check is on pages 139–142.

Open Response, *Analyzing Jumping-Jack Data*

Description

For this task, students use data landmarks to compare two data sets.

Focus

◆ **Use data landmarks and measures of spread to answer questions and draw conclusions.**
[Data and Chance Goal 2]

◆ **Compare and contrast the median and mean of a data set.**
[Data and Chance Goal 2]

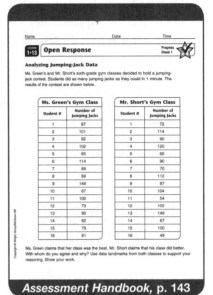

Assessment Handbook, p. 143

Implementation Tips

◆ Have students use the *Student Reference Book* to review the definitions for different landmarks and measures of spread.

◆ Emphasize that students may not need to find all of the data landmarks and measures of spread in order to answer the question.

Modifications for Meeting Diverse Needs

◆ Enlarge and copy the data for each class on a different colored paper. Have students cut out the numbers and make a line plot for each data set. Use index cards to make a label for each landmark. After students have made the line plot, have them place the landmark labels on the correct pieces of data.

◆ Have students explain how and why their responses would or would not change if another student who jumped 90 jumping jacks in one minute were added to each class.

Improving Open Response Skills

After students complete the task, have them discuss the difference between mean and median. Emphasize that outliers have no effect on median. Have students describe how mean and median are useful in solving this problem. Have students discuss in groups what a good *mathematical* explanation should include. Record a list of suggestions on chart paper. *(Sample answer: Refers back to the data, uses numbers and data landmarks, and answers the original question.)* Have students go back and try to improve their explanations based on the class discussion.

Note: The wording and formatting of the text on the student samples that follow may vary slightly from the actual task your children will complete. These minor discrepancies will not affect the implementation of the task.

Rubric

This rubric is designed to help you assess levels of mathematical performance on this task. It emphasizes mathematical understanding with only a mention of clarity of explanation. Consider the expectations of standardized tests in your area when applying a rubric. Modify this sample rubric as appropriate.

4	Correctly calculates one or more landmarks, and uses the landmark(s) to support a claim for which class did better. Explains reasoning clearly and completely, and uses mathematical vocabulary, such as *mean, median, average, compared,* and so on.
3	Calculates one or more landmarks with only minor errors, and uses the landmark(s) to support a claim for which class did better. There might be unnecessary information included. Explains some steps for solving the problem, and might use some mathematical vocabulary, such as *mean, median, average, compared,* and so on.
2	Recognizes that data landmarks can be used to solve the problem, but might not clearly describe how they are used to solve the problem. Explains some steps of the solution strategy, but there might be steps missing or incorrect.
1	Might mention or identify data landmarks on the paper, but might not use landmarks to solve the problem. The explanation might not make sense in the context of the problem.
0	Does not attempt to solve the problem.

Sample Student Responses

This Level 4 paper illustrates the following features: The values of the range, mode, median, and mean are calculated correctly for each class. The explanation clearly states that Mr. Short's class is better because the median for Mr. Short's class is greater. Mathematical vocabulary is used in the explanation.

This Level 4 paper illustrates the following features: The values the minimum, maximum, range, and mean are calculated correctly for each class. The explanation clearly states that the classes performed equally well because the mean for the two classes is identical. Mathematical vocabulary is used in the explanation.

This Level 3 paper illustrates the following features: The values of the minimum, maximum, mode, range, median, and mean are calculated correctly for each class. The explanation states that Mr. Short's class is better because the mode, median, and range for Mr. Short's class are higher numbers. The explanation treats the three landmarks as though they were equally important in determining an answer.

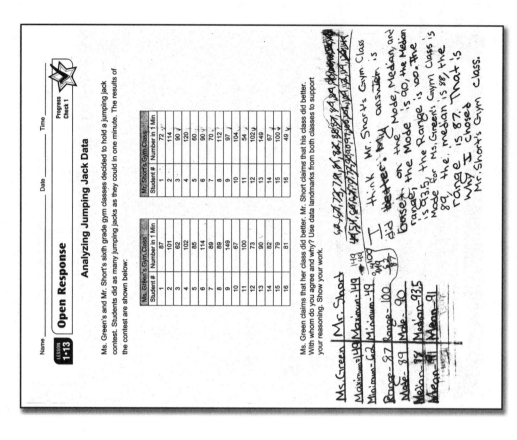

This Level 3 paper illustrates the following features: The values of the minimum, maximum, mode, and mean are calculated correctly for each class. The explanation states that Mr. Short's class is better because even though the mean for the two classes is identical, some students in Mr. Short's class "had higher scores." This last statement must be interpreted based on the notes near the data sets.

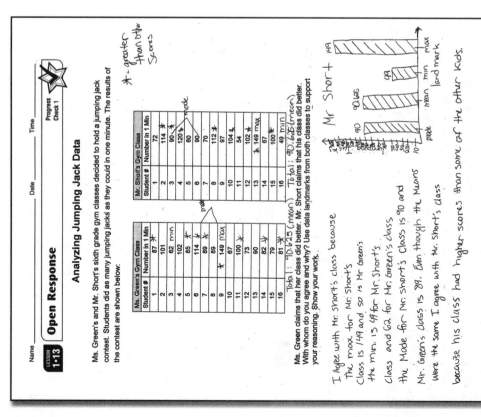

This Level 1 paper illustrates the following features: The number of jumping jacks are totaled for each class, but no data landmarks are calculated or referenced in the answer.

This Level 2 paper illustrates the following features: Some landmarks are calculated incorrectly. Instead of comparing landmarks to solve the problem, the landmarks are totaled for each class and the sums are compared.

Level 1 paper

Name _____ Date _____ Time _____

LESSON 1·13 | **Open Response** Progress Check 1

Analyzing Jumping Jack Data

Ms. Green's and Mr. Short's sixth grade gym classes decided to hold a jumping jack contest. Students did as many jumping jacks as they could in one minute. The results of the contest are shown below:

Ms. Green's Gym Class

Student #	Number in 1 Min
1	87
2	101
3	62
4	102
5	85
6	114
7	89
8	89
9	149
10	67
11	100
12	73
13	90
14	82
15	79
16	81

Mr. Short's Gym Class

Student #	Number in 1 Min
1	72
2	114
3	90
4	120
5	60
6	90
7	70
8	112
9	97
10	104
11	54
12	102
13	149
14	67
15	100
16	49

(handwritten column of sums ... 149 = 1,450)

Ms. Green claims that her class did better. Mr. Short claims that his class did better. With whom do you agree and why? Use data landmarks from both classes to support your reasoning. Show your work.

(handwritten) 149 = 1,450

Mr. Short's Gym class did more Jumping Jacks than ms. Green's Gym class.

Level 2 paper

Name _____ Date _____ Time _____

LESSON 1·13 | **Open Response** Progress Check 1

Analyzing Jumping Jack Data

Ms. Green's and Mr. Short's sixth grade gym classes decided to hold a jumping jack contest. Students did as many jumping jacks as they could in one minute. The results of the contest are shown below:

Ms. Green's Gym Class

Student #	Number in 1 Min
1	87
2	101
3	62
4	102
5	85
6	114
7	89
8	89
9	149
10	97
11	100
12	73
13	90
14	82
15	79
16	81

(handwritten landmarks)
Mode : 89
Maximum: 149
Minimum ; 62
Mean: 91
Median : 89
Range : 87
567

Mr. Short's Gym Class

Student #	Number in 1 Min
1	72
2	114
3	90
4	120
5	60
6	90
7	70
8	112
9	97
10	104
11	54
12	102
13	149
14	67
15	100
16	49

(handwritten landmarks)
Mode : 90
Maximum: 149
Minimum : 54
Mean : 91
Median : 90
Range : 95
569

Ms. Green claims that her class did better. Mr. Short claims that his class did better. With whom do you agree and why? Use data landmarks from both classes to support your reasoning. Show your work.

(handwritten)

I agree with Mr Shorts because I looked at the landmarks and then I add up the landmarks and for Ms. Green and I got 567 and for Mr Shorts and I got then I add Mr Shorts + 569 thats why I think its Mr Shorts.

Assessment Overview

In this unit, students review computation algorithms for decimals and explore scientific notation for writing very large and very small numbers. Use the information in this section to develop your assessment plan for Unit 2.

Ongoing Assessment

Opportunities for using and collecting ongoing assessment information are highlighted in Informing Instruction and Recognizing Student Achievement notes. Student products, along with observations and suggested writing prompts, provide a range of useful assessment information.

Informing Instruction

The Informing Instruction notes highlight students' thinking and point out common misconceptions. Informing Instruction in Unit 2: Lessons 2-1, 2-4, 2-7, and 2-9.

Recognizing Student Achievement

The Recognizing Student Achievement notes highlight specific tasks from which teachers can collect assessment data to monitor and document student progress toward meeting Grade-Level Goals.

Lesson	Content Assessed	Where to Find It
2•1	Write whole numbers to billions. [Number and Numeration Goal 1]	*TLG*, p. 104
2•2	Compare decimals through thousandths. [Number and Numeration Goal 6]	*TLG*, p. 111
2•3	Align the digits of whole and decimal numbers by place value. [Number and Numeration Goal 1]	*TLG*, p. 114
2•4	Write decimals to thousandths. [Number and Numeration Goal 1]	*TLG*, p. 121
2•5	Estimate products of decimals. [Operations and Computation Goal 5]	*TLG*, p. 126
2•6	Make reasonable estimates for products and multiply decimals. [Operations and Computation Goal 2]	*TLG*, p. 133
2•7	Make reasonable estimates for quotients and divide whole numbers by 2-digit divisors. [Operations and Computation Goal 2]	*TLG*, p. 139
2•8	Make reasonable estimates for quotients and solve a division problem. [Operations and Computation Goal 2]	*TLG*, p. 145
2•9	Determine the power of 10 needed to move the decimal point in the other factor to the right or left. [Number and Numeration Goal 1]	*TLG*, p. 148
2•10	Interpret exponential notation and use the power key on the calculator. [Number and Numeration Goal 1]	*TLG*, p. 155
2•11	Translate from scientific notation to standard notation. [Number and Numeration Goal 1]	*TLG*, p. 160

Math Boxes

Math Boxes, one of several types of tasks highlighted in the Recognizing Student Achievement notes, have an additional useful feature. Math Boxes in most lessons are paired or linked with Math Boxes in one or two other lessons that have similar problems. Paired or linked Math Boxes in Unit 2: 2-1 and 2-3; 2-2 and 2-4; 2-5 and 2-7; 2-6, 2-8, and 2-10; and 2-9 and 2-11.

Writing/Reasoning Prompts

In Unit 2, a variety of writing prompts encourage students to explain their strategies and thinking, to reflect on their learning, and to make connections to other mathematics or life experiences. Here are some of the Unit 2 suggestions:

Lesson	Writing/Reasoning Prompts	Where to Find It
2•2	Explain why each of the other three answers is not the best choice.	*TLG*, p. 111
2•5	Explain why the product 77 * 0.1 is less than 77.	*TLG*, p. 127
2•6	Explain why the product is always less than either of the two factors, when each factor is less than 1.	*TLG*, p. 133
2•9	Explain how you decided where to place the decimal point in a product and a quotient.	*TLG*, p. 150
2•10	Describe something you notice in the number pairs you moved from *P* to *Q* on the line graph.	*TLG*, p. 155

Portfolio Opportunities

Portfolios are a versatile tool for assessment. They help students reflect on their mathematical growth and help teachers understand and document that growth. Each unit identifies several student products that can be selected and stored in a portfolio. Here are some of the Unit 2 suggestions:

Lesson	Portfolio Opportunities	Where to Find It
2•1	Students solve a multistep problem and explain their solution strategies.	*TLG*, p. 107
2•4	Students compare the powers of 10 in the factors to the power of 10 in the product.	*TLG*, p. 122
2•5	Students compare products and factors.	*TLG*, p. 127
2•5	Students construct a table to find how many food items they can buy with $25.	*TLG*, p. 128
2•6	Students review examples of a halving-and-doubling strategy and use it to mentally compute products.	*TLG*, p. 134

Periodic Assessment

Every Progress Check lesson includes opportunities to observe student progress and to collect student products in a variety of ways—Self Assessment, Oral and Slate Assessment, Written Assessment, and an Open Response task. For more details, see the first page of Progress Check 2, Lesson 2-12, page 162, of the *Teacher's Lesson Guide*.

Progress Check Modifications

Written Assessments are one way students demonstrate what they know. The table below shows modifications for the Written Assessment in this unit. Use these to maximize opportunities for students to demonstrate what they know. Modifications can be given individually or written on the board for the class.

Problem(s)	Modifications for Written Assessment
1–3	For Problems 1–3, place each digit in a place-value chart before recording your final digit or number.
8, 9	For Problems 8 and 9, build the numbers with base-10 blocks or use pictures of base-10 blocks to model the problems.
12	For Problem 12, explain how writing numbers in expanded notation is connected to place value.
15–18	For Problems 15–18, label each interval on the number line with its decimal name before solving the problems.

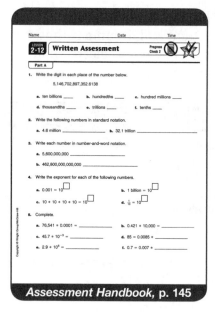

Assessment Handbook, p. 145

The Written Assessment for the Unit 2 Progress Check is on pages 145–148.

Open Response, *Planning a Pizza Party*

Description

For this task, students find the best buy for a pizza party based on the number of slices in each pizza and the cost of each one.

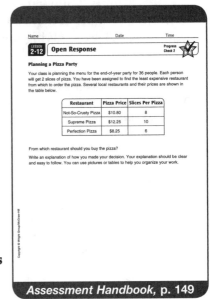

Assessment Handbook, p. 149

Focus

◆ **Use paper-and-pencil algorithms to solve problems involving the multiplication and division of whole numbers and decimals; describe the strategies used and explain how they work.** [Operations and Computation Goal 2]

◆ **Make reasonable estimates for whole number and decimal multiplication and division problems; explain how the estimates were obtained.** [Operations and Computation Goal 5]

Implementation Tips

◆ Review what information is in the chart. Remind students that they need to find the best buy for the amount of pizza they must buy, not just the least-expensive pizza.

Modifications for Meeting Diverse Needs

◆ Have students illustrate the problem on a separate piece of paper. They can draw pizzas and slices in the pizzas, and label them with the name of the shop and the price. First, have them compute how many of each kind of pizza they would have to buy to get 72 slices. Then have them compute the total cost for each multiple purchase.

◆ Have students compute the absolute best buy (assuming they can buy from more than one pizza place). *(Sample answer: 2 pizzas from Perfection Pizza and 6 pizzas from Not-So-Crusty Pizza.)* Have them explain how they found their answer.

Improving Open Response Skills

Before students begin the task, have them read the problem independently. Have the class identify a list of numbers needed to solve the problem. Record the students' list of numbers on the board or on chart paper, and display it during the task.

Note: The wording and formatting of the text on the student samples that follow may vary slightly from the actual task your children will complete. These minor discrepancies will not affect the implementation of the task.

Rubric

This rubric is designed to help you assess levels of mathematical performance on this task. It emphasizes mathematical understanding with only a mention of clarity of explanation. Consider the expectations of standardized tests in your area when applying a rubric. Modify this sample rubric as appropriate.

4 Calculates that 72 slices need to be purchased and how many pizzas are needed. Calculates and compares the total cost for each restaurant. Justifies the choice of least expensive. Explains or illustrates all of the solution steps clearly and completely.

3 Calculates that 72 slices need to be purchased and how many pizzas are needed. Calculates and compares the total cost for each restaurant with minor errors. Justifies the choice of least expensive. Explains or illustrates some steps of the strategy used to solve the problem.

2 Might calculate that 72 slices need to be purchased. Attempts to calculate which restaurant has the best deal. Might make calculation errors. Attempts to explain or illustrate some steps of the solution strategy, but might omit necessary steps or list incorrect steps.

1 Attempts to solve the problem, but the solution strategy might not make sense in the context of the problem.

0 Does not attempt to solve the problem.

Sample Student Responses

This Level 4 paper illustrates the following features: It identifies Not-So-Crusty as the best buy. The explanation clearly describes all the solution steps. First the total number of pizzas required is determined (mentioning that since no multiple provides exactly 72 slices, an additional pizza is required from Supreme), and each number of pizzas is multiplied by the cost per pizza using a lattice. All conclusions are listed.

This Level 4 paper illustrates the following features: It identifies Not-So-Crusty as the best buy. The explanation clearly describes all the solution steps. First the total number of pizzas required from each restaurant is determined, and each number of pizzas is multiplied by the cost per pizza.

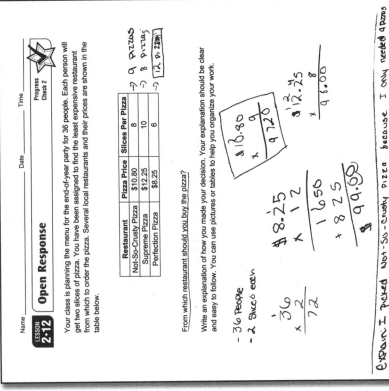

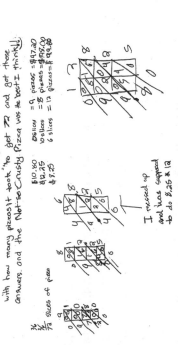

This Level 3 paper illustrates the following features: There is no written explanation; however, all of the steps for solving the problem are illustrated with pictures and numbers, and the work is labeled. The computation and the answer are correct.

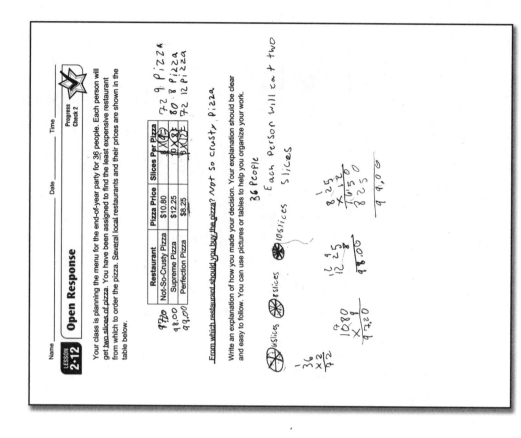

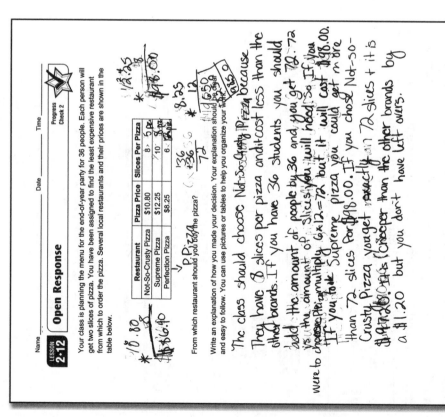

This Level 3 paper illustrates the following features: It identifies Not-So-Crusty as the best buy. The explanation describes some steps for the solution. The total of 72 is explained, and the computation is all described, but there are no reasons included in the explanation. Some of the computation on the page is incorrect and does not match the explanation.

This Level 1 paper illustrates the following features: Some of the work on the page makes sense in the context of the problem, but the numbers of pizzas used for the different restaurants are incorrect. Because the totals are incorrect, the conclusion that Perfection Pizza is the best deal is also incorrect.

This Level 2 paper illustrates the following features: It identifies Supreme Pizza as the best buy. The solution strategy is partially correct. It is determined that 72 slices are required, and there is computation that indicates some understanding of the problem. There are errors in the computation, and the explanation for the second way does not take into account that an extra pizza is required from Supreme.

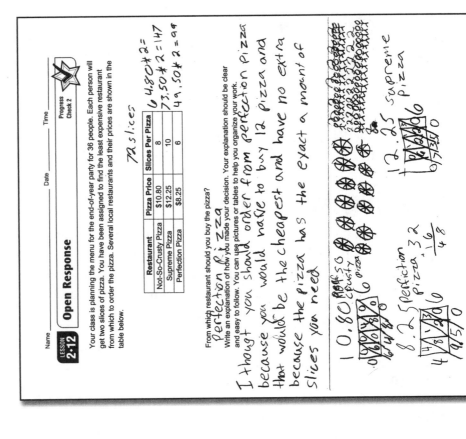

In this unit, students build on their work from previous grade levels exploring the relationships between rules, tables, and graphs, including writing rules using variables. Use the information in this section to develop your assessment plan for Unit 3.

Ongoing Assessment

Opportunities for using and collecting ongoing assessment information are highlighted in Informing Instruction and Recognizing Student Achievement notes. Student products, along with observations and suggested writing prompts, provide a range of useful assessment information.

Informing Instruction
The Informing Instruction notes highlight students' thinking and point out common misconceptions. Informing Instruction in Unit 3: Lessons 3-1, 3-2, 3-5, and 3-10.

Recognizing Student Achievement
The Recognizing Student Achievement notes highlight specific tasks from which teachers can collect assessment data to monitor and document student progress toward meeting Grade-Level Goals.

Lesson	Content Assessed	Where to Find It
3•1	**Write special cases for a general pattern.** [Patterns, Functions, and Algebra Goal 1]	*TLG*, p. 183
3•2	**Write a general pattern with two variables to represent a special case.** [Patterns, Functions, and Algebra Goal 1]	*TLG*, p. 188
3•3	**Find decimal solutions to whole-number division problems.** [Operations and Computation Goal 2]	*TLG*, p. 194
3•4	**Use algebraic notation to describe general patterns.** [Patterns, Functions, and Algebra Goal 1]	*TLG*, p. 197
3•5	**Complete a table from a formula and graph the data.** [Patterns, Functions, and Algebra Goal 1]	*TLG*, p. 205
3•6	**Complete a table from a formula and graph the data.** [Patterns, Functions, and Algebra Goal 1]	*TLG*, p. 212
3•7	**Add positive and negative numbers.** [Operations and Computation Goal 1]	*TLG*, p. 217
3•8	**Solve open number sentences involving signed numbers.** [Operations and Computation Goal 1]	*TLG*, p. 220
3•9	**Analyze the shape of a graph and draw conclusions about data trends.** [Data and Chance Goal 2]	*TLG*, p. 225
3•10	**Name a spreadsheet cell and identify a spreadsheet formula for calculating a total.** [Patterns, Functions, and Algebra Goal 1]	*TLG*, p. 233

Math Boxes

Math Boxes, one of several types of tasks highlighted in the Recognizing Student Achievement notes, have an additional useful feature. Math Boxes in most lessons are paired or linked with Math Boxes in one or two other lessons that have similar problems. Paired or linked Math Boxes in Unit 3: 3-1 and 3-3; 3-2 and 3-4; 3-5 and 3-7; 3-6 and 3-9; and 3-8 and 3-10.

Writing/Reasoning Prompts

In Unit 3, a variety of writing prompts encourage students to explain their strategies and thinking, to reflect on their learning, and to make connections to other mathematics or life experiences. Here are some of the Unit 3 suggestions:

Lesson	Writing/Reasoning Prompts	Where to Find It
3♦1	Explain how you know where to place the decimal point in the quotient.	*TLG*, p. 183
3♦2	Describe the general pattern you wrote in words.	*TLG*, p. 188
3♦5	Explain how you can use 2^4 to write 2^8 in standard notation.	*TLG*, p. 206
3♦6	Describe the strategy you used to rename 0.3 as a percent.	*TLG*, p. 212
3♦8	Explain the strategy you used to compare numbers.	*TLG*, p. 222

Portfolio Opportunities

Portfolios are a versatile tool for assessment. They help students reflect on their mathematical growth and help teachers understand and document that growth. Each unit identifies several student products that can be selected and stored in a portfolio. Here are some of the Unit 3 suggestions.

Lesson	Portfolio Opportunities	Where to Find It
3♦1	Students use "What's My Rule?" tables to make connections between general number patterns and special cases.	*TLG*, p. 184
3♦4	Students are given several approaches to explore the process of deriving a formula for a brick wall.	*TLG*, p. 200
3♦8	Students evaluate a formula by substituting specific values for a variable.	*TLG*, p. 221
3♦9	Students construct original mystery graphs and describe the situations the graphs represent.	*TLG*, p. 229
3♦10	Students review and practice writing a rule, completing a table, or making a graph representing a situation.	*TLG*, p. 234

Periodic Assessment

Every Progress Check lesson includes opportunities to observe student progress and to collect student products in a variety of ways—Self Assessment, Oral and Slate Assessment, Written Assessment, and an Open Response task. For more details, see the first page of Progress Check 3, Lesson 3-11, page 236, of the *Teacher's Lesson Guide*.

Progress Check Modifications

Written Assessments are one way students demonstrate what they know. The table below shows modifications for the Written Assessment in this unit. Use these to maximize opportunities for students to demonstrate what they know. Modifications can be given individually or written on the board for the class.

Problem(s)	Modifications for Written Assessment
3, 5	For Problems 3 and 5, use a ruler to estimate the equivalent number of centimeters.
7	For Problem 7, rewrite each expression, replacing *x* with 3, and then solve the problems.
11	For Problem 11, explain how you chose the matching graph and explain why the graph matches the situation.
16	For Problem 16, use factor rainbows to find the greatest common factor for each pair of numbers.

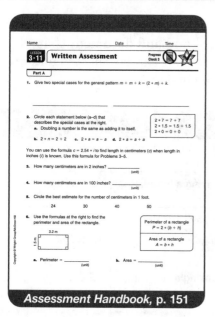

Assessment Handbook, p. 151

The Written Assessment for the Unit 3 Progress Check is on pages 151–154.

Open Response, *Representing Rates*

Description

For this task, students use various representations of rate functions to compare and analyze how membership numbers of two school clubs increase over time.

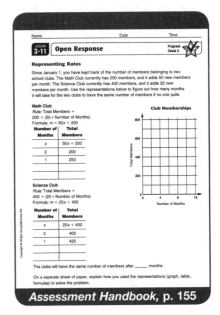

Assessment Handbook, p. 155

Focus

◆ **Extend and describe rules for patterns and use them to solve problems.**
[Patterns, Functions, and Algebra Goal 1]

◆ **Represent functions using words, algebraic notation, tables, and graphs.**
[Patterns, Functions, and Algebra Goal 1]

◆ **Translate from one representation to another and use representations to solve problems involving functions.**
[Patterns, Functions, and Algebra Goal 1]

Implementation Tips

◆ Review graphing ordered pairs on a coordinate grid.

◆ Review the meaning of a variable in a formula.

Modifications for Meeting Diverse Needs

◆ Extend the tables on a separate sheet of paper so students have enough rows to find where the two data sets intersect *(8 months)*. Enlarge the graph and label the intermediate grid lines to make plotting points easier.

◆ Have students determine which representation best helps them calculate when the Math Club will have 1.5 times as many members as the Science Club. *(Sample answer: The table could work if I skip around for a number of months until I narrow down the possibilities; for example, try 10 months, then 15 months.)* Have students find the point at which the Math Club has 1.5 times as many members. *(32 months)*

Improving Open Response Skills

Before students begin the task, have them read the problem together. Review Level 4 of the rubric using the board or overhead projector. Have students brainstorm the qualities of a Level 4 paper and rewrite the rubric for Level 4 in their own words. Record the students' Level 4 description on chart paper, and display this during the task. Have students compare their work with the posted Level 4 description of qualities before turning in their papers.

Note: The wording and formatting of the text on the student samples that follow may vary slightly from the actual task your children will complete. These minor discrepancies will not affect the implementation of the task.

Rubric

This rubric is designed to help you assess levels of mathematical performance on this task. It emphasizes mathematical understanding with only a mention of clarity of explanation. Consider the expectations of standardized tests in your area when applying a rubric. Modify this sample rubric as appropriate.

4 Completes the tables and plots ordered pairs correctly. Connects plotted points and indicates the graphed lines intersect at the correct coordinates. Clearly explains all of the steps for how a representation (formula, table, graph) is used to solve the problem.

3 Completes the tables and plots ordered pairs correctly. Connects plotted points and indicates the graphed lines intersect at the correct coordinates. Explains some steps for how a representation (formula, table, graph) is used, but the steps might require clarification or additional information.

2 Completes the tables and plots some ordered pairs, but not all are plotted correctly. Might or might not connect the plotted points. Attempts to use the rules, the table patterns, or the graph to solve the problem, but the strategy used is unclear or might have errors.

1 Attempts to complete the table and plot the ordered pairs, but there might be errors. The explanation describes a strategy that might be incorrect or make no sense in the context of the problem.

0 Does not attempt to solve the problem.

Sample Student Responses

This Level 4 paper illustrates the following features: Tables are completed correctly and extended to 12 months according to the table rules. All points are plotted and connected correctly on the grid and the lines intersect at (8,600). The explanation clearly describes using the formula to extend the tables to identify when the number of members for both clubs is the same.

This Level 4 paper illustrates the following features: Tables are completed correctly and extended to 10 months according to the table rules. All points are plotted and connected correctly on the grid and the lines intersect at (8,600). The explanation clearly describes repeating the pattern for the rule to identify when the number of members for both clubs is the same. This information is illustrated in an extended table.

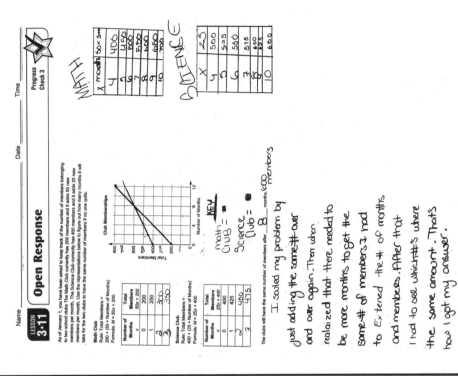

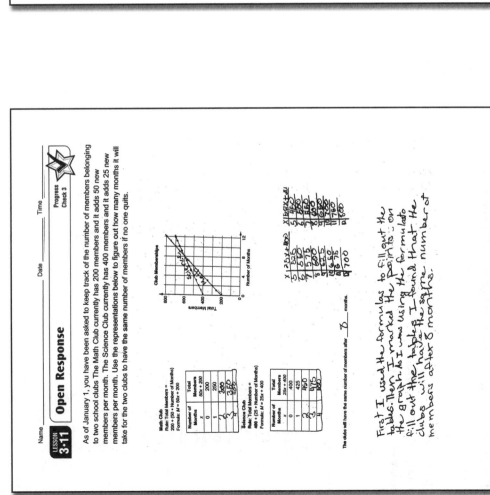

This Level 3 paper illustrates the following features: Tables are completed correctly. All points are plotted and connected correctly on the grid and the lines are extended to intersect at (8,600). The explanation refers to completing the graph, but it is unclear how the answer is determined.

This Level 3 paper illustrates the following features: Tables are completed correctly and extended to 8 months according to the table rules. All points are plotted and connected correctly on the grid and the lines intersect at (8,600). The explanation refers to completing the tables and graph, but it is unclear how the answer is determined.

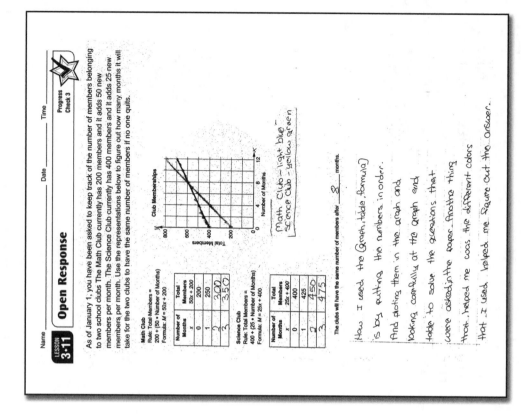

LESSON 3·11 Open Response Progress Check 3

As of January 1, you have been asked to keep track of the number of members belonging to two school clubs The Math Club currently has 200 members and it adds 50 new members per month. The Science Club currently has 400 members and it adds 25 new members per month. Use the representations below to figure out how many months it will take for the two clubs to have the same number of members if no one quits.

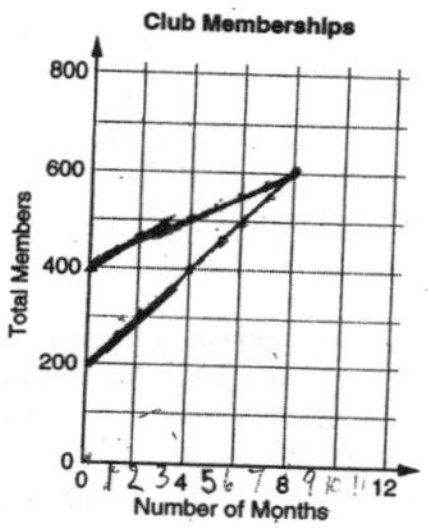

Math Club
Rule: Total Members =
200 + (50 • Number of Months)
Formula: M = 50x + 200

Number of Months x	Total Members 50x + 200
0	200
1	250
2	300
3	350

Science Club
Rule: Total Members =
400 + (25 • Number of Months)
Formula: M = 25x + 400

Number of Months x	Total Members 25x + 400
0	400
1	425
2	450
3	475

The clubs will have the same number of members after __8__ months.

(handwritten) How I used the Graph, table, formula is by putting the numbers in order. And ploting them in the graph and looking carefully at the graph and table to solve the questions that were asked in the paper. Anothe thing that helped me was the different colors that I used helped me figure out the answer.

Math Club - light blue
Science Club - yellow green

LESSON 3·11 Open Response Progress Check 3

As of January 1, you have been asked to keep track of the number of members belonging to two school clubs The Math Club currently has 200 members and it adds 50 new members per month. The Science Club currently has 400 members and it adds 25 new members per month. Use the representations below to figure out how many months it will take for the two clubs to have the same number of members if no one quits.

Math Club
Rule: Total Members =
200 + (50 • Number of Months)
Formula: M = 50x + 200

Number of Months x	Total Members 50x + 200
0	200
1	250
2	300
3	350

Science Club
Rule: Total Members =
400 + (25 • Number of Months)
Formula: M = 25x + 400

Number of Months x	Total Members 25x + 400
0	400
1	425
2	450
3	475

The clubs will have the same number of members after __8__ months.

(handwritten Math table)

# of Months	Total Numbers
4	400
5	450
6	500
7	550
8	600

Math

(handwritten Science table)

# of Months	Total Members
4	500
5	525
6	550
7	575
8	600

Science

(handwritten) I got answer by filling the numbers in. I used it by going from one to eight. then, I move my lines up to 600.

This Level 2 paper illustrates the following features: The correct answer is recorded, but it is unclear how the answer is determined based on the work that is shown. The explanation simply restates part of the rule, and only one table is completed far enough to determine the necessary number of months. The graph is completed correctly.

This Level 1 paper illustrates the following features: There is evidence of using the rule to complete the table; however, there are computation errors resulting in incorrect entries in the table. The correct answer is recorded, but no work on the page supports this answer.

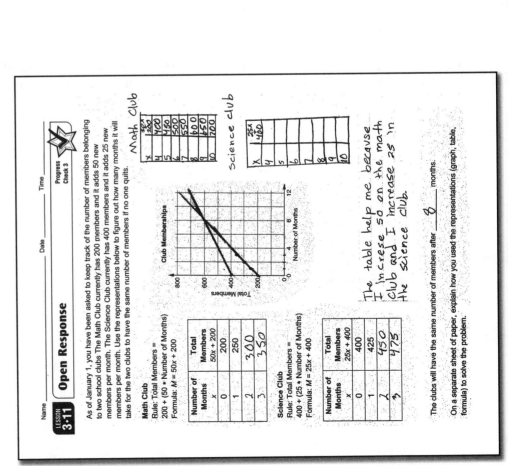

In this unit, students continue their exploration of operations with fractions and mixed numbers, and review the meaning and uses of percents. Use the information in this section to develop your assessment plan for Unit 4.

Ongoing Assessment

Opportunities for using and collecting ongoing assessment information are highlighted in Informing Instruction and Recognizing Student Achievement notes. Student products, along with observations and suggested writing prompts, provide a range of useful assessment information.

Informing Instruction
The Informing Instruction notes highlight students' thinking and point out common misconceptions. Informing Instruction in Unit 4: Lessons 4-1, 4-6, and 4-9.

Recognizing Student Achievement
The Recognizing Student Achievement notes highlight specific tasks from which teachers can collect assessment data to monitor and document student progress toward meeting Grade-Level Goals.

Lesson	Content Assessed	Where to Find It
4•1	**Rename fractions in simplest form.** [Number and Numeration Goal 5]	*TLG*, p. 257
4•2	**Name the least common multiple (LCM) for a number pair.** [Number and Numeration Goal 3]	*TLG*, p. 261
4•3	**Add and subtract fractions with unlike denominators.** [Operations and Computation Goal 3]	*TLG*, p. 269
4•4	**Add mixed numbers with like denominators.** [Operations and Computation Goal 3]	*TLG*, p. 275
4•5	**Subtract mixed numbers.** [Operations and Computation Goal 3]	*TLG*, p. 281
4•6	**Add and subtract fractions with unlike denominators.** [Operations and Computation Goal 3]	*TLG*, p. 286
4•7	**Multiply fractions.** [Operations and Computation Goal 4]	*TLG*, p. 290
4•8	**Convert between fractions, decimals, and percents.** [Number and Numeration Goal 5]	*TLG*, p. 296
4•9	**Multiply a whole number by a fraction to find a fractional part of the number.** [Operations and Computation Goal 4]	*TLG*, p. 305
4•10	**Rename fractions as decimals and percents.** [Number and Numeration Goal 5]	*TLG*, p. 308
4•11	**Convert between fractions, decimals, and percents.** [Number and Numeration Goal 5]	*TLG*, p. 316

Math Boxes

Math Boxes, one of several types of tasks highlighted in the Recognizing Student Achievement notes, have an additional useful feature. Math Boxes in most lessons are paired or linked with Math Boxes in one or two other lessons that have similar problems. Paired or linked Math Boxes in Unit 4: 4-1 and 4-3; 4-2 and 4-4; 4-5 and 4-7; 4-6, 4-8, and 4-10; and 4-9 and 4-11.

Writing/Reasoning Prompts

In Unit 4, a variety of writing prompts encourage students to explain their strategies and thinking, to reflect on their learning, and to make connections to other mathematics or life experiences. Here are some of the Unit 4 suggestions:

Lesson	Writing/Reasoning Prompts	Where to Find It
4◆1	Explain how you found the missing term in the proportion.	*TLG*, p. 258
4◆2	Explain how you solved fraction addition problems involving unlike denominators.	*TLG*, p. 264
4◆5	Explain why $302.7 * 10^{-3}$ is equal to $302.7 \div 1,000$.	*TLG*, p. 281
4◆6	Explain the strategy you used to compare fractions.	*TLG*, p. 286
4◆9	Explain the strategy you used to compare and order a set of 5 fractions.	*TLG*, p. 305

Portfolio Opportunities

Portfolios are a versatile tool for assessment. They help students reflect on their mathematical growth and help teachers understand and document that growth. Each unit identifies several student products that can be selected and stored in a portfolio. Here are some of the Unit 4 suggestions:

Lesson	Portfolio Opportunities	Where to Find It
4◆3	Students play *Paper Pool* to explore patterns related to the least common multiple.	*TLG*, p. 271
4◆6	Students explain the strategy they used to compare fractions.	*TLG*, p. 286
4◆6	Students model fraction multiplication.	*TLG*, p. 287
4◆10	Students conduct a survey, collect the data, and use a spreadsheet or graphing program to make a circle graph of the results.	*TLG*, p. 312
4◆11	Students conduct a survey and compare their results with the results in the original study.	*TLG*, p. 317

Periodic Assessment

Every Progress Check lesson includes opportunities to observe student progress and to collect student products in a variety of ways—Self Assessment, Oral and Slate Assessment, Written Assessment, and an Open Response task. For more details, see the first page of Progress Check 4, Lesson 4-12, page 318, of the *Teacher's Lesson Guide*.

Progress Check Modifications

Written Assessments are one way students demonstrate what they know. The table below shows modifications for the Written Assessment in this unit. Use these to maximize opportunities for students to demonstrate what they know. Modifications can be given individually or written on the board for the class.

Problem(s)	Modifications for Written Assessment
3	For Problem 3, use the Fraction-Stick and Decimal Number-Line Chart on *Student Reference Book*, page 373, to make the comparisons.
7a	For Problem 7a, explain how you figured out what fraction of the garden contains lilies.
8	For Problem 8, use a calculator to figure out the percent of students for each number of students.
11	For Problem 11, rewrite each expression, replacing x with 5, and then solve the problems.

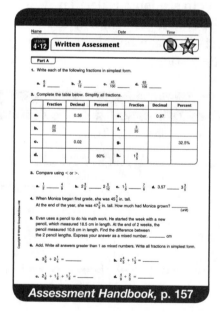

Assessment Handbook, p. 157

The Written Assessment for the Unit 4 Progress Check is on pages 157–159.

Open Response, *Making a Wooden Rack*

  45-55 Min.

Description

For this task, students calculate the measurements for a wooden rack based on a set of requirements.

Focus

◆ **Estimate length with and without tools.**
[Measurement and Reference Frames Goal 1]

◆ **Use mental arithmetic and paper-and-pencil algorithms to solve problems involving the addition and subtraction of fractions and mixed numbers.**
[Operations and Computation Goal 3]

Implementation Tips

◆ Review the meaning of *diameter*.

◆ Discuss how the illustration is related to the problem.

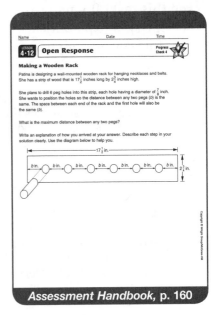

Assessment Handbook, p. 160

Modifications for Meeting Diverse Needs

◆ Provide a $17\frac{1}{2}$-inch strip of adding machine tape that has six circles drawn on it each with a diameter of $\frac{7}{8}$ inch so students can model the problem. Have students check their answers against their model.

◆ Have students develop a formula for calculating the length of the wooden rack for *N* pegs. Assume all relationships in the problem stay consistent, that is, the distance between the holes, the diameters of the holes, and the border of the surrounding wood.

Improving Open Response Skills

After students complete the task, have them organize their answers into two columns on a separate sheet of paper—*What* each step is, and *Why* each step is required. For example, in the *What* column, students might write *multiply $\frac{7}{8}$ by 6*. In the *Why* column, they might record *to determine how much of the length the pegs will occupy*. Have students attach this explanation to their original task. Remind students that when they explain their answers, the explanation should include the information from both of the columns on their charts.

Note: The wording and formatting of the text on the student samples that follow may vary slightly from the actual task your children will complete. These minor discrepancies will not affect the implementation of the task.

Rubric

This rubric is designed to help you assess levels of mathematical performance on this task. It emphasizes mathematical understanding with only a mention of clarity of explanation. Consider the expectations of standardized tests in your area when applying a rubric. Modify this sample rubric as appropriate.

4	Uses the given information to compute the maximum distance between two pegs. Uses number sentences and notation correctly. Converts between mixed numbers and fractions. Clearly and completely explains and/or shows all steps of the solution strategy. The strategy can be generalized to similar situations.
3	Uses the given information to compute the maximum distance between two pegs. Uses number sentences and notation has only minor errors. Converts between mixed numbers and fractions. There might be minor computation errors. Explains and/or shows some steps of the solution strategy, but the explanation might require clarification or additional information.
2	Attempts to compute the maximum distance between two pegs. Converts between mixed numbers and fractions but might have minor errors. Uses number sentences and notation has only minor errors. The strategy makes sense in the context of the problem, but might have errors or be incomplete.
1	Attempts to compute the maximum distance between two pegs. Converts between mixed numbers and fractions incorrectly. Uses a strategy that might not make sense in the context of the problem.
0	Does not attempt to solve the problem.

Sample Student Responses

This Level 4 paper illustrates the following features: All the computation steps are clearly explained. The problem-solving process begins with subtracting the total length of all the peg holes from the length of the rack. This distance is then divided by 7. The computation is recorded correctly with fraction number sentences.

This Level 4 paper illustrates the following features: All the computation steps along with some justifications are clearly explained. The problem-solving process begins with converting fractions in the problem to decimals for easier computing. All work is shown.

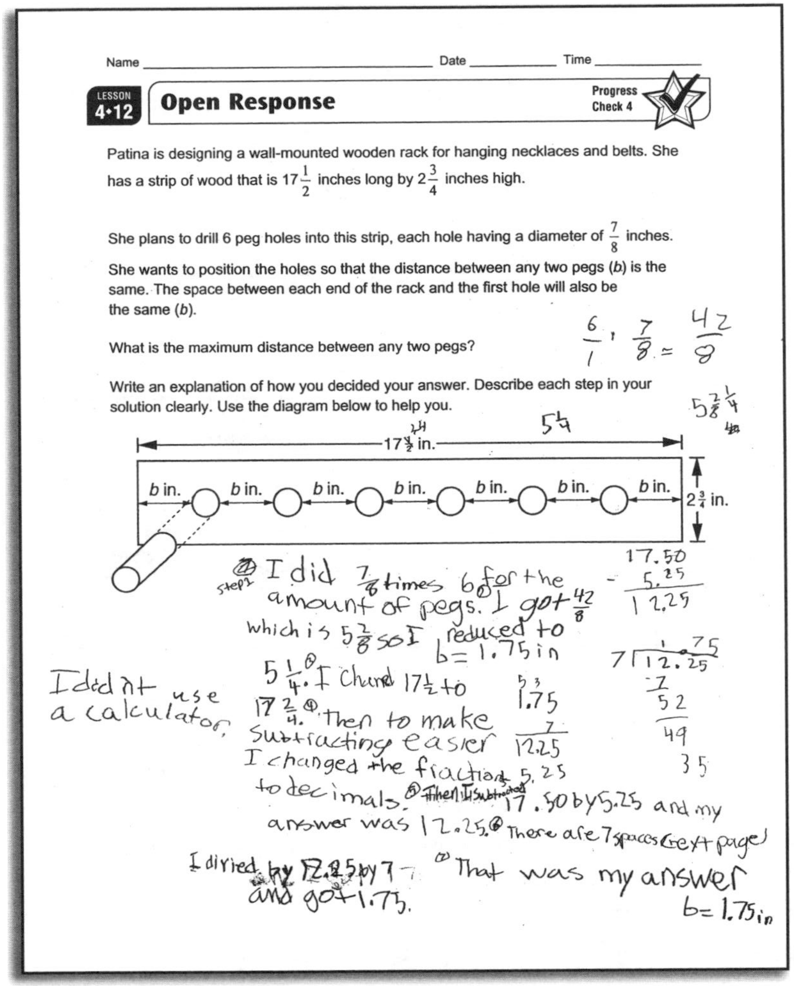

Name _____ **Date** _____ **Time** _____

LESSON 4·12 Open Response — Progress Check 4

Patina is designing a wall-mounted wooden rack for hanging necklaces and belts. She has a strip of wood that is $17\frac{1}{2}$ inches long by $2\frac{3}{4}$ inches high.

She plans to drill 6 peg holes into this strip, each hole having a diameter of $\frac{7}{8}$ inches.

She wants to position the holes so that the distance between any two pegs (b) is the same. The space between each end of the rack and the first hole will also be the same (b).

What is the maximum distance between any two pegs?

Write an explanation of how you decided your answer. Describe each step in your solution clearly. Use the diagram below to help you.

(Left sample — handwritten student work)

Data — $17\frac{1}{2}$ in long
- holes $\frac{7}{8}$ in diameter
- Need 7 spaces between

3rd step

1st I multiplied $\frac{7}{8} \times 6 =$ and that equaled $5\frac{2}{8}$.

2nd I subtracted $17\frac{4}{8} - 5\frac{2}{8} =$ and that equaled $12\frac{2}{8} = 12\frac{1}{4}$

3rd When I divided $12\frac{2}{8} \div 7 =$ one that equal $1\frac{2}{8}$ because $2\frac{1}{8} \div 7 = 3$ $28 \div 7 = 4$ so than I finally got $1\frac{2}{8}$. That's how I got my answer. But after I'm done I check my work again. My final answer was $1\frac{1}{4}$ inch.

$\frac{7}{8} \times 6 = 5\frac{2}{8}$

$17\frac{1}{2} - 5\frac{2}{8} = 12\frac{2}{8} = 12\frac{4}{8}$

$12\frac{2}{4} \div 7 = 1\frac{21}{28} = 1\frac{1}{8}$

$\boxed{12\frac{1}{4}}$

(Right sample — handwritten student work)

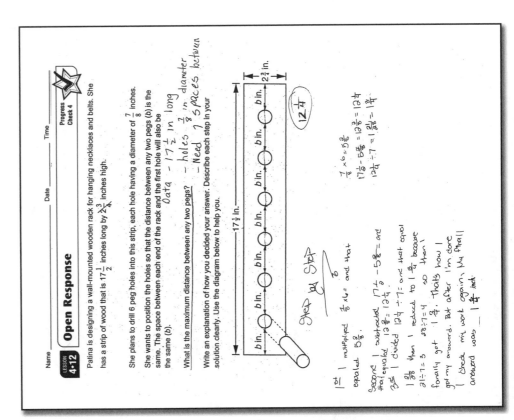

① I did $\frac{7}{8}$ times 6 for the amount of pegs. I got $\frac{42}{8}$ which is $5\frac{2}{8}$ so I reduced to $b=1.75$ in

$\frac{6}{1} , \frac{7}{8} = \frac{42}{8}$

② $5\frac{1}{8}$ 4. I think $17\frac{1}{2}$ to $17\frac{4}{8}$ 4. Then to make subtracting easier I changed the fractions to decimals. Then I subtracted 17.50 by 5.25 and my answer was 12.25. ③ There are 7 spaces (next page)

I did not use a calculator.

$\begin{array}{r} 17.50 \\ -\ 5.25 \\ \hline 12.25 \end{array}$

$\begin{array}{r} 1.75 \\ 7\overline{)12.25} \\ -7 \\ \hline 52 \\ 49 \\ \hline 35 \end{array}$

I divided 12.25 by 7 and got 1.75. ④ That was my answer. $b=1.75$ in

This Level 3 paper illustrates the following features: All the computation steps are illustrated on the page. Some of the steps are explained, but the explanation does not describe how the numbers are related in the problem. The explanation includes a description of how to check the answer by comparing it to the original length.

This Level 3 paper illustrates the following features: All the computation steps are described. The problem-solving process begins with converting some fractions to decimals. All computation is correct, but some notation is written incorrectly. All work is shown. The explanation describes the computation rather than the steps for the solution strategy.

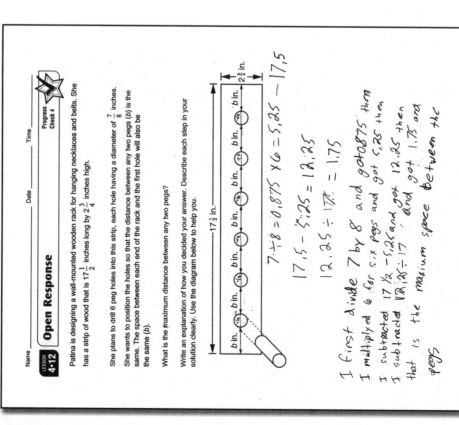

Name _____ Date _____ Time _____

LESSON 4·12 Open Response   Progress Check 4

Patina is designing a wall-mounted wooden rack for hanging necklaces and belts. She has a strip of wood that is $17\frac{1}{2}$ inches long by $2\frac{3}{4}$ inches high.

She plans to drill 6 peg holes into this strip, each hole having a diameter of $\frac{7}{8}$ inches.

She wants to position the holes so that the distance between any two pegs (b) is the same. The space between each end of the rack and the first hole will also be the same (b).

What is the maximum distance between any two pegs?

Write an explanation of how you decided your answer. Describe each step in your solution clearly. Use the diagram below to help you.

Copyright © Wright Group/McGraw-Hill

This Level 1 paper illustrates the following features: A lot of computation is shown and explained on the page; however, it does not make sense in the context of the problem.

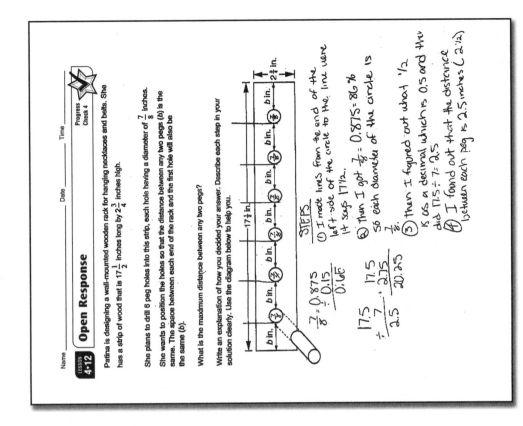

This Level 2 paper illustrates the following features: All computation listed on the page is correct. The steps progress in a logical order. Because numbers are rounded, the final answer is incorrect but is as close as rounding to the tenths will get it. There is no explanation in words.

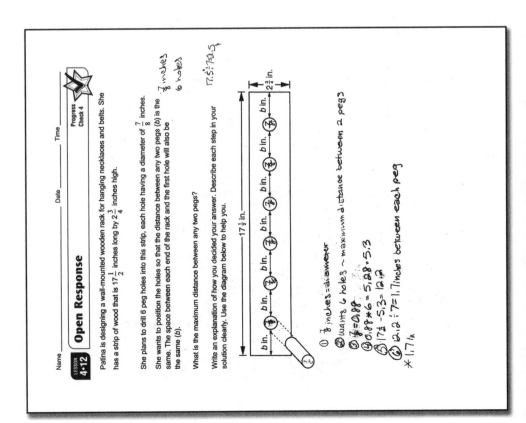

In this unit, students explore the relationships between angles in geometric figures and the concept of congruence. Use the information in this section to develop your assessment plan for Unit 5.

Ongoing Assessment

Opportunities for using and collecting ongoing assessment information are highlighted in Informing Instruction and Recognizing Student Achievement notes. Student products, along with observations and suggested writing prompts, provide a range of useful assessment information.

Informing Instruction

The Informing Instruction notes highlight students' thinking and point out common misconceptions. Informing Instruction in Unit 5: Lessons 5-2, 5-4, 5-7, and 5-9.

Recognizing Student Achievement

The Recognizing Student Achievement notes highlight specific tasks from which teachers can collect assessment data to monitor and document student progress toward meeting Grade-Level Goals.

Lesson	Content Assessed	Where to Find It
5♦1	Use a half-circle protractor to measure an angle. [Measurement and Reference Frames Goal 1]	*TLG*, p. 339
5♦2	Name, label, and measure angles. [Measurement and Reference Frames Goal 1; Geometry Goal 1]	*TLG*, p. 343
5♦3	Find the measures of supplementary and vertical angles using angle relationships. [Geometry Goal 1]	*TLG*, p. 347
5♦4	Use a strategy for solving problems involving percents and discounts. [Number and Numeration Goal 2]	*TLG*, p. 354
5♦5	Name ordered pairs in the third quadrant of a coordinate grid. [Measurement and Reference Frames Goal 3]	*TLG*, p. 358
5♦6	Rotate a figure and name points on a coordinate grid. [Measurement and Reference Frames Goal 3; Geometry Goal 3]	*TLG*, p. 366
5♦7	Convert between fraction and decimal equivalents. [Number and Numeration Goal 5]	*TLG*, p. 372
5♦8	Add, subtract, and multiply fractions and mixed numbers. [Operations and Computation Goals 3 and 4]	*TLG*, p. 375
5♦9	Determine angle measures by applying the properties of adjacent angles, supplementary angles, and sums of angle measures in triangles and quadrangles. [Geometry Goal 1]	*TLG*, p. 381
5♦10	Calculate the degree measures of the sectors of a circle graph. [Number and Numeration Goal 2; Measurement and Reference Frames Goal 1]	*TLG*, p. 390

Math Boxes

Math Boxes, one of several types of tasks highlighted in the Recognizing Student Achievement notes, have an additional useful feature. Math Boxes in most lessons are paired or linked with Math Boxes in one or two other lessons so that they have similar problems. Paired or linked Math Boxes in Unit 5: 5-1 and 5-3; 5-2 and 5-4; 5-5 and 5-7; 5-6 and 5-9; and 5-8 and 5-10.

Writing/Reasoning Prompts

In Unit 5, a variety of writing prompts encourage students to explain their strategies and thinking, reflect on their learning, and make connections to other mathematics or life experiences. Here are some of the Unit 5 suggestions:

Lesson	Writing/Reasoning Prompts	Where to Find It
5♦1	Explain how to convert fractions to decimals.	*TLG*, p. 339
5♦2	Explain how you might find the sum of interior angle measures of 2 intersecting lines without using a protractor.	*TLG*, p. 344
5♦5	Explain how fractions are used to express division problems as multiplication problems.	*TLG*, p. 360
5♦6	Identify another rotation that will produce an image with vertices at the same location as the image you got by performing a 90° counterclockwise rotation.	*TLG*, p. 366
5♦8	Explain how you used angle relationships to determine missing angle measures in a figure.	*TLG*, p. 378

Portfolio Opportunities

Portfolios are a versatile tool for assessment. They help students reflect on their mathematical growth and help teachers understand and document that growth. Each unit identifies several student products that can be selected and stored in a portfolio. Here are some of the Unit 5 suggestions:

Lesson	Portfolio Opportunities	Where to Find It
5♦1	Students construct a hexagon according to a set of specifications.	*TLG*, p. 340
5♦2	Students extend the sides of a regular pentagon to construct a five-pointed star and find the measure of each angle in the construction.	*TLG*, p. 345
5♦6	Students use pentaminoes to explore isometry transformations and congruence.	*TLG*, p. 368
5♦8	Students bisect an angle using a compass and a straightedge.	*TLG*, p. 379

Periodic Assessment

Every Progress Check lesson includes opportunities to observe student progress and to collect student products in a variety of ways—Self Assessment, Oral and Slate Assessment, Written Assessment, and an Open Response task. For more details, see the first page of Progress Check 5, Lesson 5-11 on page 392, of the *Teacher's Lesson Guide*.

Progress Check Modifications

Written Assessments are one way students demonstrate what they know. The table below shows modifications for the Written Assessment in this unit. Use these to maximize opportunities for students to demonstrate what they know. Modifications can be given individually or written on the board for the class.

Problem(s)	Modifications for Written Assessment
1, 2	For Problems 1 and 2, classify each angle before measuring.
4	For Problem 4, to make naming coordinates easier, use a colored pencil to draw lines connecting the vertex to its coordinates on both the *x*- and *y*-axes.
9	For Problem 9, describe two different ways to solve the fraction subtraction problem.
12, 13	For Problems 12 and 13, draw number lines to help you solve the problems. For Problem 12, the number line can be labeled by 2s and for Problem 13, by 10s.

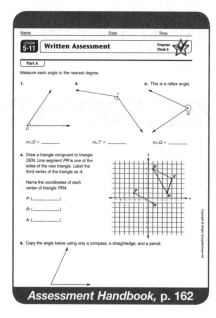

Assessment Handbook, p. 162

The Written Assessment for the Unit 5 Progress Check is on pages 162–164.

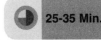

Open Response, *Measuring Angles*

Description

For this task, students find the missing measures of angles in triangles using angle relationships.

Focus

◆ **Use mental arithmetic and paper-and-pencil algorithms to solve problems involving the addition and subtraction of whole numbers.** [Operations and Computation Goal 1]

◆ **Determine angle measures by applying properties of orientations of angles and of sums of angle measures in triangles and quadrangles.** [Geometry Goal 1]

Implementation Tips

◆ Have students use a different color to trace each triangle.

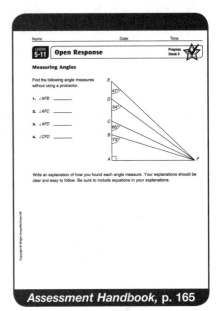

Assessment Handbook, p. 165

Modifications for Meeting Diverse Needs

◆ Enlarge the figure and provide each student with four copies. Have them cut out the triangle for which they are finding the missing measure.

◆ Have students write a number sentence that could be used to find m∠*CFD*.

Improving Open Response Skills

After students complete the task, create a mock paper that contains mistakes. Have students find, explain, and correct the mistakes. When they have finished, have the class discuss the misconceptions that would yield such mistakes.

Possible Mistakes

Problem 1: The answer is 73°. *(incorrectly classified the triangle as isosceles)*

Problem 2: The answer is 42°. *(incorrectly added 73 and 65, instead of 90 and 65, and then subtracted from 180)*

Problem 3: The answer is 115°. *(used a supplementary angle relationship, 65 + 115 = 180, but did not continue to find the designated angle measure)*

Problem 4: The answer is 43°. *(found the large/total angle measure [by completing the pattern begun in the other problems] instead of computing the measurement of the single, designated angle)*

Note: The wording and formatting of the text on the student samples that follow may vary slightly from the actual task your children will complete. These minor discrepancies will not affect the implementation of the task.

Rubric

This rubric is designed to help you assess levels of mathematical performance on this task. It emphasizes mathematical understanding with only a mention of clarity of explanation. Consider the expectations of standardized tests in your area when applying a rubric. Modify this sample rubric as appropriate.

4 Uses angle relationships to calculate the measures of all specified angles. Clearly explains a strategy and describes all the steps followed to solve both types of missing-angle problems. Includes equations in the explanation and uses correct notation.

3 Appears to use angle relationships to calculate the measures of all specified angles, but might make some computation errors. Describes some of the steps followed to solve the problem, but there might be minor omissions. Includes equations in the explanation, but there might be errors in the notation.

2 Calculates the angle measures for the first three problems, but might make minor computation errors. Attempts to solve Problem 4 and explain a strategy. Demonstrates some understanding of angle relationships in the work shown. Might attempt to write equations, but might make errors.

1 Attempts to calculate the measures of some angles, but might make errors. Might attempt to explain a strategy but the explanation includes little or no evidence of an understanding of angle relationships.

0 Does not attempt to solve the problem.

Sample Student Responses

This Level 4 paper illustrates the following features: All angle measures are listed correctly. The explanation includes a description of how to find the measure of the third angle by subtracting the sum of the other 2 angles from 180°. In Problem 4, the explanation describes using supplementary angles to find the second angle measure and subtracting from 180° to find the third angle measure.

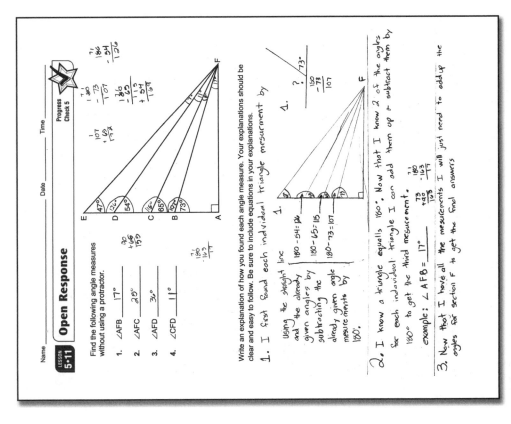

This Level 4 paper illustrates the following features: There is a generalized explanation for all problems on the page. Supplementary angles are used to find a second angle in each small triangle. The third angle for each small triangle is found by subtracting the sum of the first 2 from 180°. Finally, the small angles are added to find the missing angles for the larger triangles as specified.

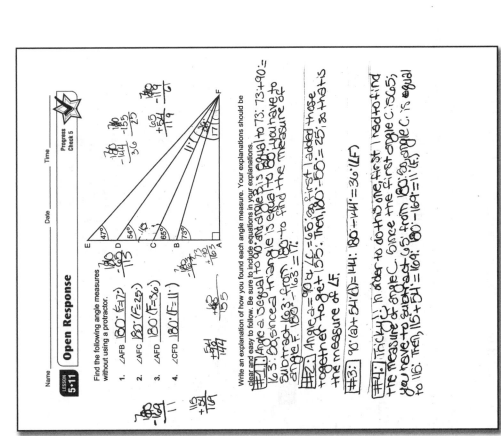

This Level 3 paper illustrates the following features: All angle measures are listed correctly. The explanation includes a description of how to find the specified angle measure by subtracting from 90°. In subsequent problems, the small angles are found by first determining supplementary angle measures. The supplementary angle measures are then subtracted from 180°. The small angles are added together to get the correct answers for each problem.

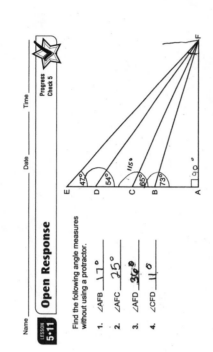

This Level 3 paper illustrates the following features: All angle measures are listed correctly. The explanation includes a description of how to add 2 angles to find the third; however, there is no mention of the angle measures in a triangle totaling 180°. In Problem 4, the explanation describes how to find the smaller missing angle by finding the difference in the measures of the 2 larger angles.

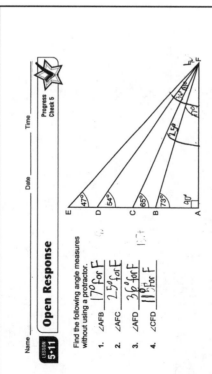

This Level 1 paper illustrates the following features: The strategy described for the first problem is correct and makes sense. The explanations for the last three problems all involve slightly different mathematics, none of which is correct.

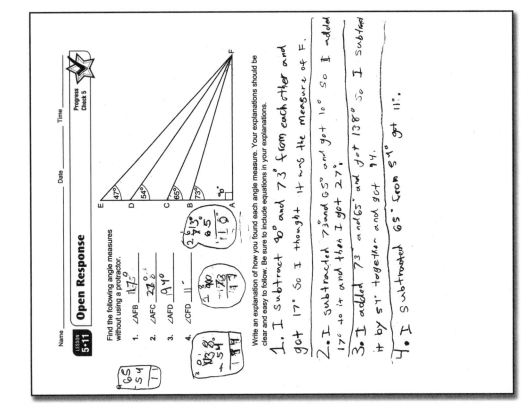

This Level 2 paper illustrates the following features: All angle measures are listed correctly. The explanation includes a description of how to find the third angle by subtracting the measure of the angle that is not a right angle from 90°. The description only includes the example from the first problem. There is no mention of how Problem 4 is solved.

Mid-Year Assessment Goals

The Mid-Year Assessment (pages 203–210) provides an additional opportunity that you may use as part of your balanced assessment plan. It covers some of the important concepts and skills presented in *Sixth Grade Everyday Mathematics*. It should be used to complement the ongoing and periodic assessments that appear within lessons and at the end of units. The following table provides the goals for all the problems in the Mid-Year Assessment.

Problem(s)	Grade-Level Goal
1a, 20b, 22, 25a	**Data and Chance 1:** Collect and organize data or use given data to create graphic displays with reasonable titles, labels, keys, and intervals.
1b, 2, 3, 20a, 20c, 25b	**Data and Chance 2:** Use data landmarks, measures of spread, and graphs to ask and answer questions, draw conclusions, and make predictions; compare and contrast the median and mean of a data set.
4–11, 23	**Number and Numeration 1:** Read and write whole numbers and decimals; identify places in such numbers and the values of the digits in those places; use expanded notation, number-and-word notation, exponential notation, and scientific notation to represent whole numbers and decimals.
12, 13, 16, 24	**Operations and Computation 1:** Use mental arithmetic, paper-and-pencil algorithms and models, and calculators to solve problems involving the addition and subtraction of whole numbers, decimals, and signed numbers; describe the strategies used and explain how they work.
14, 15, 17–19, 21, 24	**Operations and Computation 2:** Use mental arithmetic, paper-and-pencil algorithms and models, and calculators to solve problems involving the multiplication and division of whole numbers, decimals, and signed numbers; describe the strategies used and explain how they work.

Assessment Overview

In this unit, students extend their previous work with algorithms to rational numbers, and they explore equations and inequalities. Use the information in this section to develop your assessment plan for Unit 6.

Ongoing Assessment

Opportunities for using and collecting ongoing assessment information are highlighted in Informing Instruction and Recognizing Student Achievement notes. Student products, along with observations and suggested writing prompts, provide a range of useful assessment information.

Informing Instruction
The Informing Instruction notes highlight students' thinking and point out common misconceptions. Informing Instruction in Unit 6: Lessons 6-2, 6-3, 6-6, and 6-12.

Recognizing Student Achievement
The Recognizing Student Achievement notes highlight specific tasks from which teachers can collect assessment data to monitor and document student progress toward meeting Grade-Level Goals.

Lesson	Content Assessed	Where to Find It
6♦1	Name and identify the reciprocal of a number. [Patterns, Functions, and Algebra Goal 4]	*TLG*, p. 533
6♦2	Solve fraction division problems. [Operations and Computation Goal 4]	*TLG*, p. 541
6♦3	Understand the inverse relationship between addition and subtraction. [Patterns, Functions, and Algebra Goal 4]	*TLG*, p. 546
6♦4	Calculate and compare sums and differences of signed numbers. [Operations and Computation Goal 1]	*TLG*, p. 551
6♦4a	Use a formula to find the volume of a rectangular prism. [Measurement and Reference Frames Goal 2]	*TLG*, p. 552E
6♦5	Divide fractions and mixed numbers. [Operations and Computation Goal 4]	*TLG*, p. 554
6♦6	Evaluate numeric expressions. [Patterns, Functions, and Algebra Goal 3]	*TLG*, p. 563
6♦7	Apply the order of operations to evaluate numeric expressions. [Patterns, Functions, and Algebra Goal 3]	*TLG*, p. 567
6♦8	Use trial and error or the cover-up method to solve equations. [Patterns, Functions, and Algebra Goal 2]	*TLG*, p. 574
6♦9	Solve equations and check the solutions. [Patterns, Functions, and Algebra Goal 2]	*TLG*, p. 578
6♦10	Use a pan-balance model to solve an equation. [Patterns, Functions, and Algebra Goal 2]	*TLG*, p. 587
6♦11	Solve equations and check solutions. [Patterns, Functions, and Algebra Goal 2]	*TLG*, p. 591
6♦12	Determine whether inequalities are *true* or *false*. [Patterns, Functions, and Algebra Goal 2]	*TLG*, p. 599

Math Boxes

Math Boxes, one of several types of tasks highlighted in the Recognizing Student Achievement notes, have an additional useful feature. Math Boxes in most lessons are paired or linked with Math Boxes in one or two other lessons that have similar problems. Paired or linked Math Boxes in Unit 6: 6-1 and 6-3; 6-2 and 6-4; 6-4a, 6-5, and 6-7; 6-6 and 6-8; 6-9 and 6-11; and 6-10 and 6-12.

Writing/Reasoning Prompts

In Unit 6, a variety of writing prompts encourage students to explain their strategies and thinking, reflect on their learning, and make connections to other mathematics or life experiences. Here are some of the Unit 6 suggestions:

Lesson	Writing/Reasoning Prompts	Where to Find It
6◆1	Explain strategies to mentally calculate products of fractions and mixed numbers.	*TLG*, p. 534
6◆2	Explain how you converted feet to centimeters.	*TLG*, p. 541
6◆6	Explain how you apply properties of corresponding sides and angles of a triangle.	*TLG*, p. 564
6◆9	Explain how you might mentally calculate 15% of 90.	*TLG*, p. 582
6◆10	Explain how you solved an equation and checked its solution.	*TLG*, p. 587

Portfolio Opportunities

Portfolios are a versatile tool for assessment. They help students reflect on their mathematical growth and help teachers understand and document that growth. Each unit identifies several student products that can be selected and stored in a portfolio. Here are some of the Unit 6 suggestions:

Lesson	Portfolio Opportunities	Where to Find It
6◆4	Students examine patterns in products and quotients of signed numbers.	*TLG*, p. 552
6◆5	Students explain why $\frac{3}{4}$ of 80 is less than 80, while $\frac{9}{8}$ of 2 is greater than 2.	*TLG*, p. 557
6◆7	Students examine the various word phrases that can be used to refer to an operation.	*TLG*, p. 570
6◆8	Students use a trial-and-error method to solve equations involving multiple variables.	*TLG*, p. 576
6◆12	Students graph the solution set of compound inequalities and write compound inequalities to describe graphs.	*TLG*, p. 601

Periodic Assessment

Every Progress Check lesson includes opportunities to observe student progress and to collect student products in a variety of ways—Self Assessment, Oral and Slate Assessment, Written Assessment, and an Open Response task. For more details, see the first page of Progress Check 6, Lesson 6-13, page 524, of the *Teacher's Lesson Guide*.

Progress Check Modifications

Written Assessments are one way students demonstrate what they know. The table below shows modifications for the Written Assessment in this unit. Use these to maximize opportunities for students to demonstrate what they know. Modifications can be given individually or written on the board for the class.

Problem(s)	Modifications for Written Assessment
4	For Problem 4, describe how to use a common-denominator method to solve this division problem.
13, 14, 16	For Problems 13, 14, and 16, find the value of the expressions inside the parentheses and record this value above the expression. Rewrite the number sentences with these values inserted before determining whether each number sentence is true or false.
18–21	For Problems 18–21, perform the first operation; then rewrite the expression with the value from the first operation inserted. Repeat for each subsequent operation until you have one value for the expression.
28, 29	For Problems 28 and 29, put dots on the vertex and each endpoint of the greater-than, less-than symbols. Remember that the greater number is on the same side as the two dots.

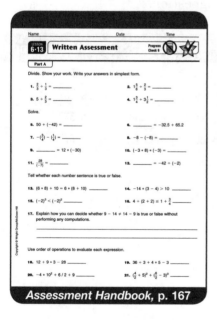

Assessment Handbook, p. 167

The Written Assessment for the Unit 6 Progress Check is on pages 167–169.

Open Response, *Calculating Tree Growth*

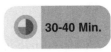 30-40 Min.

Description

For this task, students identify and use a rule to solve a problem involving patterns.

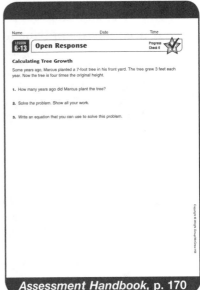

Focus

◆ **Extend and describe numeric patterns.**
   [Patterns, Functions, and Algebra Goal 1]

◆ **Describe rules for patterns and use them to solve problems.**
   [Patterns, Functions, and Algebra Goal 1]

Implementation Tips

◆ Have students check their answers by working backward.

Modifications for Meeting Diverse Needs

◆ Provide students with a labeled drawing of a tree. One label might say *7 feet in Year 0*. Have them write a number sentence to represent the total height for each year and describe any patterns they notice in words or numbers.

◆ Have students write an equation using variables. Have them list what each variable represents.

Assessment Handbook, p. 170

Improving Open Response Skills

Before students begin the task, have them read through the problem. Ask the class to list problem-solving strategies they could use to solve the problem. *(Sample answer: make a table, draw a picture, find a pattern, and so on.)*

Note: The wording and formatting of the text on the student samples that follow may vary slightly from the actual task your children will complete. These minor discrepancies will not affect the implementation of the task.

Rubric

This rubric is designed to help you assess levels of mathematical performance on this task. It emphasizes mathematical understanding with only a mention of clarity of explanation. Consider the expectations of standardized tests in your area when applying a rubric. Modify this sample rubric as appropriate.

4	States that the tree was planted 7 years ago. Labels all work. Identifies and makes use of the pattern of adding 3. Writes an equation with or without variables. Clearly shows or explains the steps of the strategy used.
3	States that the tree was planted 7 years ago. Identifies and makes use of the pattern of adding 3. Writes an equation with or without variables, but might make errors. Shows or explains the steps of the strategy.
2	Attempts to figure out when the tree was planted, but might make computation errors. Identifies and uses the pattern of adding 3 to solve the problem, but might incorrectly apply the pattern. Might attempt to record equations, but might make errors. Might not explain the strategy used.
1	Attempts to solve the problem. Might recognize a pattern, but might not apply the pattern to solving the problem. Might explain a strategy, but it might not make sense in the context of the problem.
0	Does not attempt to solve the problem.

Sample Student Responses

This Level 4 paper illustrates the following features: The answer states the tree was planted 7 years ago. All work is labeled according to height in feet or years. The pattern of adding 3 is described. Each step is clearly written out as an equation, and the notation is correct.

This Level 4 paper illustrates the following features: The answer states the tree was planted 7 years ago. All work is labeled according to height in feet or years. The pattern of adding 3 is shown in a table. The solution is written as an equation and is explained.

Name _____ Date _____ Time _____

LESSON 6·13 **Open Response** Progress Check 6

Some years ago, Marcus planted a 7-foot tree in his front yard. The tree grew 3 feet each year. This year, the tree is four times the original height.

How many years ago did Marcus plant the tree?
Write an equation that you can use to solve this problem.
Solve the problem. Show all of your work.

Marcus planted the tree 7 years ago.

I got 7x4

Equation
7*4 = Hight of the new tree
7+3+3+3+3+3+3+3 = Hight

Amount of 3's equals the
number of years

year	hight
1	10 ft
2	13 ft
3	16 ft
4	19 ft
5	22 ft
6	25 ft
7	28 ft
8	

I did 7*4 because this year it was 4 times the original hight. Then I added 3 ft to 7 so that I had how much it grew in the first year. Then I added 3 to the hight amount until I got to 28.

Name _____ Date _____ Time _____

LESSON 6·13 **Open Response** Progress Check 6

Some years ago, Marcus planted a 7-foot tree in his front yard. The tree grew 3 feet each year. This year, the tree is four times the original height.

1. How many years ago did Marcus plant the tree?
   7 years ago

2. Solve the problem. Show all your work.

3. Write an equation that you can use to solve this problem. H = 7 + 3 · Y

1. M. planted a 7' tree, some years ago

2. grew 3' each year

3. Tree is now 4y it's orig.
   4·(7!)

Patterns 28' tall

Yr.	Hight
0	7'
1·3	7+3=10
2·3	10+3=13
3·3	13+3=16
4·3	16+3=19
5·3	19+3=22
6·3	22+3=25
7·3	25+3=28

Yr.
0   7'
1   7+3 = 7+3·1
2   7+3+3 = 7+3·2
3   7+3+3+3 = 7+3·3
4   7+3+3+3+3 = 7+3·4
5   7+3+3+3+3+3 = 7+3·5
6   7+3+3+3+3+3+3 = 7+3·6
7   7+3+3+3+3+3+3+3 = 7+3·7

H = 7+3·Y = 28'

This Level 3 paper illustrates the following features: The work is organized in a table in which the pattern is shown in each row. Although two columns of the table are labeled with Y and h, the Y column includes more information than the year. An unlabeled third column lists the total change in each year. The number model represents the problem, but it is not an equation because there is no equal sign.

This Level 3 paper illustrates the following features: The explanation describes a strategy of using the pattern by subtracting 3s from 28 and counting the number of subtractions that are possible. The equation matches the work. Instead of representing the number of years, as stated, the variable Y represents the original height.

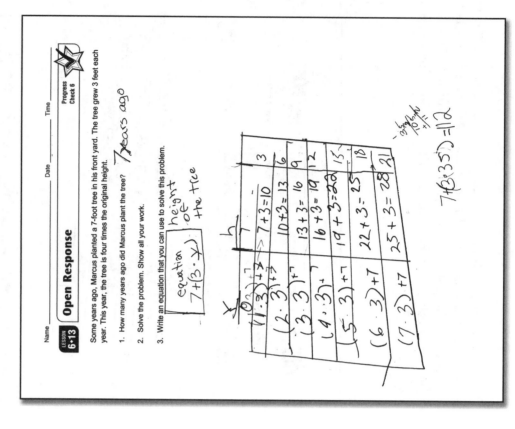

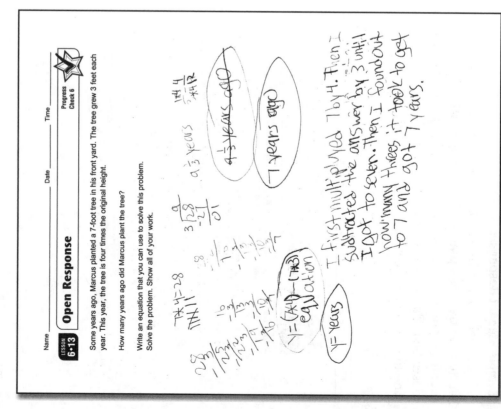

This Level 1 paper illustrates the following features: There is some evidence of recognizing the pattern of adding 3 feet each year. However, there is no evidence of how the final answer is found.

This Level 2 paper illustrates the following features: The final height is calculated by multiplying the initial height of 7 by 4, as indicated. However, the initial height is ignored in finding a solution. The pattern is used when the total height is divided by 3 (the number of feet the tree grows each year) resulting in an incorrect answer.

Level 1 paper

Name _____ Date _____ Time _____

LESSON 6·13

Open Response

Progress Check 6

Some years ago, Marcus planted a 7-foot tree in his front yard. The tree grew 3 feet each year. This year, the tree is four times the original height.

1. How many years ago did Marcus plant the tree? 7 years ago

2. Solve the problem. Show all your work.

3. Write an equation that you can use to solve this problem.

In my

x 3
+ 28

$7 + 3 = 10$
$7 + 3 = 13$
$7 + 3 = 16$
$7 + 3 = 19$
$7 + 3 = 28$

Yrs	hight
1	7
2	10
3	13
4	16

It was planted 7 years ago. Ever year it grows 3 feet bigger. Now the tree is 4 times bigger.

Level 2 paper

Name _____ Date _____ Time _____

LESSON 6·13

Open Response

Progress Check 6

Some years ago, Marcus planted a 7-foot tree in his front yard. The tree grew 3 feet each year. This year, the tree is four times the original height.

How many years ago did Marcus plant the tree? 9 years & 4 months ago

Write an equation that you can use to solve this problem.
Solve the problem. Show all your work.

EQUATION
$7 * 4 = 28$ ft
$28 ÷ 3 = 9\tfrac{1}{3}$ years

Marcus tree was 7ft when he planted it. Each year his tree grew 3ft. This year is $4 * 3$
This years hight = 28ft
Planted $9\tfrac{1}{3}$ years ago (9 years 4 months)

This year to it original hight to solve this problem you need a simple equasion to multiply

7 (original hight) * 4
(fou times its orignal hight) equals 28 (the hight of Marcus tree this year) then ÷ 28
by 3 (# of feet his tree grew each year) and you get 9.3 ($9\tfrac{1}{3}$)

9.33
3)27.99 about 28

4)28
   28
   00

In this unit, students explore probability and chance events and use probabilities to judge the "fairness" of situations. Use the information in this section to develop your assessment plan for Unit 7.

Ongoing Assessment

Opportunities for using and collecting ongoing assessment information are highlighted in Informing Instruction and Recognizing Student Achievement notes. Student products, along with observations and suggested writing prompts, provide a range of useful assessment information.

Informing Instruction

The Informing Instruction notes highlight students' thinking and point out common misconceptions. Informing Instruction in Unit 7: Lessons 7-4, 7-5, and 7-6.

Recognizing Student Achievement

The Recognizing Student Achievement notes highlight specific tasks from which teachers can collect assessment data to monitor and document student progress toward meeting Grade-Level Goals.

Lesson	Content Assessed	Where to Find It
7♦1	Identify outcomes and calculate probabilities. [Data and Chance Goal 3]	*TLG*, p. 623
7♦2	Explain how sample size affects outcomes. [Data and Chance Goal 3]	*TLG*, p. 629
7♦3	Solve equations using a trial-and error method. [Patterns, Functions, and Algebra Goal 2]	*TLG*, p. 636
7♦4	Calculate probabilities. [Data and Chance Goal 3]	*TLG*, p. 643
7♦5	Determine expected outcomes and use a tree diagram to calculate probabilities of chance events. [Data and Chance Goal 3]	*TLG*, p. 649
7♦6	Calculate probabilities, and use a tree diagram to find the probability of a compound event. [Data and Chance Goal 3]	*TLG*, p. 652
7♦7	Use a tree diagram to calculate probabilities. [Data and Chance Goal 3]	*TLG*, p. 663
7♦8	Calculate probabilities and determine expected outcomes for chance events. [Data and Chance Goal 3]	*TLG*, p. 666

Math Boxes

Math Boxes, one of several types of tasks highlighted in the Recognizing Student Achievement notes, have an additional useful feature. Math Boxes in most lessons are paired or linked with Math Boxes in one or two other lessons that have similar problems. Paired or linked Math Boxes in Unit 7: 7-1 and 7-3; 7-2 and 7-4; 7-5 and 7-7; and 7-6 and 7-8.

Writing/Reasoning Prompts

In Unit 7, a variety of writing prompts encourage students to explain their strategies and thinking, to reflect on their learning, and to make connections to other mathematics or life experiences. Here are some of the Unit 7 suggestions:

Lesson	Writing/Reasoning Prompts	Where to Find It
7♦1	Explain what happens to the solution when you multiply each term of the equation by 2.	*TLG*, p. 624
7♦2	Explain why two events are dependent.	*TLG*, p. 630
7♦5	Explain why the graph does not represent the set of counting numbers.	*TLG*, p. 649
7♦6	Explain how to estimate percent equivalents of fractions.	*TLG*, p. 654

Portfolio Opportunities

Portfolios are a versatile tool for assessment. They help students reflect on their mathematical growth and help teachers understand and document that growth. Each unit identifies several student products that can be selected and stored in a portfolio. Here are some of the Unit 7 suggestions:

Lesson	Portfolio Opportunities	Where to Find It
7♦1	Students compare theoretical probabilities with experimental results.	*TLG*, p. 626
7♦2	Students explore the relationship between sample size and reliability of predictions.	*TLG*, p. 631
7♦4	Students predict and test outcomes in a maze contest.	*TLG*, p. 644
7♦6	Students explain why a graph does not represent a set of counting numbers.	*TLG*, p. 649
7♦7	Students explain how they estimate percent equivalents.	*TLG*, p. 654

Periodic Assessment

Every Progress Check lesson includes opportunities to observe student progress and to collect student products in a variety of ways—Self Assessment, Oral and Slate Assessment, Written Assessment, and an Open Response task. For more details, see the first page of Progress Check 7, Lesson 7-9 on page 672, of the *Teacher's Lesson Guide*.

Progress Check Modifications

Written Assessments are one way students demonstrate what they know. The table below shows modifications for the Written Assessment in this unit. Use these to maximize opportunities for students to demonstrate what they know. Modifications can be given individually or written on the board for the class.

Problem(s)	Modifications for Written Assessment
1–4	Before solving Problems 1–4, figure out the fraction of the circle occupied by each color.
5–7	For Problems 5–7, construct a table listing favorable outcomes in the first column and possible outcomes in the second. Refer to the table when finding each probability.
9	For Problem 9, Matilda said that since 60 marbles are dropped and there are 5 exits, she would expect 12 marbles to go down each branch of the maze. Explain Matilda's mistake.
14–17	Before solving Problems 14–17, use a red pencil to lightly shade the Science Olympiad ring; use a blue pencil to lightly shade the Science Fair ring.

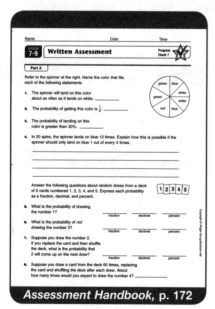

Assessment Handbook, p. 172

The Written Assessment for the Unit 7 Progress Check is on pages 172–174.

Open Response, *Card Products*

Description

For this task, students create a solitaire game that has an equal chance of winning or losing.

Focus

◆ **Describe events using basic probability terms.** [Data and Chance Goal 3]

◆ **Predict the outcomes of experiments; express the probability of an event as a fraction, decimal, or percent.** [Data and Chance Goal 3]

Implementation Tips

◆ Review the definition of *fair*—that there is an equal chance of winning or losing. Remind students that they need to find all possible outcomes to know if they have created a fair game.

◆ Remind students that they need to generate a list of rules for the game and justify why their proposed game is fair.

Modifications for Meeting Diverse Needs

◆ Provide number cards so that students can experiment with the game. Encourage students to make an organized list or tree diagram for all possible outcomes.

◆ Have students explain how the game changes if there are four cards for each number instead of one card. Increasing the number of cards results in new outcomes for the game and, depending on the student's rules, may change whether or not the game is fair.

Improving Open Response Skills

After students complete the task, have them analyze several sample game rules and explanations. Consider using some of the samples included in the Sample Student Responses beginning on page 107 of this book. Record a set of game rules and the matching explanation on a piece of chart paper, and give one to each group. Have students determine and record information that is missing from the rules and explanation. Have them work together to write an explanation that is clearer and more complete.

Note: the wording and formatting of the text on the student samples that follow may vary slightly from the actual task your students will complete. These minor discrepancies will not affect the implementation of the task.

Assessment Handbook, p. 175

Rubric

This rubric is designed to help you assess levels of mathematical performance on this task. It emphasizes mathematical understanding with only a mention of clarity of explanation. Consider the expectations of standardized tests in your area when applying a rubric. Modify this sample rubric as appropriate.

4 Clearly describes rules for the game that include finding the product of 2 cards. Uses a method for organizing and determining outcomes. Designs a game in which the player has an equal chance of winning or losing. Clearly describes how to win the game. Shows or explains why the game is a fair game.

3 Might describe some rules for a game that includes finding the product of 2 cards. Uses a method for organizing and determining outcomes. Designs a game in which the player has an equal chance of winning or losing. Describes how to win the game. Shows or explains why the game is a fair game.

2 Might attempt to describe some rules for a game that includes finding the product of 2 cards. Might design a game in which the player has an equal chance of winning or losing. Attempts to describe how to win the game, and to explain why the game is a fair game.

1 Might attempt to describe some rules for a game. There might be no attempt to record the outcomes. Might not demonstrate an understanding of a fair game.

0 Does not attempt to solve the problem.

Sample Student Responses

This Level 4 paper illustrates the following features: The game instructions are clearly stated step by step. The outcomes are organized in a tree diagram and listed. The game is fair as designed, with a 50-50 chance of winning. The game rules clearly describe how to win and how to lose.

This Level 4 paper illustrates the following features: The game rules describe how to generate the products and how to lose the game. The outcomes are organized in a tree diagram with the winning outcomes circled. The game is fair as designed, with a 50-50 chance of winning.

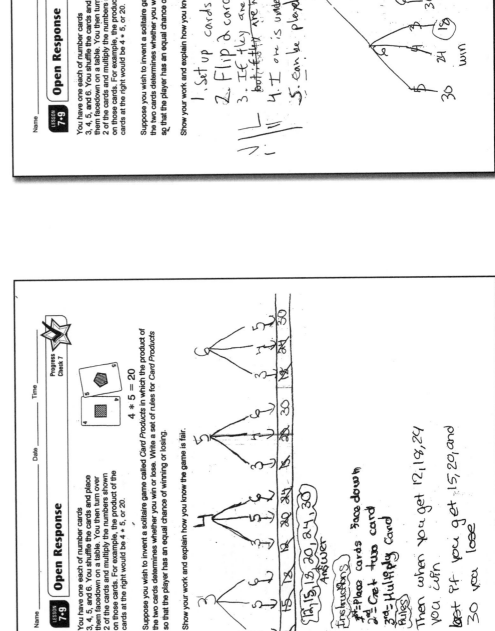

This Level 3 paper illustrates the following features: There are some rules listed for the game, but they are confusing. The outcomes are organized in a tree diagram and listed. The rules state how to win or lose, but it is unclear what happens if the product is 20. The game is fair if the rules are interpreted to say that 20 and up are the winning products.

This Level 3 paper illustrates the following features: The explanation describes how to win the game, but no rules on how to play the game are listed. The outcomes are organized in a tree diagram and listed. The game is fair as designed, with a 50-50 chance of winning.

Name _____ Date _____ Time _____

LESSON 7·9 · **Open Response** · Progress Check 7

You have one each of number cards 3, 4, 5, and 6. You shuffle the cards and place them facedown on a table. You then turn over 2 of the cards and multiply the numbers shown on those cards. For example, the product of the cards at the right would be 4 * 5, or 20.

4 * 5 = 20

Suppose you wish to invent a solitaire game called *Card Products* in which the product of the two cards determines whether you win or lose. Write a set of rules for *Card Products* so that the player has an equal chance of winning or losing.

Show your work and explain how you know the game is fair.

(Right-hand student response)

3, 1   4, 1   5, 1   6, 1
4 5 6   3 5 6   3 4 6   3 4 5
12 15 18 12 20 27 15 20 30 18 20 30

1. You have to pick four cards and shufale them and you pick 2 cards and turne them and you multiply it two cards and number. (i.e. 5 x 6 = 30) and leafts of the product.

2. The player gets four cards 3 4 5 6

3. To win or lose or 50% chance he got to get the higgest number from 20 and up (1) down (9)

(Left-hand student response)

The rules of the game are a 50 - 50 chance of winning. All you have to do is get the following Numbers and you win 12, 24, 15, + 30 - winning #'s.
12, 20, 18 - losing #'s.

3
4 5 6
12 15 18

4
3 5 6
12 20 24

5
3 4 6
15 20 30

6
3 4 5
18 24 30

possible - 12, 20, 24, 30, 18, 16,
answers

This Level, 1 paper illustrates the following features: The rules for a card game are written, but there is no record of the possible outcomes and no evidence of an understanding of how to make the game a fair game.

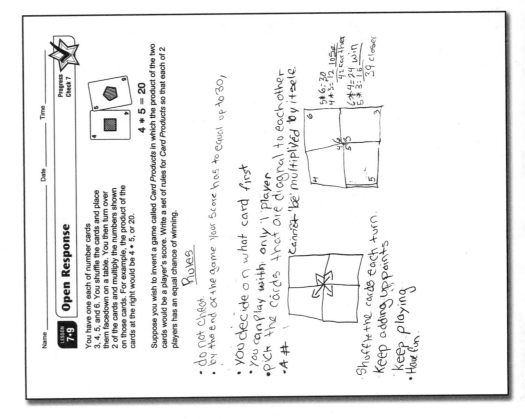

This Level 2 paper illustrates the following features: Some rules for a card game are written, but it is unclear what the tree diagram represents. There is a point system added to the game, which complicates the rules. The rules state that a game is 16 rounds, but there is no clear description of winning or losing. It appears that 20 and up is considered the winning category, which would indicate some understanding of a fair game.

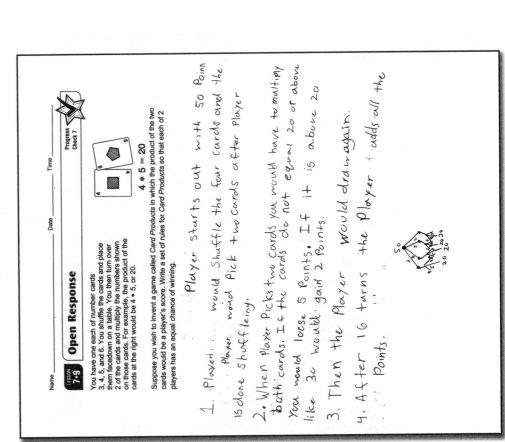

In this unit, students explore proportional thinking through the study of rates and ratios. Use the information in this section to develop your assessment plan for Unit 8.

Ongoing Assessment

Opportunities for using and collecting ongoing assessment information are highlighted in Informing Instruction and Recognizing Student Achievement notes. Student products, along with observations and suggested writing prompts, provide a range of useful assessment information.

Informing Instruction
The Informing Instruction notes highlight students' thinking and point out common misconceptions. Informing Instruction in Unit 8: Lessons 8-2, 8-3, 8-4, 8-6, and 8-9.

Recognizing Student Achievement
The Recognizing Student Achievement notes highlight specific tasks from which teachers can collect assessment data to monitor and document student progress toward meeting Grade-Level Goals.

Lesson	Content Assessed	Where to Find It
8◆1	Apply the per-unit-rate and rate-table methods to solve problems. [Patterns, Functions, and Algebra Goal 1]	*TLG*, p. 694
8◆2	Use proportions to model, summarize, and solve rate problems. [Operations and Computation Goal 6]	*TLG*, p. 697
8◆3	Use cross products to write an open number sentence. [Operations and Computation Goal 6]	*TLG*, p. 706
8◆4	Use unit rates, rate tables, or proportions to solve simple rate problems. [Operations and Computation Goal 6]	*TLG*, p. 711
8◆5	Use proportions to model and solve rate problems. [Operations and Computation Goal 6]	*TLG*, p. 720
8◆6	Use proportions to model and solve ratio problems. [Operations and Computation Goal 6]	*TLG*, p. 727
8◆7	Use open proportions to solve percent problems. [Operations and Computation Goal 6]	*TLG*, p. 732
8◆8	Express ratios as fractions and percents. [Number and Numeration Goal 5]	*TLG*, p. 738
8◆9	Measure line segments to the nearest $\frac{1}{16}$ inch. [Measurement and Reference Frames Goal 1]	*TLG*, p. 745
8◆10	Use ratios to solve problems involving similar polygons. [Operations and Computation Goal 6]	*TLG*, p. 753
8◆11	Use fraction equivalents or proportions to solve percent-of problems. [Number and Numeration Goal 2]	*TLG*, p. 756
8◆12	Find corresponding side lengths of similar polygons and use proportions to find the length of the unknown side. [Operations and Computation Goal 6]	*TLG*, p. 764

Math Boxes

Math Boxes, one of several types of tasks highlighted in the Recognizing Student Achievement notes, have an additional useful feature. Math Boxes in most lessons are paired or linked with Math Boxes in one or two other lessons that have similar problems. Paired or linked Math Boxes in Unit 8: 8-1 and 8-3; 8-2 and 8-4; 8-5 and 8-7; 8-6 and 8-8; 8-9 and 8-11; and 8-10 and 8-12.

Writing/Reasoning Prompts

In Unit 8, a variety of writing prompts encourage students to explain their strategies and thinking, to reflect on their learning, and to make connections to other mathematics or life experiences. Here are some of the Unit 8 suggestions:

Lesson	Writing/Reasoning Prompts	Where to Find It
8◆1	Explain how to calculate the number of possible meal combinations without making a list or tree diagram.	*TLG*, p. 694
8◆2	Explain how you used the information given to complete the Venn diagram.	*TLG*, p. 701
8◆5	Explain how you found the area of triangle *APE*.	*TLG*, p. 720
8◆6	Explain how to translate a word problem into an equation you could use to find the number of counters.	*TLG*, p. 727
8◆9	Explain how to subtract a mixed number from an improper fraction.	*TLG*, p. 745

Portfolio Opportunities

Portfolios are a versatile tool for assessment. They help students reflect on their mathematical growth and help teachers understand and document that growth. Each unit identifies several student products that can be selected and stored in a portfolio. Here are some of the Unit 8 suggestions:

Lesson	Portfolio Opportunities	Where to Find It
8◆2	Students write rate problems for which the information can be summarized in a table and by a proportion.	*TLG*, p. 701
8◆3	Students practice solving rate problems by calculating how much of each ingredient is needed to make 1 pound and 80 pounds of peanut butter fudge.	*TLG*, p. 709
8◆5	Students use information from a menu to make a table and a circle graph.	*TLG*, p. 721
8◆10	Students reduce designs and find the scale factors of their reductions.	*TLG*, p. 754
8◆11	Students use a variety of notations for writing equivalent ratios.	*TLG*, p. 760

Periodic Assessment

Every Progress Check lesson includes opportunities to observe student progress and to collect student products in a variety of ways—Self Assessment, Oral and Slate Assessment, Written Assessment, and an Open Response task. For more details, see the first page of Progress Check 8, Lesson 8-13 on page 766, of the *Teacher's Lesson Guide*.

Progress Check Modifications

Written Assessments are one way students demonstrate what they know. The table below shows modifications for the Written Assessment in this unit. Use these to maximize opportunities for students to demonstrate what they know. Modifications can be given individually or written on the board for the class.

Problem(s)	Modifications for Written Assessment
10	In Problem 10, use equivalent fractions to complete the rate table.
18	For Problem 18, use actual cards or draw pictures to model the problem. Make groups of 2 facedown cards and 3 faceup cards until you have a total of 25 cards.
19, 21, 22	For Problems 19, 21, and 22, use counters to model the shaded and unshaded circles.
25, 26	For Problems 25 and 26, write a number sentence containing variables. Choose one of the number sentences and explain how you would use it to solve the problem.

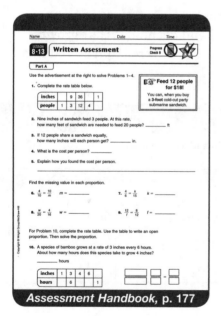

Assessment Handbook, p. 177

The Written Assessment for the Unit 8 Progress Check is on pages 177–180.

Open Response, *Designing a Banner*

Description

For this task, students use scale factors to enlarge a design to full size.

Focus

◆ **Use numerical expressions to find and represent equivalent names for fractions.**
[Number and Numeration Goal 5]

◆ **Choose and apply strategies for comparing and ordering rational numbers.**
[Number and Numeration Goal 6]

◆ **Use ratios expressed as words and fractions to solve problems; use scaling to model multiplication.**
[Operations and Computation Goal 6]

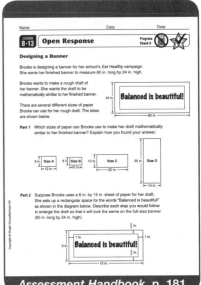

Assessment Handbook, p. 181

Implementation Tips

◆ Review solving proportions and finding equivalent fractions.

Modifications for Meeting Diverse Needs

◆ Students sometimes find it easier to first figure out a relationship that they know works. Have students begin with Part 2. They should focus on figuring out the relationship between the dimensions of the draft and the final banner. Then they can go back and do Part 1.

◆ Have students use proportional reasoning to figure out where the letters should be placed and then write a description of how they would place them on the final banner. The description should include directions that refer to the height of the letters and their approximate distance from the border.

Improving Open Response Skills

Before students begin the task, have them read the problem independently, then think about it, and record the information they know as well as questions they need to answer before solving the problem. Have students share what they wrote in small groups. Before solving the problem, have each group make a list of information and questions to refer to while completing the task.

Note: The wording and formatting of the text on the student samples that follow may vary slightly from the actual task your students will complete. These minor discrepancies will not affect the implementation of the task.

Rubric

This rubric is designed to help you assess levels of mathematical performance on this task. It emphasizes mathematical understanding with only a mention of clarity of explanation. Consider the expectations of standardized tests in your area when applying a rubric. Modify this sample rubric as appropriate.

4   Clearly explains how to derive and apply ratios to determine which paper sizes work. Describes why C and D work in terms of the ratios. Clearly explains how to derive and apply a scale factor to enlarge the plan to full size. Describes enlarging the borders based on the given dimensions.

3   Explains how to derive and apply ratios to determine which paper sizes work. Describes why C or D work. Explains some steps of how to derive and apply a scale factor to enlarge the plan to full size. Refers to enlarging everything on the draft by a factor of four, and might refer to the border.

2   Explains some steps for deriving and applying ratios to determine which paper sizes work. Lists and justifies paper choices, but there might be errors. Identifies and describes using a scale factor of four to enlarge the plan to full size.

1   Attempts to explain some steps for deriving and applying ratios to determine which paper sizes work, but there might be errors. There is little evidence of understanding how to apply ratios to solve the problem.

0   Does not attempt to solve the problem.

Copyright © Wright Group/McGraw-Hill

Sample Student Responses

This Level 4 paper illustrates the following features: Scale factors are used to check each of the possible draft-paper sizes. The dimensions of both C and D are found to have a constant scale factor, but not A and B. C is selected as the best because the scale factor is closer to a whole number. For Part 2, a scale factor of 4 is identified. There is a clear explanation for how to scale up from the draft size. The final dimensions are shown.

This Level 4 paper illustrates the following features: The explanation clearly describes how to use a scale factor to check each of the possible draft-paper sizes. There is a constant scale factor for both dimensions of C and D. For Part 2, a scale factor of 4 is identified, and how to multiply each dimension by 4 is described.

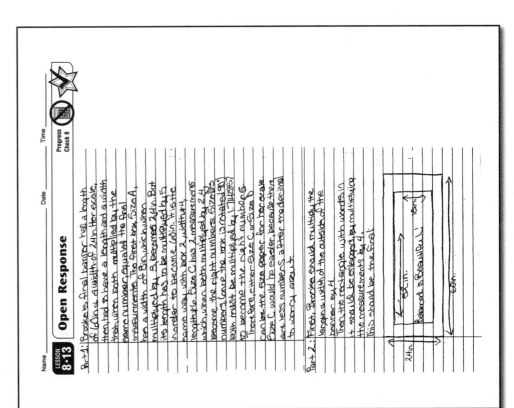

This Level 3 paper illustrates the following features: C and D are selected as the best sizes. The explanation does not specifically find a scale factor but suggests that both C and D have a scale factor that works. For Part 2, a scale factor of 4 is identified, and the explanation describes multiplying each measurement by 4 to create the final banner.

LESSON 8·13   **Open Response**   Progress Check 8

Part 1 I believe size Card size D are mathimatically similar to the final banner because both the length and with of both sizes can be multiplied by a certain number to eqoal 24in. by 6in.

Part 2 First I would divide 24 by 6in to find out how many threes 6 goes into 24. Then I divided 60 by 15in to figure out how many times 15 goes into 60. Since both answers wode ×4 I just have to mult iply all of the measurements by 4 on the rough draft to get the final measurements for the final object.

This Level 3 paper illustrates the following features: The explanation clearly describes how to use a scale factor to check each of the possible draft-paper sizes. There is a constant scale factor for both dimensions of C. For Part 2, a scale factor of 4 is identified. The explanation describes how to scale up from the draft size to the actual size of the banner, and there is a description of how to work with the borders of the banner.

LESSON 8·13   **Open Response**   Progress Check 8

I think size C would be the paper that Brooke could use because 10 and 25 can be multiplied by the same number to get 24 and 60. 10 can be multiplied by 2.4 to get 24 and 25 can be multiplied by 2.4 to get 60.

6 am 15 would get to 24 and 60 by multiplying 4 by 6 and 15. 6×4 = 24 and 15×4 = 60 to get the real measurement of the rectangular shape for the words you have to subtract 1.5 from 6 and 2 from 15, as a result you get 4.5 and 6. Since I had to multiply 15 and 6 by 4 I have to multiply 4.5 and 13 by 4 which is 18 and 52.

This Level 2 paper illustrates the following features: B is chosen as the best draft size because each dimension can be multiplied by some number to get the final dimensions. The multipliers are different numbers. For Part 2, the illustration shows multiplying every dimension by 4 to create the final banner.

This Level 1 paper illustrates the following features: A and B are chosen as possible draft sizes because each of their dimensions can be multiplied by some number to get the final dimension. The multipliers are different. For Part 2, the explanation describes multiplying the outer dimensions by 4, and subtracting the draft border measurements from the draft dimensions to find the final border measurements.

In this unit, students extend their experience with algebra and explore geometry and measurement using the language and notation of algebra. Use the information in this section to develop your assessment plan for Unit 9.

Ongoing Assessment

Opportunities for using and collecting ongoing assessment information are highlighted in Informing Instruction and Recognizing Student Achievement notes. Student products, along with observations and suggested writing prompts, provide a range of useful assessment information.

Informing Instruction

The Informing Instruction notes highlight students' thinking and point out common misconceptions. Informing Instruction in Unit 9: Lessons 9-2, 9-4, 9-6, 9-7, 9-9, and 9-12.

Recognizing Student Achievement

The Recognizing Student Achievement notes highlight specific tasks from which teachers can collect assessment data to monitor and document student progress toward meeting Grade-Level Goals.

Lesson	Content Assessed	Where to Find It
9◆1	Use a trial-and-error strategy to solve for an unknown value. [Patterns, Functions, and Algebra Goal 2]	*TLG*, p. 787
9◆2	Find the total number of objects in a set when a fractional part of the set is given. [Number and Numeration Goal 2]	*TLG*, p. 796
9◆3	Solve equations and check the solution using substitution. [Patterns, Functions, and Algebra Goal 2]	*TLG*, p. 802
9◆4	Write an expression for an area model and then evaluate that expression for a given value. [Patterns, Functions, and Algebra Goal 3]	*TLG*, p. 805
9◆5	Simplify equations and recognize equivalent equations. [Patterns, Functions, and Algebra Goal 2]	*TLG*, p. 813
9◆6	Use a distributive strategy to mentally calculate quotients. [Operations and Computation Goal 2]	*TLG*, p. 817
9◆7	Evaluate algebraic expressions using order of operations. [Patterns, Functions, and Algebra Goal 3]	*TLG*, p. 823
9◆8	Apply area formulas. [Measurement and Reference Frames Goal 2]	*TLG*, p. 829
9◆9	Simplify and solve equations. [Patterns, Functions, and Algebra Goal 2]	*TLG*, p. 837
9◆10	Use a trial-and-error method to approximate solutions of equations. [Patterns, Functions, and Algebra Goal 2]	*TLG*, p. 843

Lesson	Content Assessed *cont.*	Where to Find It
9◆11	**Substitute known values in appropriate formulas and then solve the resulting equations.** [Patterns, Functions, and Algebra Goal 2]	*TLG*, p. 849
9◆12	**Use the appropriate formula to solve an area problem.** [Measurement and Reference Frames Goal 2]	*TLG*, p. 857
9◆13	**Apply a size-change factor to find missing lengths of similar figures.** [Operations and Computation Goal 6]	*TLG*, p. 861

Math Boxes

Math Boxes, one of several types of tasks highlighted in the Recognizing Student Achievement notes, have an additional useful feature. Math Boxes in most lessons are paired or linked with Math Boxes in one or two other lessons that have similar problems. Paired or linked Math Boxes in Unit 9: 9-1, 9-3, and 9-5; 9-2 and 9-4; 9-6 and 9-8; 9-7 and 9-9; 9-10 and 9-12; and 9-11 and 9-13.

Writing/Reasoning Prompts

In Unit 9, a variety of writing prompts encourage students to explain their strategies and thinking, to reflect on their learning, and to make connections to other mathematics or life experiences. Here are some of the Unit 9 suggestions:

Lesson	Writing/Reasoning Prompts	Where to Find It
9◆1	**Explain how you identified the regular polygons.**	*TLG*, p. 790
9◆3	**Explain how the ratio is related to the ratio of the corresponding sides.**	*TLG*, p. 801
9◆6	**Explain how you found the number of faceup cards.**	*TLG*, p. 819
9◆7	**Describe each step you followed to draw the circle.**	*TLG*, p. 826
9◆11	**Explain how you calculated the height.**	*TLG*, p. 850

Portfolio Opportunities

Portfolios are a versatile tool for assessment. They help students reflect on their mathematical growth and help teachers understand and document that growth. Each unit identifies several student products that can be selected and stored in a portfolio. Here are some of the Unit 9 suggestions:

Lesson	Portfolio Opportunities	Where to Find It
9◆5	**Students translate word sentences into equations and then solve the equations.**	*TLG*, p. 815
9◆7	**Students complete a spreadsheet, answer questions about the data, and make graphs based on the data.**	*TLG*, p. 827
9◆11	**Students write, illustrate, and solve volume and area number stories.**	*TLG*, p. 851
9◆12	**Students explore the Pythagorean theorem by manipulating squares to form the sides of a triangle.**	*TLG*, p. 858
9◆13	**Students solve an indirect measurement problem.**	*TLG*, p. 863

Periodic Assessment

Every Progress Check lesson includes opportunities to observe student progress and to collect student products in a variety of ways—Self Assessment, Oral and Slate Assessment, Written Assessment, and an Open Response task. For more details, see the first page of Progress Check 9, Lesson 9-14 on page 864, of the *Teacher's Lesson Guide*.

Progress Check Modifications

Written Assessments are one way students demonstrate what they know. The table below shows modifications for the Written Assessment in this unit. Use these to maximize opportunities for students to demonstrate what they know. Modifications can be given individually or written on the board for the class.

Problem(s)	Modifications for Written Assessment
5	For Problems 5a and 5b, rewrite the formula, replacing one of the variables with its given value. Solve for the variable that remains. Show all of your steps.
7	For Problem 7, solve for *x* when a second rod weight of 2 is placed 9 units to the right of the fulcrum.
12	For Problem 12, identify corresponding sides and set up proportions before solving the problems.
17	For Problem 17, identify congruent angles by circling their angle numbers with a colored pencil. Use a separate color for each pair or set of congruent angles.

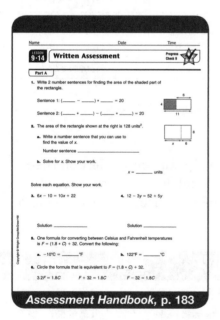

Assessment Handbook, p. 183

The Written Assessment for the Unit 9 Progress Check is on pages 183–186.

Open Response, *Area of an Octagon*

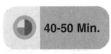
Description

For this task, students apply area formulas for various polygons to devise a procedure for finding the area of an octagon.

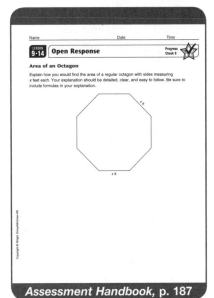

Assessment Handbook, p. 187

Focus

◆ **Use appropriate formulas to calculate the areas of polygons.**
[Measurement and Reference Frames Goal 2]

◆ **Write an open sentence containing a variable to model a situation.**
[Patterns, Functions, and Algebra Goal 2]

Implementation Tips

◆ Review "Area" pages 214–218 in the *Student Reference Book*.

Modifications for Meeting Diverse Needs

◆ Have students generate a list of polygons for which they know area formulas such as triangles, rectangles, and parallelograms. Record each formula under a picture of the polygon to which it applies. Have students refer to the labeled polygons and formulas as they work on the task.

◆ Have students attempt to find the area in terms of x. Note that they will need to use a square root if applying the Pythagorean theorem. Encourage students to share and discuss their equations as they work.

Improving Open Response Skills

After students complete the task, ask them to demonstrate a variety of solution strategies and share their explanations. Have them compare their explanations. Use questions like the following: *How are they alike and how are they different? What components are necessary in the explanation for it to be complete?* Have students make a list of the necessary components. For example, they use what they know about other shapes to find the area of the octagon. For each shape they use, they have to list the area formula and describe what to do with the area they calculate. When students have finished making a list of the necessary components, have them improve their own explanations.

Note: the wording and formatting of the text on the student samples that follow may vary slightly from the actual task your students will complete. These minor discrepancies will not affect the implementation of the task.

Rubric

This rubric is designed to help you assess levels of mathematical performance on this task. It emphasizes mathematical understanding with only a mention of clarity of explanation. Consider the expectations of standardized tests in your area when applying a rubric. Modify this sample rubric as appropriate.

4 Clearly and completely describes a strategy to determine the area of the regular octagon. Explains how to use relationships between figures to find the area. Labels the drawing to clarify the explanation. Uses formulas and geometric language in describing the strategy.

3 Describes a strategy to determine the area of the regular octagon, but some steps might require clarification or additional information. Explains how to use relationships between figures to find the area. Uses formulas and some geometric language in describing the strategy.

2 Describes some steps of a strategy that can be used to find the area of the regular octagon. There might be errors or some steps might be missing. Attempts to explain how to use relationships between figures to find the area, and there is evidence of some understanding. Might use formulas in the description.

1 Attempts to describe some steps of a strategy that can be used to find the area of the regular octagon. Attempts to explain how to identify and use relationships between figures to find the area, but there is little evidence of understanding the problem. Might attempt to use formulas in the description, but there might be errors.

0 Does not attempt to solve the problem.

Sample Student Responses

This Level 4 paper illustrates the following features: A large square is drawn around the octagon, and 4 small right triangles are added to the figure. The explanation uses formulas and clearly describes applying the Pythagorean theorem to determine the missing dimensions and then calculating areas and finding their differences.

This Level 4 paper illustrates the following features: Two methods for finding the area are described. The first one suggests dividing the octagon into 8 congruent triangles. The second involves creating 4 right triangles by enclosing the octagon in a square. The areas for the triangles are determined and subtracted from the area of the square. The explanation refers to both the Pythagorean theorem and the area formula for triangles.

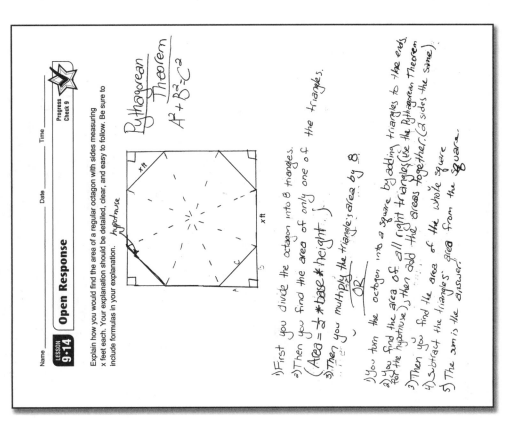

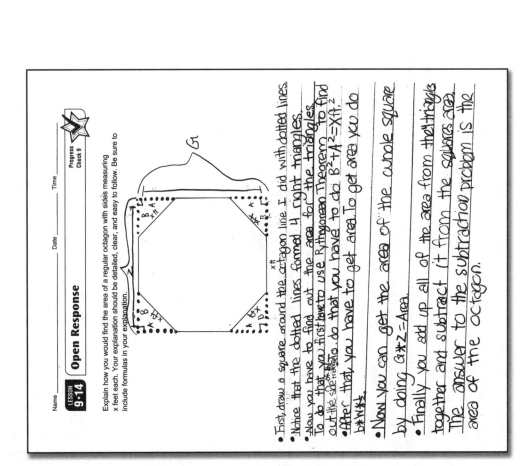

This Level 3 paper illustrates the following features: A large square is drawn around the octagon, and 4 small right triangles are added to the figure. There is a note incorrectly stating that the triangles might not be the same size. The Pythagorean theorem is mentioned but the formula is not recorded. The explanation uses area formulas, and describes finding the sum of the area of the triangles and subtracting that area from the square's area to find the area of the octagon.

This Level 2 paper illustrates the following features: A large square is drawn around the octagon, and 4 small right triangles are added to the figure. Area formulas are listed with accompanying drawings. The explanation describes subtracting the area of the triangles from the octagon to find the total area. The explanation does not clearly describe how to use all the formulas.

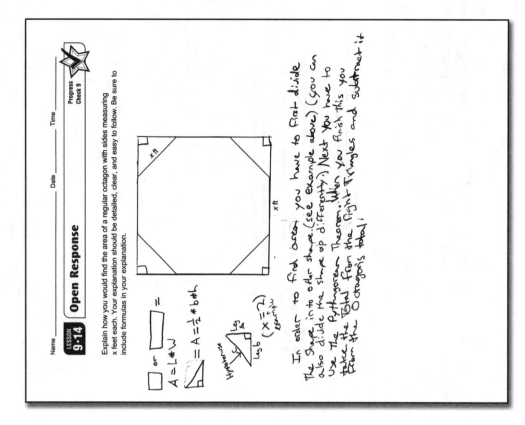

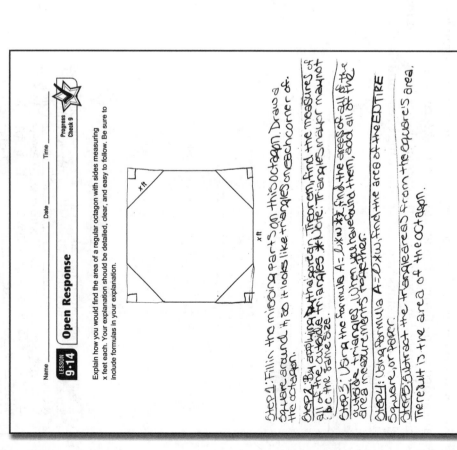

This Level 2 paper illustrates the following features: A large square is drawn around the octagon, and 4 small right triangles are added to the figure. The explanation describes finding the area of the triangles, and subtracting that area from the square's area to find the area of the octagon. The octagon is labeled with hypothetical lengths, and these measurements are used to calculate the area.

This Level 1 paper illustrates the following features: The octagon is divided into trapezoids and a rectangle, and then a square is drawn around the outside. The explanation describes finding the total angle measures of the triangles, the hypotenuse, and then suggests that the Pythagorean theorem can somehow be used to solve the problem.

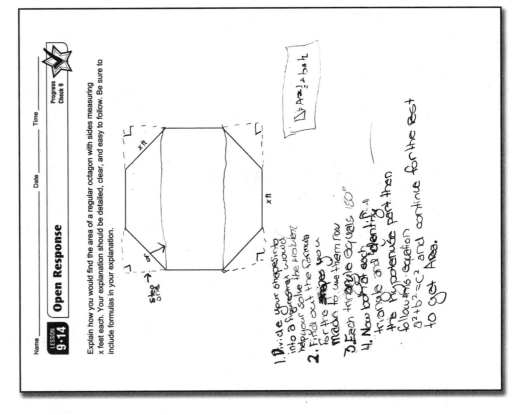

Assessment Overview

In this unit, students explore geometric transformations, cross sections of 3-dimensional shapes, and ideas from topology. Use the information in this section to develop your assessment plan for Unit 10.

Ongoing Assessment

Opportunities for using and collecting ongoing assessment information are highlighted in Informing Instruction and Recognizing Student Achievement notes. Student products, along with observations and suggested writing prompts, provide a range of useful assessment information.

Informing Instruction

The Informing Instruction notes highlight students' thinking and point out common misconceptions. Informing Instruction in Unit 10: Lessons 10-3 and 10-4.

Recognizing Student Achievement

The Recognizing Student Achievement notes highlight specific tasks from which teachers can collect assessment data to monitor and document student progress toward meeting Grade-Level Goals.

Lesson	Content Assessed	Where to Find It
10♦1	Apply the definitions of supplementary and vertical angles. [Geometry Goal 1]	*TLG*, p. 884
10♦2	Compare rational numbers. [Number and Numeration Goal 6]	*TLG*, p. 887
10♦3	Apply properties of angle orientations. [Geometry Goal 1]	*TLG*, p. 894
10♦4	Apply order of operations to write numerical expressions for rational numbers. [Number and Numeration Goal 4]	*TLG*, p. 901
10♦5	Identify instances of reflection and rotation symmetry. [Geometry Goal 3]	*TLG*, p. 906

Math Boxes

Math Boxes, one of several types of tasks highlighted in the Recognizing Student Achievement notes, have an additional useful feature. Math Boxes in most lessons are paired or linked with Math Boxes in one or two other lessons that have similar problems. Paired or linked Math Boxes in Unit 10: 10-1, 10-3 and 10-5; and 10-2 and 10-4.

Writing/Reasoning Prompts

In Unit 10, a variety of writing prompts encourage children to explain their strategies and thinking, to reflect on their learning, and to make connections to other mathematics or life experiences. Here are some of the Unit 10 suggestions:

Lesson	Writing/Reasoning Prompts	Where to Find It
10♦1	Explain how you decided whether the inequalities are true or false.	*TLG*, p. 884
10♦2	Explain how you estimated the product.	*TLG*, p. 888

Portfolio Opportunities

Portfolios are a versatile tool for assessment. They help children reflect on their mathematical growth and help teachers understand and document that growth. Each unit identifies several student products that can be selected and stored in a portfolio. Here are some of the Unit 10 suggestions:

Lesson	Portfolio Opportunities	Where to Find It
10♦1	Students use pattern blocks to explore which of several regular polygons they can use to create same-tile tessellations.	*TLG*, p. 885
10♦2	Students estimate the product.	*TLG*, p. 888
10♦3	Students draw a shape with rotation symmetry of order 3, and explore ways to draw shapes with rotation symmetry of other orders.	*TLG*, p. 895
10♦3	Students use transparent mirrors to identify and explore lines of symmetry in figures and drawings.	*TLG*, p. 894
10♦5	Students investigate networks and why some networks are traceable.	*TLG*, p. 907

Periodic Assessment

Every Progress Check lesson includes opportunities to observe student progress and to collect student products in a variety of ways—Self Assessment, Oral and Slate Assessment, Written Assessment, and an Open Response task. For more details, see the first page of Progress Check 10, Lesson 10-6 on page 908, of the *Teacher's Lesson Guide*.

Progress Check Modifications

Written Assessments are one way students demonstrate what they know. The table below shows modifications for the Written Assessment in this unit. Use these to maximize opportunities for students to demonstrate what they know. Modifications can be given individually or written on the board for the class.

Problem(s)	Modifications for Written Assessment
1	For Problem 1, explain how you used the given angle measures to find the measure of ∠E.
2	For Problems 2, cut out several enlarged copies of each figure. Use these copies to determine whether each figure will tessellate.
3	For Problem 3, use the isosceles triangle on your Geometry Template to determine the transformation that would move triangle A onto triangle B.
5	For Problem 5, cut out enlarged copies of each figure. Fold each figure identify the number and position of its line(s) of symmetry. Label the "top" of each figure and then rotate it to determine the order of rotation symmetry.

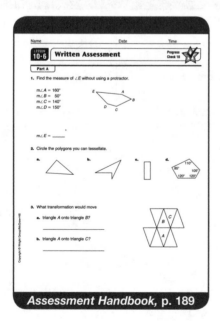

Assessment Handbook, p. 189

The Written Assessment for the Unit 10 Progress Check is on pages 189–191.

Open Response, *Finding Symmetry*

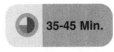
Description

For this task, students find patterns relating lines of symmetry and rotational symmetry in polygons.

Focus

◆ **Describe, compare, and classify plane figures using appropriate geometric terms.**
[Geometry Goal 2]

◆ **Identify lines of symmetry.**
[Geometry Goal 3]

◆ **Describe patterns and rules for patterns, and use them to solve problems.**
[Patterns, Functions, and Algebra Goal 1]

Implementation Tips

◆ Review lines of symmetry and rotating figures.

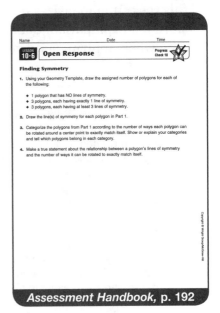

Assessment Handbook, p. 192

Modifications for Meeting Diverse Needs

◆ Have students draw each of their polygons on a quarter-sheet of paper so that they can model rotating the figure. Have them label the 4 sides of the quarter sheet as 0°/360°, 90°, 180°, and 270° so they can model the various degrees of rotation.

◆ Have students determine how many degrees each polygon is rotated to match itself with each rotation. For example, every time a square is rotated 90°, it will exactly match itself.

Improving Open Response Skills

After students complete the task, have them reflect on what was easy and what was difficult about the task. Have them write down ways that they might improve their responses. When they have finished, ask them to share their reflections in small groups. After the discussion, return their papers and have them attempt to improve their work.

Note: the wording and formatting of the text on the student samples that follow may vary slightly from the actual task your students will complete. These minor discrepancies will not affect the implementation of the task.

Rubric

This rubric is designed to help you assess levels of mathematical performance on this task. It emphasizes mathematical understanding with only a mention of clarity of explanation. Consider the expectations of standardized tests in your area when applying a rubric. Modify this sample rubric as appropriate.

4 Draws 1 polygon with 0 lines of symmetry, 3 polygons with exactly 1 line of symmetry, and 3 polygons with at least 3 lines of symmetry. Draws all possible lines of symmetry. Divides the shapes into categories according to how many ways they can be rotated to match the original shape. Clearly explains how the categories are determined and why the shapes fit into the categories.

3 Draws 1 polygon with 0 lines of symmetry, 3 polygons with at least 1 line of symmetry, and 3 polygons with at least 3 lines of symmetry. Draws some lines of symmetry. Divides the shapes into categories according to how many ways they can be rotated to match the original shape. Attempts to explain how the categories are determined and why the shapes fit into the categories, but there might be errors.

2 Draws 1 polygon with 0 lines of symmetry, 3 polygons with at least 1 line of symmetry, and 3 polygons with at least 3 lines of symmetry. Draws some lines of symmetry. Attempts to divide the shapes into categories and to explain the categories, but the categories or explanation might be confusing or incorrect.

1 Draws some polygons and some lines of symmetry. Might attempt to divide the shapes into categories and explain the categories, but the categories or explanation might not make sense in the context of the problem.

0 Does not attempt to solve the problem.

Sample Student Responses

This Level 4 paper illustrates the following features: The specified polygons are drawn for each category and clearly labeled as to whether they have 0, 1, or at least 3 lines of symmetry. The polygons are clearly categorized into two groups—polygons having 0 or 1 line of symmetry that have to be rotated 360° to match the original and polygons with at least 2 lines of symmetry that can be rotated less than 360° to match the original.

This Level 4 paper illustrates the following features: The specified polygons are drawn for each category and clearly labeled as to whether they have 0, 1, or at least 3 lines of symmetry. The polygons are clearly categorized into two groups—"Do" and "Don't." The "Do" group contains polygons that can be rotated less than 360° to match the original. The "Don't" group contains polygons that must be rotated 360° to match the original.

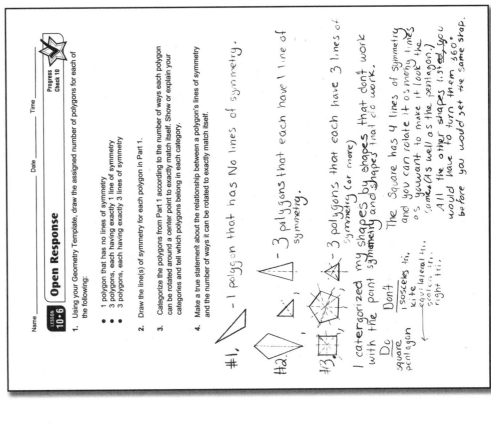

This Level 3 paper illustrates the following features: The specified polygons are drawn for each category and clearly labeled as to whether they have 0, 1, or at least 3 lines of symmetry (LOS). Except for the scalene triangle the polygons are correctly labeled with an order of rotational symmetry (ROS). There are no categories, but the final statement describes a relationship between LOS and ROS.

This Level 3 paper illustrates the following features: The specified polygons are drawn for each category and clearly labeled as to whether they have 0, 1, or at least 3 lines of symmetry. The polygons appear to be categorized according to the number of degrees the polygon must be rotated to match the original, but the degrees of rotation assigned to several polygons are incorrect. The final statement indicates an understanding that with 0 or 1 line of symmetry, the figure must be rotated 360°.

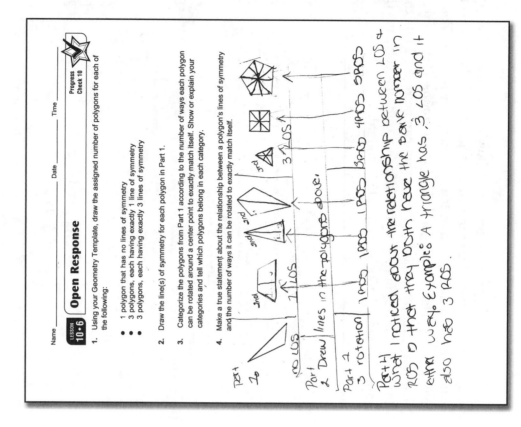

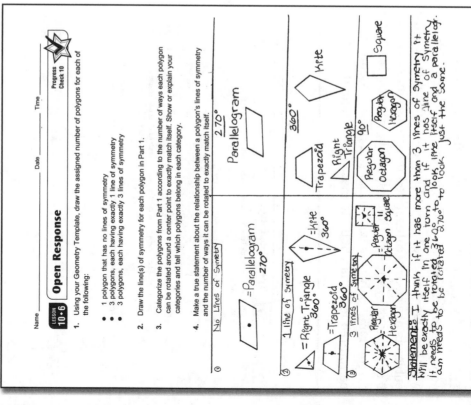

This Level 2 paper illustrates the following features: The specified polygons are drawn for each category. Then, one polygon from each category is drawn as it would look rotated 90°, 180°, and 270°. The final statement explains that rotation does not affect the number of lines of symmetry.

This Level 1 paper illustrates the following features: The specified polygons are drawn for each category. Not all lines of symmetry are recorded on those polygons having at least three lines of symmetry. There is a table comparing lines of symmetry (LOS) with rotation symmetry (ROS), but the table contains errors. The explanation does not make sense.

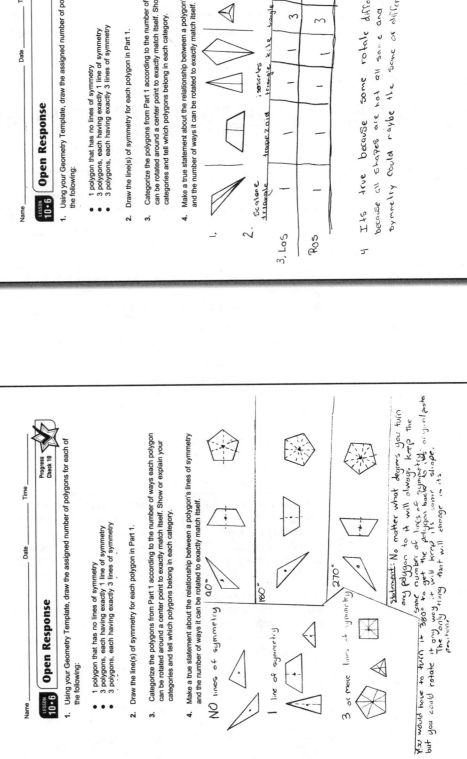

End-of-Year Assessment Goals

The End-of-Year Assessment (pages 211–219) provides an additional opportunity that you may use as part of your balanced assessment plan. It covers some of the important concepts and skills presented in *Sixth Grade Everyday Mathematics*. It should be used to complement the ongoing and periodic assessments that appear within lessons and at the end of units. The following table provides the goals for all the problems in the End-of-Year Assessment.

Problem(s)	Grade-Level Goal
1, 25	**Number and Numeration 6:** Choose and apply strategies for comparing and ordering rational numbers; explain those choices and strategies.
2, 25	**Number and Numeration 1:** Read and write whole numbers and decimals; identify places in such numbers and the values of the digits in those places; use expanded notation, number-and-word notation, exponential notation, and scientific notation to represent whole numbers and decimals.
3	**Patterns, Functions, and Algebra 3:** Describe and apply the conventional order of operations.
4a, 4d, 15, 18	**Operations and Computation 1:** Use mental arithmetic, paper-and-pencil algorithms and models, and calculators to solve problems involving the addition and subtraction of whole numbers, decimals, and signed numbers; describe the strategies used and explain how they work.
4b, 4c, 16, 20	**Operations and Computation 2:** Use mental arithmetic, paper-and-pencil algorithms and models, and calculators to solve problems involving the multiplication and division of whole numbers, decimals, and signed numbers; describe the strategies used and explain how they work.
5, 34	**Patterns, Functions, and Algebra 1:** Extend, describe, and create numeric patterns; describe rules for patterns and use them to solve problems; represent patterns and rules using algebraic notation; represent functions using words, algebraic notation, tables, and graphs; translate from one representation to another and use representations to solve problems involving functions.
6–11, 34	**Patterns, Functions, and Algebra 2:** Determine whether equalities and inequalities are true or false; solve open number sentences and explain the solutions; use a pan-balance model to solve linear equations in one or two unknowns; use trial-and-error and equivalent equations strategies to solve linear equations in one unknown.
12, 13	**Data and Chance 3:** Use the Multiplication Counting Principle, tree diagrams, and other counting strategies to identify all possible outcomes for a situation; predict results of experiments, test the predictions using manipulatives, and summarize the findings; compare predictions based on theoretical probability with experimental results; calculate probabilities and express them as fractions, decimals, and percents; explain how sample size affects results; use the results to predict future events.
14, 23b, 24a, 24d	**Operations and Computation 6:** Use ratios and scaling to model size changes and to solve size-change problems; represent ratios as fractions, percents, and decimals, and using a colon; model and solve problems involving part-to-whole and part-to-part ratios; model rate and ratio number stories with proportions; use and explain cross multiplication and other strategies to solve proportions.

Problem(s)	Grade-Level Goal
15–22	**Operations and Computation 5:** Make reasonable estimates for whole number, decimal, fraction, and mixed number addition, subtraction, multiplication, and division problems; explain how the estimates were obtained.
17, 19	**Operations and Computation 4:** Use mental arithmetic, paper-and-pencil algorithms and models, and calculators to solve problems involving the multiplication and division of fractions and mixed numbers; describe the strategies used and explain how they work.
21, 22	**Operations and Computation 3:** Use mental arithmetic, paper-and-pencil algorithms and models, and calculators to solve problems involving the addition and subtraction of fractions and mixed numbers; describe the strategies used and explain how they work.
23a, 39	**Measurement and Reference Frames 1:** Estimate length with and without tools; measure length with tools to the nearest $\frac{1}{16}$ inch and millimeter; estimate the measure of angles with and without tools; use tools to draw angles with given measures.
24b, 24c, 34	**Measurement and Reference Frames 2:** Choose and use appropriate formulas to calculate the circumference of circles and to solve area, perimeter, and volume problems.
26	**Number and Numeration 5:** Find equivalent fractions and fractions in simplest form by applying multiplication and division rules and concepts from number theory; convert between fractions, mixed numbers, decimals, and percents.
27–29	**Number and Numeration 2:** Solve problems involving percents and discounts; explain strategies used; identify the unit whole in situations involving fractions, decimals, and percents.
30, 31	**Number and Numeration 3:** Use GCFs, LCMs, and divisibility rules to manipulate fractions.
32	**Number and Numeration 4:** Apply the order of operations to numerical expressions to give equivalent names for rational numbers.
33	**Geometry 2:** Identify and describe similar and congruent figures and describe their properties; construct a figure that is congruent to another figure using a compass and straightedge.
35	**Geometry 1:** Identify, describe, classify, name, and draw angles; determine angle measures by applying properties of orientations of angles and of sums of angle measures in triangles and quadrangles.
36	**Measurement and Reference Frames 3:** Use ordered pairs of numbers to name, locate, and plot points in all four quadrants of a coordinate grid.
36	**Geometry 3:** Identify, describe, and sketch (including plotting on the coordinate plane) instances of reflections, translations, and rotations.
37a	**Data and Chance 1:** Collect and organize data or use given data to create graphic displays with reasonable titles, labels, keys, and intervals.
37b, 37c	**Data and Chance 2:** Use data landmarks, measures of spread, and graphs to ask and answer questions, draw conclusions, and make predictions; compare and contrast the median and mean of a data set.
38	**Patterns, Functions, and Algebra 4:** Describe and apply properties of arithmetic and multiplicative and additive inverses.

Assessment Masters

Contents

LESSON 1·13

Self Assessment

Progress
Check 1

Think about each skill listed below. Assess your own progress by checking the most appropriate box.

Skills	I can do this on my own and explain how to do it.	I can do this on my own.	I can do this if I get help or look at an example.
1. Find the mean of a set of numbers.			
2. Find the median of a set of numbers.			
3. Make a line plot.			
4. Make a stem-and-leaf plot.			
5. Make a bar graph.			
6. Read a broken-line graph.			
7. Use the Percent Circle to measure sectors of a circle graph.			

LESSON 1·13 — Written Assessment

Progress Check 1

Part A

1. Emperor penguins are the largest of all penguins. Some weights (in pounds) for these penguins are represented by the following data set.

   60, 59, 66, 64, 61, 64, 60, 59, 65, 64, 65, 60

   a. Construct a line plot to represent the penguin data.

   Weights of Emperor Penguins

   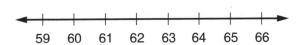

   59   60   61   62   63   64   65   66

   b. Use your line plot to find the following landmarks.

   maximum _____   minimum _____

   mode(s) _____   range _____

2. The ages of some Nobel Peace Prize winners since 1990 appear in the following data set.

   56, 78, 62, 75, 61, 54, 47, 38, 46, 87, 65, 71, 72, 75, 57, 33, 46

   a. Construct a stem-and-leaf plot of the ages of prize winners.

   Ages of Some Nobel Peace Prize Winners since 1990

Stems (10s)	Leaves (1s)

   b. Use your stem-and-leaf plot to find the following landmarks.

   maximum _____

   minimum _____

   mode(s) _____

   range _____

LESSON 1·13 | **Written Assessment** *continued*

3. The ages of the students in a Saturday art class are 14, 18, 43, 14, 15, 18, and 11.

a. Find the median age and the mean age.   median _____   mean _____

b. Which landmark, the mean or median, is the better representation of the ages of students in the art class? Explain.

_____

_____

4. Suppose you are dealt the hand shown below in a game of *Landmark Shark*.

Which landmark, the range, median, or mode, will show you the highest score for your hand? _____

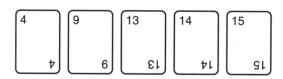

5. Study the double-line graph at the right. On average, what is the

a. warmest month of the year? _____

b. coldest month of the year? _____

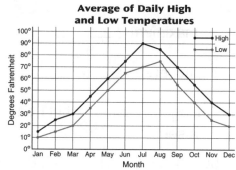

c. Compare the average daily high and low temperatures in July. About how much warmer is the high temperature? _____

6. Construct a bar graph to represent the data in the table below. Label each axis.

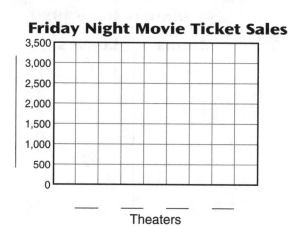

Friday Night Movie Ticket Sales	
Theater	**Average Number of Tickets Sold**
Theater A	2,250
Theater B	1,750
Theater C	1,500
Theater D	3,000

LESSON 1·13 | **Written Assessment** *continued*

7. A small company produces video games. The marketing manager claims that sales fell 50% between the third and fourth quarters.

End-of-Quarter Sales 2005

a. According to the graph, what were the first quarter sales? _____

b. Between which two quarters was the increase in sales the greatest?

_____

c. Is the marketing manager's claim misleading? Explain.

_____

_____

_____

8. Through a survey that used random sampling, 3,000 American adults were asked how much time they spend on various activities during an average day. The circle graph displays the results.

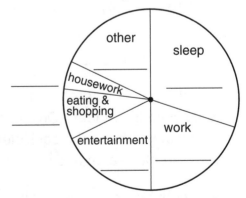

Daily Activities

Use your estimation skills and your Percent Circle to find the percent for the following activities.

a. sleep: About _____

b. work: About _____

c. entertainment: About _____

d. other: About _____

LESSON 1·13 | **Written Assessment** *continued*

---

9. The length of a rectangle is 6 cm and the width is 9 cm.

  a. Write a number sentence for the perimeter of the rectangle.

  _____

  b. What is the area of the rectangle? Area = _____ cm^2

10. Write four expressions for 25. Each must use a 7 and a 9.

  _____   _____

  _____   _____

11. Use the step graph to answer the following questions.

  a. How much would it cost to rent a canoe for

  $1\frac{1}{2}$ hours? _____ 3 hours? _____

  3 hours 5 minutes? _____

  b. Dimitri and his friends rent a canoe at
  3:15 P.M. They don't want to pay more than
  $20. By what time do they need to return
  the canoe? _____

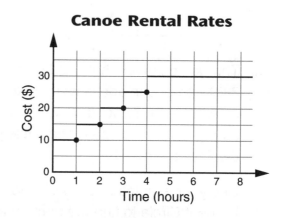

Canoe Rental Rates

12. A pedestrian is a person who travels by walking. Consider the following statistic meant to astound the reader: "On average, a pedestrian is killed by a motor vehicle every 90 minutes. That is the equivalent of a plane crash in which 110 passengers are killed every week, year in and year out."

  a. About how many pedestrians are killed by motor vehicles each year?

  _____

  b. The U.S. population is about 270 million people. About how many times as great is the estimated U.S. population than the number of pedestrians killed by motor vehicles each year?

  _____

LESSON 1·13 | Open Response

Analyzing Jumping-Jack Data

Ms. Green's and Mr. Short's sixth-grade gym classes decided to hold a jumping-jack contest. Students did as many jumping jacks as they could in 1 minute. The results of the contest are shown below.

Ms. Green's Gym Class	
Student #	Number of Jumping Jacks
1	87
2	101
3	62
4	102
5	85
6	114
7	89
8	89
9	149
10	67
11	100
12	73
13	90
14	82
15	79
16	81

Mr. Short's Gym Class	
Student #	Number of Jumping Jacks
1	72
2	114
3	90
4	120
5	60
6	90
7	70
8	112
9	97
10	104
11	54
12	102
13	149
14	67
15	100
16	49

Ms. Green claims that her class was the best. Mr. Short claims that his class did better. With whom do you agree and why? Use data landmarks from both classes to support your reasoning. Show your work.

LESSON 2·12

Self Assessment

Think about each skill listed below. Assess your own progress by checking the most appropriate box.

Skills	I can do this on my own and explain how to do it.	I can do this on my own.	I can do this if I get help or look at an example.
1. Read and write numbers to trillions.			
2. Read and write numbers to thousandths.			
3. Write numbers in scientific notation.			
4. Add and subtract decimals.			
5. Multiply by positive and negative powers of 10.			
6. Multiply decimals.			
7. Divide whole numbers.			
8. Estimate products and quotients of decimal numbers.			

LESSON 2·12

Written Assessment

Progress
Check 2

Part A

1. Write the digit in each place of the number below.

5,146,702,897,352.6138

a. ten billions ____   **b.** hundredths ____   **c.** hundred millions ____

d. thousandths ____   **e.** trillions ____   **f.** tenths ____

2. Write the following numbers in standard notation.

a. 4.6 million _____   **b.** 32.1 trillion _____

3. Write each number in number-and-word notation.

a. 5,600,000,000 _____

b. 462,800,000,000,000 _____

4. Write the exponent for each of the following numbers.

a. $0.001 = 10^{\square}$ **b.** $1 \text{ billion} = 10^{\square}$

c. $10 * 10 * 10 * 10 = 10^{\square}$ **d.** $\frac{1}{10} = 10^{\square}$

5. Complete.

a. $76{,}541 * 0.0001 = $ _____   **b.** $0.421 * 10{,}000 = $ _____

c. $45.7 * 10^{-3} = $ _____   **d.** $85 = 0.0085 * $ _____

e. $2.9 * 10^5 = $ _____   **f.** $0.7 = 0.007 * $ _____

LESSON 2·12 | **Written Assessment** *continued*

6. Suppose that Pluto is about $2.8 * 10^9$ miles from the sun. Write $2.8 * 10^9$ in standard notation. _____

7. Suppose that Earth travels about 600,000,000 miles in its orbit around the sun every year. Write 600,000,000 in scientific notation. _____

Add or subtract.

8. $9.394 + 5.67 =$ _____

9. $4.4 - 3.82 =$ _____

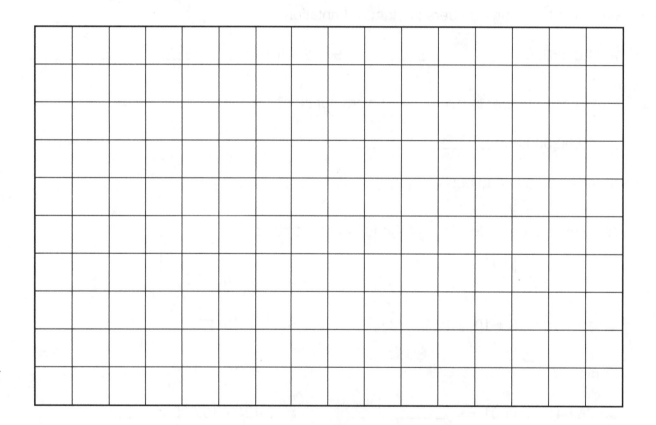

Multiply or divide.

10. _____ $= 72.3 * 5.6$

11. $990 / 36$ _____

LESSON 2·12 | **Written Assessment** *continued*

Part B

12. Write each of the following numbers in expanded notation.
Example: $23.89 = (2 * 10) + (3 * 1) + (8 * 0.1) + (9 * 0.01)$

a. 67,051 _____

b. 2.904 _____

13. Use a calculator to help you convert the numbers written in exponential notation to standard notation.

a. $13^5 = $ _____   b. $8^{-6} = $ _____

Metric Measurements		
Length	**Capacity**	**Mass**
1 meter (m) = 100 centimeters (cm)	1 liter (L) = 1,000 milliliters (mL)	1 kilogram (kg) = 1,000 grams (g)
1 centimeter (cm) = 10 millimeters (mm)	1 kiloliter (kL) = 1,000 liters (L)	1 gram (g) = 1,000 milligrams (mg)

14. Use the table of metric measurements above to complete the following.

a. 245 cm = _____ m   b. 3.6 L = _____ mL

c. 19,200 g = _____ kg   d. 591 mL = _____ L

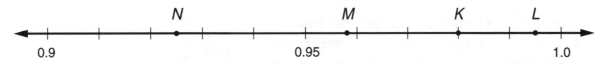

Name the point on the number line above that represents each of the following numbers.

15. 0.958 _____   **16.** 0.925 _____   **17.** 0.995 _____

18. Use the number line above to help you round 0.908
to the nearest hundredth.   _____

LESSON 2·12 | **Written Assessment** *continued*

19. The scores for a math quiz appear in the table at the right.

Math Quiz Scores
83 91 88 91 95 66 91 81 85 71
98 91 41 63 49 74 85 80 75

a. Make a stem-and-leaf plot for the quiz data.

Math Quiz Scores

Stems (10s)	Leaves (1s)

b. Use your stem-and-leaf plot to find the following landmarks.

median _____ mean (round to nearest tenth) _____

c. Which landmark, mean or median, is the better indicator of students' overall performance on the math quiz? Explain.

_____

_____

_____

20. Gabriella is trying to convince her boss that she deserves a salary increase. She claims that over the past 8 weeks, her number of working hours has greatly increased. She uses the broken-line graph at the right to support her claim.

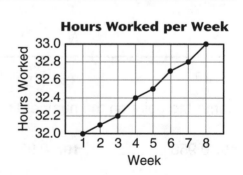

Hours Worked per Week

a. According to the graph, how many hours did Gabriella work during Week 7? _____

b. Is Gabriella's claim misleading? Explain.

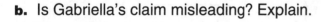

_____

_____

LESSON 2·12

Open Response

Planning a Pizza Party

Your class is planning the menu for the end-of-year party for 36 people. Each person will get 2 slices of pizza. You have been assigned to find the least expensive restaurant from which to order the pizza. Several local restaurants and their prices are shown in the table below.

Restaurant	Pizza Price	Slices Per Pizza
Not-So-Crusty Pizza	$10.80	8
Supreme Pizza	$12.25	10
Perfection Pizza	$8.25	6

From which restaurant should you buy the pizza?

Write an explanation of how you made your decision. Your explanation should be clear and easy to follow. You can use pictures or tables to help you organize your work.

LESSON 3·11

Self Assessment

Think about each skill listed below. Assess your own progress by checking the most appropriate box.

Skills	I can do this on my own and explain how to do it.	I can do this on my own.	I can do this if I get help or look at an example.
1. Describe a general number pattern in words and with a number sentence.			
2. Use a formula.			
3. Complete a table for a given rule. Then graph the data.			
4. Apply multiplication and division facts and strategies to solve problems.			
5. Mentally add positive and negative numbers.			
6. Write spreadsheet cell names and formulas.			

LESSON 3·11 Written Assessment

Part A

1. Give two special cases for the general pattern $m + m + k = (2 * m) + k$.

   _____   _____

2. Circle each statement below (a–d) that describes the special cases at the right.
   a. Doubling a number is the same as adding it to itself.

   b. $2 * n = 2 + 2$ c. $2 * a = a - a$ d. $2 * a = a + a$

   > $2 * 7 = 7 + 7$
   > $2 * 1.5 = 1.5 + 1.5$
   > $2 * 0 = 0 + 0$

You can use the formula $c = 2.54 * i$ to find length in centimeters (c) when length in inches (i) is known. Use this formula for Problems 3–5.

3. How many centimeters are in 2 inches? _____
   (unit)

4. How many centimeters are in 100 inches? _____
   (unit)

5. Circle the best estimate for the number of centimeters in 1 foot.

   24   30   40   50

6. Use the formulas at the right to find the perimeter and area of the rectangle.

   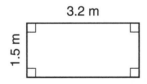

   3.2 m
   1.5 m

   > Perimeter of a rectangle
   > $P = 2 * (b + h)$
   >
   > Area of a rectangle
   > $A = b * h$

   a. Perimeter = _____
      (unit)

   b. Area = _____
      (unit)

LESSON 3·11

Written Assessment *continued*

7. Evaluate each expression when $x = 3$.

a. $2.7 * 10^x$ _____

b. $x^4 + 3^x$ _____

c. $x * 10^{-5}$ _____

d. $x^0 + -3$ _____

8. Mr. Ricco used the spreadsheet at the right to record his students' scores on 3 math quizzes. The mean score for the 3 quizzes appears in Column E.

	A	B	C	D	E
1	**Student**	**Quiz 1**	**Quiz 2**	**Quiz 3**	**Mean**
2	Cheri	100	100	100	100
3	Briana	50	80	74	68
4	Lamar	100	95	95	97
5	Sam	80	100	90	

a. Name the cell that contains Lamar's score on Quiz 2. _____

b. Calculate Sam's mean score and record it in cell E5.

c. Using cell names, write a formula for calculating the value in E5.

_____

9. Complete the table for the given rule. Then plot and connect the points to make a line graph.

Rule: $y = (\frac{1}{2} * x) + 1$

in	out
x	y
0	1
1	
2	
	3
5	

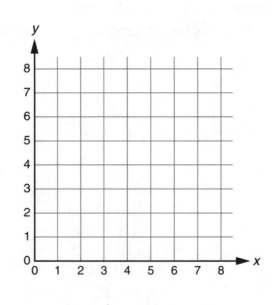

LESSON 3·11 **Written Assessment** *continued*

Each of the graphs represents one of the situations described below. Match each situation with its graph.

Graph A

Graph B

Graph C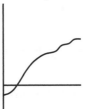

Graph D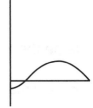

10. The height of a plant, starting as a seed. Graph _____

11. The height of a human male between the ages of 5 and 12. Graph _____

12. The height of the red liquid in a thermometer during a January day in

Chicago, Illinois. Graph _____

13. The height of the grass in a soccer field during a playing season. Graph _____

Part B

14. Rename each fraction as a mixed number or whole number.

a. $\frac{29}{4}$ _____ b. $\frac{32}{8}$ _____ c. $\frac{15}{2}$ _____ d. $\frac{80}{16}$ _____

15. Rename each mixed number as a fraction.

a. $5\frac{3}{8}$ _____ b. $4\frac{1}{2}$ _____ c. $7\frac{9}{16}$ _____ d. $4\frac{3}{4}$ _____

16. Name the greatest common factor of each pair of numbers.

a. 8 and 24 _____   b. 49 and 50 _____

Written Assessment *continued*

17. List the first 6 multiples of each number.

60 _____

90 _____

Name the least common multiple (LCM) of 60 and 90. _____

18. Use estimation to insert the decimal point in each quotient.

a. $1{,}401.4 / 77 = 1\ 8\ 2$ **b.** $309.68 / 9.8 = 3\ 1\ 6\ 0$

19. Multiply mentally.

a. $3.944 * 10^{-3} =$ _____   **b.** $7.56 * 10^{5} =$ _____

20. Adena rode her bike from her home to the park, where she had a picnic with her friend Meredith. Then she rode her bike home.

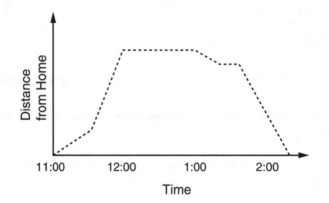

Use the graph to tell a story about Adena's bike ride.

_____

_____

_____

LESSON 3·11 | **Open Response**

Representing Rates

Since January 1, you have kept track of the number of members belonging to two school clubs. The Math Club currently has 200 members, and it adds 50 new members per month. The Science Club currently has 400 members, and it adds 25 new members per month. Use the representations below to figure out how many months it will take for the two clubs to have the same number of members if no one quits.

Math Club

Rule: Total Members = 200 + (50 * Number of Months)

Formula: $m = 50x + 200$

Number of Months	Total Members
x	50x + 200
0	200
1	250

Science Club

Rule: Total Members = 400 + (25 * Number of Months)

Formula: $m = 25x + 400$

Number of Months	Total Members
x	25x + 400
0	400
1	425

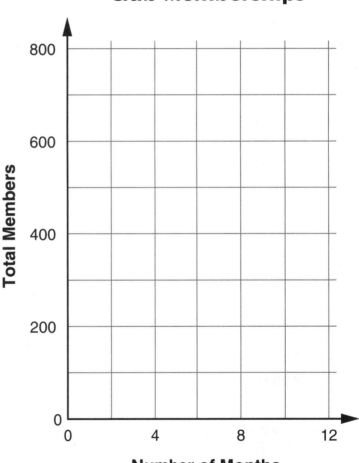

Club Memberships

The clubs will have the same number of members after _____ months.

On a separate sheet of paper, explain how you used the representations (graph, table, formulas) to solve the problem.

LESSON 4·12   Self Assessment

Think about each skill listed below. Assess your own progress by checking the most appropriate box.

Skills	I can do this on my own and explain how to do it.	I can do this on my own.	I can do this if I get help or look at an example.
1. Write fractions in simplest form.			
2. Convert between fractions and mixed numbers.			
3. Find equivalent fractions, mixed numbers, decimals, and percents.			
4. Compare fractions.			
5. Add or subtract fractions and mixed numbers with unlike denominators.			
6. Multiply fractions and mixed numbers.			
7. Find the percent of a number.			
8. Use the Percent Circle to make a circle graph.			

LESSON 4·12 | **Written Assessment**

Part A

1. Write each of the following fractions in simplest form.

a. $\frac{6}{8}$ _____   **b.** $\frac{9}{12}$ _____   **c.** $\frac{45}{100}$ _____   **d.** $\frac{63}{108}$ _____

2. Complete the table below. Simplify all fractions.

	Fraction	Decimal	Percent		Fraction	Decimal	Percent
a.		0.36		**e.**		0.97	
b.	$\frac{22}{25}$			**f.**	$\frac{3}{20}$		
c.		0.02		**g.**			32.5%
d.			60%	**h.**	$1\frac{3}{5}$		

3. Compare using < or >.

a. $\frac{1}{2}$ _____ $\frac{4}{9}$ **b.** $2\frac{3}{8}$ _____ $2\frac{5}{12}$ **c.** $1\frac{1}{3}$ _____ $\frac{7}{6}$ **d.** 3.57 _____ $3\frac{3}{5}$

4. When Monica began first grade, she was $45\frac{3}{4}$ in. tall.
At the end of the year, she was $47\frac{3}{8}$ in. tall. How much had Monica grown? _____
(unit)

5. Evan uses a pencil to do his math work. He started the week with a new
pencil, which measured 18.5 cm in length. At the end of 2 weeks, the
pencil measured 10.8 cm in length. Find the difference between
the 2 pencil lengths. Express your answer as a mixed number. _____ cm

6. Add. Write all answers greater than 1 as mixed numbers. Write all fractions in simplest form.

a. $3\frac{5}{6} + 2\frac{1}{4} =$ _____   **b.** $2\frac{4}{5} + 1\frac{1}{3} =$ _____

c. $2\frac{1}{8} + 1\frac{1}{6} + 1\frac{7}{8} =$ _____   **d.** $\frac{4}{9} + \frac{2}{3} =$ _____

LESSON 4·12   **Written Assessment** *continued*

7. Use the diagram to solve the problems below. Write your answers in simplest form.

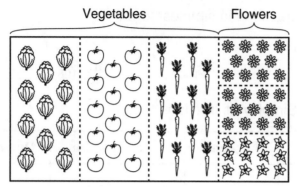

Vegetables   Flowers

Mr. Dahli plants $\frac{3}{4}$ of his garden with vegetables and $\frac{1}{4}$ of it with flowers. He plants $\frac{2}{3}$ of the flower section with daisies and the rest of the flower section with lilies.

a. What fraction of the entire garden is lilies? _____

b. Write a number model for the fraction of the entire garden that is daisies.   _____

c. Suppose Mr. Dahli's garden has an area of 1,408 ft².
How many square feet are planted in vegetables?   _____ ft²

Part B

8. Sixth graders were asked the following question: *If you could use only one of the following forms of entertainment, which would you choose?*

Complete the table below.

	Form of Entertainment	Number of Students	Percent of Students
a.	Computer with Internet access	120	
b.	TV or DVDs		35%
c.	Video games	96	
d.	Books or magazines		5%
e.	Music CDs	72	
f.	**Total**	**480**	

Written Assessment *continued*

LESSON
4·12

9. Use the Percent Circle on the Geometry Template to make a circle graph of the data in Problem 8.

Forms of Entertainment

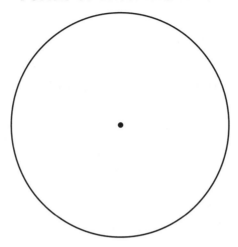

10. Find the perimeter and area of the rectangle shown below.

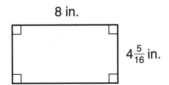

8 in.

$4\frac{5}{16}$ in.

Perimeter _____ in.   Area _____ in.^{2}

11. Evaluate each expression when $x = 5$.

a. $0.0035 * 10^x$ _____   **b.** $2^x + 3^3$ _____

c. $-(x) + -18$ _____   **d.** $x^0 + -8$ _____

12. Estimate the quotient $928.8 \div 36$. Then divide.   Estimate _____

$36\overline{)928.8}$

$928.8 \div 36 =$ _____

LESSON 4·12 **Open Response**

Making a Wooden Rack

Patina is designing a wall-mounted wooden rack for hanging necklaces and belts. She has a strip of wood that is $17\frac{1}{2}$ inches long by $2\frac{3}{4}$ inches high.

She plans to drill 6 peg holes into this strip, each hole having a diameter of $\frac{7}{8}$ inch. She wants to position the holes so the distance between any two pegs (*b*) is the same. The space between each end of the rack and the first hole will also be the same (*b*).

What is the maximum distance between any two pegs?

Write an explanation of how you arrived at your answer. Describe each step in your solution clearly. Use the diagram below to help you.

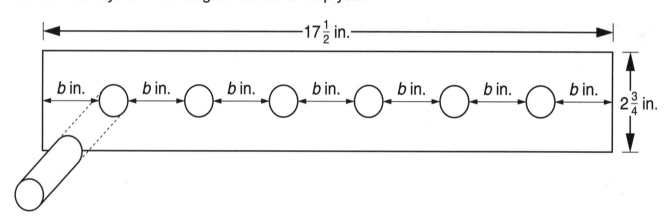

Name   Date   Time

LESSON 5·11   Self Assessment

Progress Check 5

Think about each skill listed below. Assess your own progress by checking the most appropriate box.

Skills	I can do this on my own and explain how to do this.	I can do this on my own.	I can do this if I get help or look at an example.
1. Rename fractions as mixed numbers, decimals, and percents.			
2. Estimate sums, differences, and products of fractions and mixed numbers.			
3. Add, subtract, and multiply fractions and mixed numbers.			
4. Find a percent of a number mentally.			
5. Identify, draw, and describe different types of angles (acute, obtuse, right, reflex, vertical, adjacent, supplementary).			
6. Copy a figure using a compass and a straightedge.			
7. Use a protractor to create a circle graph.			
8. Translate a figure on a coordinate grid.			

LESSON 5·11

Written Assessment

Part A

Measure each angle to the nearest degree.

1.

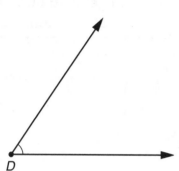

m∠D = _____

2.

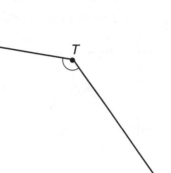

m∠T = _____

3. This is a reflex angle.

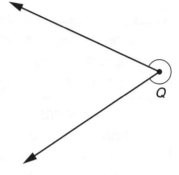

m∠Q = _____

4. Draw a triangle congruent to triangle *DEN*. Line segment *PR* is one of the sides of the new triangle. Label the third vertex of the triangle as *A*.

Name the coordinates of each vertex of triangle *PRA*.

P: (_____, _____)

R: (_____, _____)

A: (_____, _____)

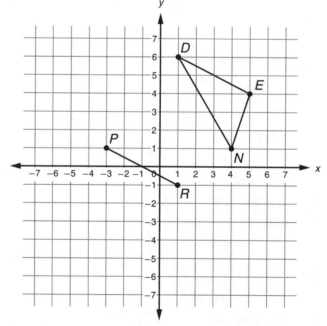

5. Copy the angle below using only a compass, a straightedge, and a pencil.

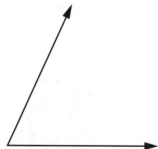

LESSON 5·11 | **Written Assessment** *continued*

6. Find the measure of each angle without using a protractor.

m∠1 = _____   m∠2 = _____

m∠3 = _____   m∠4 = _____

m∠5 = _____   m∠6 = _____

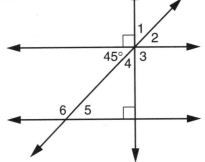

7. Quadrilateral *ABCD* is a parallelogram.
Angles *x* and *y* have the same degree
measure. What is the measure of ∠*ABE*?

m∠*ABE* = _____

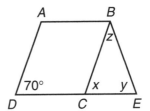

8. Celeste sold 150 boxes of candy for the school fundraiser. Complete
the table below. Round each answer to the nearest whole number.
Then use a protractor to make a circle graph of the sales information.
Write a title for your graph.

Purchased By	Number of Boxes	Percent of Total	Degree Measure of Sector
Family	27		
Friends		36%	
Parents' Coworkers	36		
Neighbors	33		
TOTAL	**150**	**100%**	**360°**

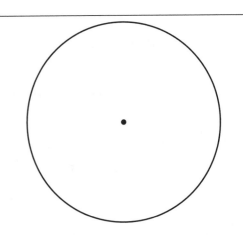

LESSON 5·11 | **Written Assessment** *continued* |

Part B

Estimate each sum, difference, or product. Then solve. Write each answer in simplest form.

9. $8\frac{1}{6} - \frac{5}{6}$ Estimate _____

$$8\frac{1}{6} - \frac{5}{6} = \text{_____}$$

10. $6\frac{2}{5} + 3\frac{1}{4}$ Estimate _____

$$6\frac{2}{5} + 3\frac{1}{4} = \text{_____}$$

11. $2\frac{7}{10} * 4\frac{4}{9}$ Estimate _____

$$2\frac{7}{10} * 4\frac{4}{9} = \text{_____}$$

Find each sum.

12. $34 + (12 + -18) = \text{_____}$ **13.** $-75 + 50 + 40 = \text{_____}$

Divide to rename each fraction as a decimal rounded to the nearest hundredth.

14. $\frac{11}{16} = 0.\text{_____}$ **15.** $\frac{5}{9} = 0.\text{_____}$

LESSON
5·11

Open Response

Measuring Angles

Find the following angle measures
without using a protractor.

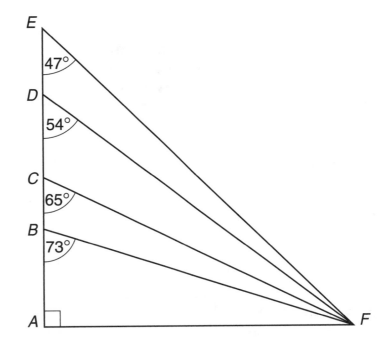

1. ∠AFB _____

2. ∠AFC _____

3. ∠AFD _____

4. ∠CFD _____

Write an explanation of how you found each angle measure. Your explanations should be
clear and easy to follow. Be sure to include equations in your explanations.

LESSON 6·13 | Self Assessment

Progress Check 6

Think about each skill listed below. Assess your own progress by checking the most appropriate box.

Skills	I can do this on my own and explain how to do it.	I can do this on my own.	I can do this if I get help or look at an example.
1. Divide fractions and mixed numbers.			
2. Add and subtract signed numbers.			
3. Multiply and divide signed numbers.			
4. Tell whether inequalities are true or false.			
5. Apply order of operations to evaluate expressions.			
6. Solve pan-balance equations.			

Part A

Divide. Show your work. Write your answers in simplest form.

1. $\frac{2}{3} \div \frac{1}{3} =$ _____

2. $1\frac{5}{6} \div \frac{2}{3} =$ _____

3. $5 \div \frac{2}{3} =$ _____

4. $1\frac{3}{4} \div 3\frac{1}{2} =$ _____

Solve.

5. $50 + (-42) =$ _____

6. _____ $= -32.5 + 65.2$

7. $-\left(\frac{3}{4}\right) - \left(\frac{1}{4}\right) =$ _____

8. $-8 - (-8) =$ _____

9. _____ $= 12 * (-30)$

10. $(-3 * 8) * (-3) =$ _____

11. $\frac{28}{(-7)} =$ _____

12. _____ $= -42 \div (-2)$

Tell whether each number sentence is true or false.

13. $(6 * 8) + 10 = 6 * (8 + 10)$ _____

14. $-14 * (3 - 4) > 10$ _____

15. $(-2)^3 < (-2)^2$ _____

16. $4 \div (2 + 2) \leq 1 + \frac{3}{4}$ _____

17. Explain how you can decide whether $9 - 14 \neq 14 - 9$ is true or false without performing any computations.

_____

_____

Use order of operations to evaluate each expression.

18. $12 + 9 * 3 - 28$ _____

19. $36 \div 3 + 4 * 5 - 3$ _____

20. $-4 * 10^2 + 6 / 2 + 9$ _____

21. $\left(\frac{4}{2} + 5\right)^2 + \left(\frac{6}{2} - 3\right)^3$ _____

LESSON 6·13 **Written Assessment** *continued*

22.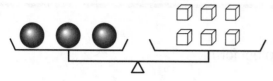

1 ball = _____ cubes

23.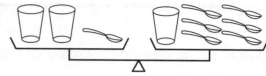

1 glass = _____ spoons

Find the solution for each equation.

24. $400 = 10^2 + y$

$y =$ _____

25. $\frac{w}{2} + 7 = 21$

$w =$ _____

Solve each equation.

26. $\frac{2}{5}x + 3 = \frac{6}{5}x - 13$

Operation

_____ _____

_____ _____

_____ _____

Solution _____

Check _____

27. $3n + 18 = 39 - 4n$

Operation

_____ _____

_____ _____

_____ _____

Solution _____

Check _____

Part B

Graph the solution set of each inequality.

28. $-2 < g$

29. $m \geq 0$

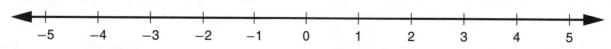

LESSON 6·13 **Written Assessment** *continued*

30. General admission to the county fair is $10. Each ride ticket costs an additional $2.50. The general pattern $y = 10 + 2.50x$ represents the total amount of money someone can spend on admission and ride tickets.

a. Use the formula to complete the table. Then graph the data and connect the points.

Rule: Total Spent = 10 + (2.50 * Number of Ride Tickets)
Formula: $y = 10 + 2.50x$

x	y
0	
	15
4	
5	

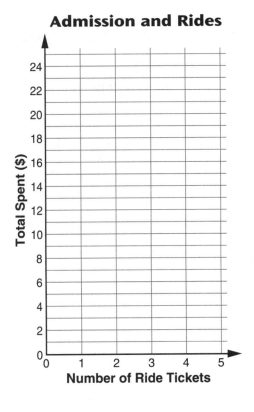

Admission and Rides

b. Use your graph to answer the following question. If someone spent $17.50 in all, how many ride tickets did that person buy? _____

31. Triangles *LMN* and *PQR* are congruent.

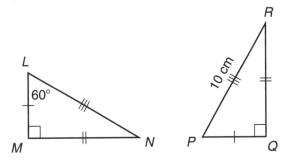

a. Find the length of $\overline{LN}$. _____ **b.** Find m∠*R*. _____

32. Give a ballpark estimate for 2,080.25 ÷ 53. Then find the exact answer. Show your work on the back of this page or on a separate sheet of paper.

a. Estimate _____ **b.** $53\overline{)2,080.25}$ = _____

LESSON 6·13

Open Response

Calculating Tree Growth

Some years ago, Marcus planted a 7-foot tree in his front yard. The tree grew 3 feet each year. Now the tree is four times the original height.

1. How many years ago did Marcus plant the tree?

2. Solve the problem. Show all your work.

3. Write an equation that you can use to solve this problem.

LESSON 7·9 **Self Assessment**

Think about each skill listed below. Assess your own progress by checking the most appropriate box.

Skills	I can do this on my own and explain how to do it.	I can do this on my own.	I can do this if I get help or look at an example.
1. Convert between fractions, decimals, and percents.			
2. Find the percent of a number.			
3. Interpret Venn diagrams.			
4. Find probabilities.			
5. Determine expected outcomes.			
6. Use tree diagrams to solve problems.			
7. Determine fairness of games.			

Written Assessment

Part A

Refer to the spinner at the right. Name the color that fits each of the following statements.

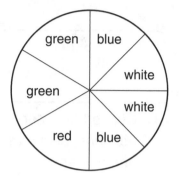

1. The spinner will land on this color about as often as it lands on white. _____

2. The probability of getting this color is $\frac{1}{6}$. _____

3. The probability of landing on this color is greater than 30%. _____

4. In 20 spins, the spinner lands on blue 12 times. Explain how this is possible if the spinner should only land on blue 1 out of every 4 times.

    _____

    _____

    _____

    _____

Answer the following questions about random draws from a deck of 5 cards numbered 1, 2, 3, 4, and 5. Express each probability as a fraction, decimal, and percent.

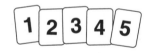

5. What is the probability of drawing the number 1?

    _____ _____ _____
    fraction   decimal   percent

6. What is the probability of *not* drawing the number 3?

    _____ _____ _____
    fraction   decimal   percent

7. Suppose you draw the number 2. If you replace the card and then shuffle the deck, what is the probability that 2 will come up on the next draw?

    _____ _____ _____
    fraction   decimal   percent

8. Suppose you draw a card from the deck 60 times, replacing the card and shuffling the deck after each draw. About how many times would you expect to draw the number 4? _____

LESSON 7·9 **Written Assessment** *continued*

9. Sixty small marbles are dropped, one at a time, into the maze shown below at the left. Each time the maze divides, the marble has an equal chance of going down any of the new paths. Complete the tree diagram at the right by writing the number of marbles you expect to go down each branch of the maze.

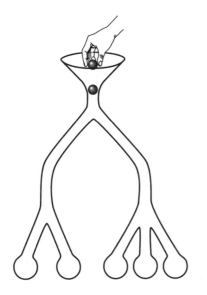

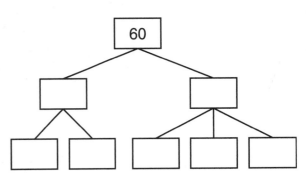

Jamie and Court designed the game *Lucky Coin* for their school carnival. A player flips a coin. If the coin lands on TAILS, the player loses. If it lands on HEADS, the player gets to flip again. If the coin lands on HEADS on the second flip, the player wins a prize; if it lands on TAILS, the player loses.

10. In the space at the right, make a tree diagram to show all possible outcomes of *Lucky Coin.* Write a fraction next to each branch to show the probability of selecting that branch.

11. What is the probability of winning *Lucky Coin?*

_____%

12. If 280 people play *Lucky Coin,* how many would you expect to win?

_____ people

13. Explain why *Lucky Coin* is not a fair game.

_____

_____

_____

Written Assessment *continued*

Part B

The Venn diagram below shows the number of sixth-grade students at Conley Middle School who participate in Science Olympiad and the regional science fair.

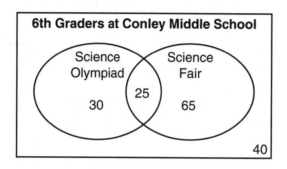

Use the Venn diagram to answer the following questions.

14. How many students participate in Science Olympiad?   _____ students

15. How many students participate in the science fair
but *not* Science Olympiad?   _____ students

16. How many sixth graders participate in both competitions?   _____ sixth graders

17. How many sixth graders are represented in the diagram?   _____ sixth graders

18. Suppose a coin is tossed at random onto the gameboard shown below.
What is the probability that it will land inside the circle? Use $\frac{22}{7}$ for π.

16 in.

7 in.

16 in.

Probability = _____   _____%

                                    fraction   percent (rounded
                                  (simplified)   to the nearest tenth)

Solve the following equations. Check each solution by substituting it for the variable in the original equation.

19. $4p - 11 = 2p + 33$

$p =$ _____

20. $\frac{y}{6} - 3 = 5 - \frac{5}{6}y$

$y =$ _____

LESSON 7·9   ## Open Response

Card Products

You have one each of number cards
3, 4, 5, and 6. You shuffle the cards and place
them facedown on a table. You then turn over
2 of the cards and multiply the numbers shown
on those cards. For example, the product of the
cards at the right would be 4 * 5, or 20.

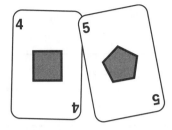

$$4 * 5 = 20$$

Suppose you wish to invent a solitaire game called *Card Products* in which the product of
the two cards determines whether you win or lose. Write a set of rules for *Card Products*
so that the player has an equal chance of winning or losing.

Show your work and explain how you know the game is fair.

LESSON 8·13 Self Assessment

Progress Check 8

Think about each skill listed below. Assess your own progress by checking the most appropriate box.

Skills	I can do this on my own and explain how to do it.	I can do this on my own.	I can do this if I get help or look at an example.
1. Use rate tables and unit rates to solve problems.			
2. Use cross multiplication to solve proportions.			
3. Solve percent problems.			
4. Set up and solve ratio problems.			
5. Identify pairs of corresponding sides in similar polygons.			
6. Use a size-change factor to solve problems.			
7. Evaluate expressions using order of operations.			
8. Solve perimeter and area problems.			
9. Divide decimal numbers.			

LESSON 8·13

Written Assessment

Progress
Check 8

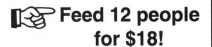

Part A

Use the advertisement at the right to solve Problems 1–4.

1. Complete the rate table below.

inches		9	36		1
people	1	3	12	4	

> 👉 **Feed 12 people for $18!**
>
> You can, when you buy a **3-foot** cold-cut party submarine sandwich.

2. Nine inches of sandwich feed 3 people. At this rate, how many feet of sandwich are needed to feed 20 people? _____ ft

3. If 12 people share a sandwich equally, how many inches will each person get? _____ in.

4. What is the cost per person? _____

5. Explain how you found the cost per person.

_____

Find the missing value in each proportion.

6. $\dfrac{4}{10} = \dfrac{10}{m}$ $m = $ _____

7. $\dfrac{4}{6} = \dfrac{k}{15}$ $k = $ _____

8. $\dfrac{w}{20} = \dfrac{4}{16}$ $w = $ _____

9. $\dfrac{12}{f} = \dfrac{8}{12}$ $f = $ _____

For Problem 10, complete the rate table. Use the table to write an open proportion. Then solve the proportion.

10. A species of bamboo grows at a rate of 3 inches every 6 hours. About how many hours does this species take to grow 4 inches?

_____ hours

inches	1	3	4	6
hours		6			1

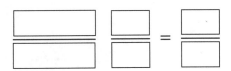

Written Assessment *continued*

For Problem 11, complete the rate table. Then use the table to write an open proportion. Solve the proportion.

11. Mr. Marconi rode his motorcycle 120 miles on 3 gallons of gasoline. How far can he ride on 4.5 gallons of gasoline?

miles	1	120		
gallons		3	1	4.5

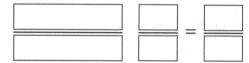

_____ miles

Write proportions to solve each problem below.

12. Jennie bought 6 boxes of pencils for $4. How many boxes of pencils can she buy for $6?

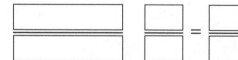

_____ boxes of pencils

13. George was reading a mystery story. He read 42 pages in 1 hour. At this rate, how many pages can he read in 40 minutes?

_____ pages

14. An astronaut standing on the Moon would weigh about 16% of her weight on Earth. If an astronaut weighs 150 lb on Earth, about how much would she weigh on the Moon?

_____ lb

15. 15% of what number is 9?

15% of _____ is 9.

16. The table below shows the calorie and fat content in 1 cup of two kinds of yogurt. Complete the table. Round the calculated fat percent to the nearest whole percent.

Food Label	Food	Calories from Fat / Total Calories	Calculated Fat Percent
Nutrition Facts Serving Size 1 cup (225 g) Servings Per Container 1 **Amount Per Serving** **Calories** 260 Calories from Fat 73	Strawberry yogurt		
Nutrition Facts Serving Size 1 cup (225 g) Servings Per Container 1 **Amount Per Serving** **Calories** 220 Calories from Fat 42	Vanilla yogurt		

Solve each problem.

17. Three out of every 5 cards are faceup. If 20 cards are facedown, how many cards are there in all?

There are _____ cards in all.

18. The ratio of facedown to faceup cards is 2 to 3. If there are 25 cards altogether, how many cards are facedown?

_____ cards are facedown.

19. Shade $\frac{4}{5}$ of the circles below.

○   ○   ○
○   ○   ○   ○
  ○ ○   ○

20. What percent of the circles in Problem 19 are shaded?

_____% of the circles are shaded.

21. What is the ratio of shaded circles to unshaded circles in Problem 19?

Ratio _____

22. How many more unshaded circles would you need to draw in Problem 19 to make the ratio of shaded circles to unshaded circles 2 to 1?

_____ unshaded circles

Written Assessment *continued*

23. Triangles *MNO* and *PQR* are similar.

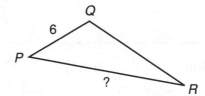

a. The length of side *RP* = _____ units

b. The size-change factor is: $\dfrac{\text{large triangle}}{\text{small triangle}}$ = _____ X

Part B

24. Use order of operations to evaluate each expression.

a. $[4(30 - 5)] \div \dfrac{-10}{2}$ = _____

b. $\left[\dfrac{6 * 2(8 - 3)}{11 - (-4)}\right] * -6$ = _____

25. Find the perimeter of triangle *PHI* when $x = 3$ units.

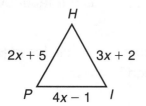

Perimeter = _____ units

26. Find the area of rectangle *YEAH* when $y = 4$ units.

E   A

$3y - 5$

Y   12   H

Area = _____ units^2

Divide. If necessary, show your work on the back of this page or on another sheet of paper.

27. $142.72 \div 16$ = _____

28. $32.48 \div 2.8$ = _____

LESSON 8·13 | **Open Response**

Designing a Banner

Brooke is designing a banner for her school's *Eat Healthy* campaign. She wants her finished banner to measure 60 in. long by 24 in. high.

Brooke wants to make a rough draft of her banner. She wants the draft to be mathematically similar to her finished banner.

There are several different sizes of paper Brooke can use for her rough draft. The sizes are shown below.

24 in.

Balanced is beautiful!

60 in.

Part 1   Which sizes of paper can Brooke use to make her draft mathematically similar to her finished banner? Explain how you found your answer.

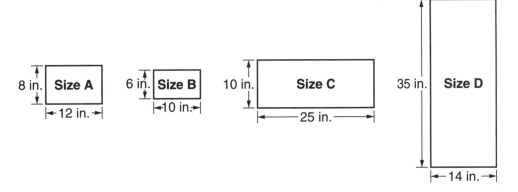

8 in. | **Size A** | 12 in.

6 in. | **Size B** | 10 in.

10 in. | **Size C** | 25 in.

35 in. | **Size D** | 14 in.

Part 2   Suppose Brooke uses a 6 in. by 15 in. sheet of paper for her draft. She sets up a rectangular space for the words "Balanced is beautiful!" as shown in the diagram below. Describe each step you would follow to enlarge the draft so that it will look the same on the full-size banner (60 in. long by 24 in. high).

$\frac{3}{4}$ in.

1 in.

Balanced is beautiful!

1 in.

6 in.

$\frac{3}{4}$ in.

15 in.

LESSON 9·14 — Self Assessment

Progress Check 9

Think about each skill listed below. Assess your own progress by checking the most appropriate box.

Skills	I can do this on my own and explain how to do it.	I can do this on my own.	I can do this if I get help or look at an example.
1. Find the number of objects in the whole when given a fractional part or a percent of the whole.			
2. Solve problems involving part-to-whole ratios.			
3. Use a size-change factor to solve problems.			
4. Use formulas to solve area and volume problems.			
5. Evaluate expressions using order of operations.			
6. Simplify and solve equations by combining like terms.			
7. Use a trial-and-error method to find an approximate solution to an equation such as $x^2 + 5 = 35$.			
8. Use the distributive property to solve equations.			

LESSON 9·14

Written Assessment

Part A

1. Write 2 number sentences for finding the area of the shaded part of the rectangle.

   Sentence 1: (_____ − _____) * _____ = 20

   Sentence 2: (_____ * _____) − (_____ * _____) = 20

2. The area of the rectangle shown at the right is 128 units².

   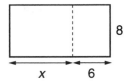

   a. Write a number sentence that you can use to find the value of *x*.

      Number sentence _____

   b. Solve for *x*. Show your work.

      $x =$ _____ units

Solve each equation. Show your work.

3. $6x − 10 = 10x + 22$

4. $12 − 3y = 52 + 5y$

Solution _____

Solution _____

5. One formula for converting between Celsius and Fahrenheit temperatures is $F = (1.8 * C) + 32$. Convert the following:

   a. $−10°C =$ _____ °F

   b. $122°F =$ _____ °C

6. Circle the formula that is equivalent to $F = (1.8 * C) + 32$.

   $3.2F = 1.8C$ $F + 32 = 1.8C$ $F − 32 = 1.8C$

LESSON 9·14 **Written Assessment** *continued*

7. The mobile shown at the right is in balance.
The fulcrum of the mobile is the center
point of the rod.

Formula:

$$(W * D) = (w * d)$$

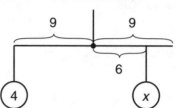

What is the weight of the object
to the right of the fulcrum?

_____ units

Use the formulas given to solve the problems below. Record the formula
you use to solve each problem.

Area	
Parallelogram	$A = b * h$
Triangle	$A = \frac{1}{2} * b * h$
Circle	$A = \pi * r^2$

Volume	
Rectangular prism	$V = B * h$
Cylinder	$V = B * h$
Sphere	$V = \frac{4}{3} * \pi * r^3$

8.

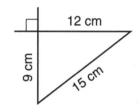

Area = _____
(unit)

Formula _____

9.

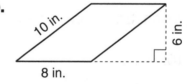

Area = _____
(unit)

Formula _____

10.

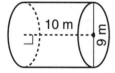

Volume = _____
(unit)

Formula _____

11.

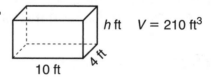

h ft $V = 210$ ft^3

$h =$ _____
(unit)

Formula _____

LESSON 9·14 Written Assessment *continued*

12. Figures *ABCD* and *LMJK* are similar. Figure *ABCD* is an enlargement of *LMJK*.

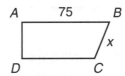
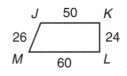

a. The size-change factor that describes the enlargement is _____ X.

b. Find the length of side *x*. $x =$ _____

c. Calculate the perimeter of *LMJK*. Then explain how you can use the size-change factor to find the perimeter of *ABCD*.

Perimeter of *LMJK* = _____ units. Explanation: _____

_____

_____

Solve each equation. Show your work.

13. $-3(m + 4) = 18$

14. $14 = \frac{1}{4}(w - 9)$

Solution _____

Solution _____

15. Using a trial-and-error-method, find an approximate solution to the equation $x^2 + 4 = 94$. Record your results in the table below. Use the suggested number to get started. Stop when your value for $x^2 + 4$ is within 1 of 94.

x	x^2	$x^2 + 4$	Compare $x^2 + 4$ to 94.
9	81	85	$85 < 94$

LESSON 9·14 | **Written Assessment** *continued*

Part B

16. There are 24 members on the school's track team. Two out of every 3 members were on the team last year. How many members were on the team?

There were _____ members last year.

17. Without using a protractor, find the measure of each numbered angle.

Lines *b* and *d* are parallel.

a. List all angles in the figure at the right that measure 115°.

_____

b. List all angles that measure 75°.

_____

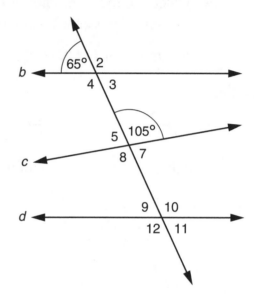

Use the order of operations to evaluate each expression.

18. $15 - 6 * 4 \div 8$ _____

19. $14 \div (9 - 2) + 2^3$ _____

20. Circle the equation that describes the relationship between the numbers in the table at the right.

$y = -4x - 3$

$y = 4x + 3$

$y = \frac{3}{4}x - 6$

$x = -4y + 3$

x	y
$\frac{3}{4}$	−6
$\frac{3}{2}$	−9
12	−51
−30	117

Open Response

Area of an Octagon

Explain how you would find the area of a regular octagon with sides measuring
x feet each. Your explanation should be detailed, clear, and easy to follow. Be sure to
include formulas in your explanation.

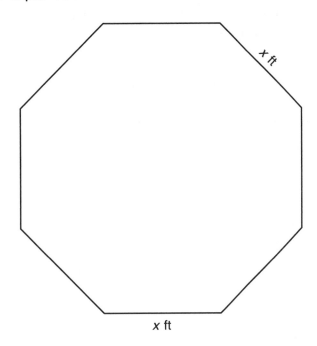

Self Assessment

Think about each skill listed below. Assess your own progress by checking the most appropriate box.

Skills	I can do this on my own and explain how to do it.	I can do this on my own.	I can do this if I get help or look at an example.
1. Apply relationships to find missing angle measures.			
2. Recognize polygons that tessellate.			
3. Identify figures that have been translated, reflected, or rotated.			
4. Draw lines of symmetry.			
5. Determine order of rotation symmetry for a figure.			
6. Write an equation or an expression to describe a situation.			
7. Simplify and solve equations by combining like terms.			
8. Use order of operations to evaluate expressions.			

LESSON 10·6

Written Assessment

Part A

1. Find the measure of ∠E without using a protractor.

m∠A = 160°
m∠B = 50°
m∠C = 140°
m∠D = 150°

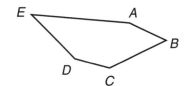

m∠E = _____ °

2. Circle the polygons you can tessellate.

a.

b.

c.

d.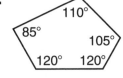

3. What transformation would move

a. triangle A onto triangle B?

_____

b. triangle A onto triangle C?

_____

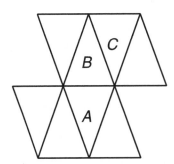

LESSON 10·6 | **Written Assessment** *continued*

4. Lines *a* and *b* are parallel.

a. Write an equation you can use to find the value of *x*.

Equation _____

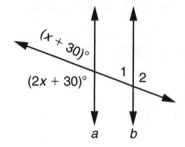

b. *x* = _____

c. Complete.   m∠1 = _____ °   m∠2 = _____ °

5. For each regular polygon, draw the line(s) of symmetry. Then determine the order of rotation symmetry for the figure.

a.

Order of rotation
symmetry   _____

b.

Order of rotation
symmetry   _____

c.

Order of rotation
symmetry   _____

d.

Order of rotation
symmetry   _____

e.

Order of rotation
symmetry   _____

f. What can you conclude about the number of sides, the number of lines of symmetry, and the order of rotation symmetry for a regular polygon?

_____

_____

_____

LESSON 10·6 | **Written Assessment** *continued*

6. Circle the objects that are topologically equivalent to the bowl.

Part B

7. Write an expression for the perimeter of the figure shown at the right.

10x

(2x + 4)   (2x + 4)

6x

   a. Expression

   _____

   b. Find the value of *x* when the perimeter is 68 units.

     Write an equation. Then solve for *x*.

     Equation _____

                     $x =$ _____

Simplify each expression using order of operations.

8. $7 + 3^2 - 4 * 3 =$ _____   **9.** $8^2 - 4 \div 2 + 2 =$ _____

10. Choose the number that makes the following number sentence true. Circle the best answer.

   $(3 + 3)^2 + 44 \div ? = 40$

   a. 2   **b.** 4   **c.** 11   **d.** 18

LESSON 10·6 **Open Response**

Finding Symmetry

1. Using your Geometry Template, draw the assigned number of polygons for each of the following:
   - ◆ 1 polygon that has NO lines of symmetry.
   - ◆ 3 polygons, each having exactly 1 line of symmetry.
   - ◆ 3 polygons, each having at least 3 lines of symmetry.

2. Draw the line(s) of symmetry for each polygon in Part 1.

3. Categorize the polygons from Part 1 according to the number of ways each polygon can be rotated around a center point to exactly match itself. Show or explain your categories and tell which polygons belong in each category.

4. Make a true statement about the relationship between a polygon's lines of symmetry and the number of ways it can be rotated to exactly match itself.

Name   Date   Time

LESSON 1·13   **Written Assessment**   Progress Check 1

Part A

1. Emperor penguins are the largest of all penguins. Some weights (in pounds) for these penguins are represented by the following data set.

   60, 59, 66, 64, 61, 64, 60, 59, 65, 64, 65, 60

   a. Construct a line plot to represent the penguin data.

   Weights of Emperor Penguins

   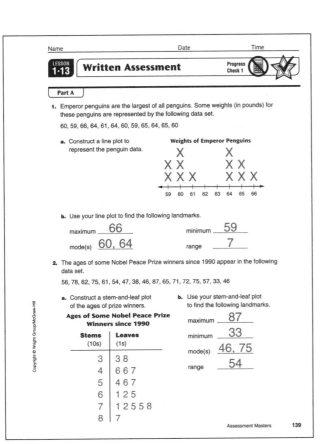

   b. Use your line plot to find the following landmarks.

   maximum   **66**   minimum   **59**

   mode(s)   **60, 64**   range   **7**

2. The ages of some Nobel Peace Prize winners since 1990 appear in the following data set.

   56, 78, 62, 75, 61, 54, 47, 38, 46, 87, 65, 71, 72, 75, 57, 33, 46

   a. Construct a stem-and-leaf plot of the ages of prize winners.

   b. Use your stem-and-leaf plot to find the following landmarks.

   maximum   **87**

   minimum   **33**

   mode(s)   **46, 75**

   range   **54**

   Ages of Some Nobel Peace Prize Winners since 1990

Stems (10s)	Leaves (1s)
3	3 8
4	6 6 7
5	4 6 7
6	1 2 5
7	1 2 5 5 8
8	7

Name   Date   Time

LESSON 1·13   **Written Assessment** *continued*

3. The ages of the students in a Saturday art class are 14, 18, 43, 14, 15, 18, and 11.

   a. Find the median age and the mean age.   median **15**   mean **19**

   b. Which landmark, the mean or median, is the better representation of the ages of students in the art class? Explain.
   median; The mean is greatly affected by the outlier 43, so the median (15) is the better representation of the age.

4. Suppose you are dealt the hand shown below in a game of *Landmark Shark*.

   Which landmark, the range, median, or mode, will show you the highest score for your hand? **median**

   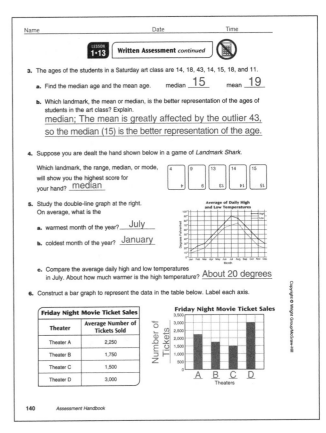

5. Study the double-line graph at the right. On average, what is the

   a. warmest month of the year? **July**

   b. coldest month of the year? **January**

   Average of Daily High and Low Temperatures

   c. Compare the average daily high and low temperatures in July. About how much warmer is the high temperature? **About 20 degrees**

6. Construct a bar graph to represent the data in the table below. Label each axis.

Friday Night Movie Ticket Sales	
Theater	Average Number of Tickets Sold
Theater A	2,250
Theater B	1,750
Theater C	1,500
Theater D	3,000

   Friday Night Movie Ticket Sales

Name   Date   Time

LESSON 1·13   **Written Assessment** *continued*

7. A small company produces video games. The marketing manager claims that sales fell 50% between the third and fourth quarters.

   a. According to the graph, what were the first quarter sales? **$45,000**

   b. Between which two quarters was the increase in sales the greatest?
   Between the 2nd and 3rd quarters

   c. Is the marketing manager's claim misleading? Explain.
   Yes. If sales had fallen 50%, the sales for the 4th quarter would be $32,500. If the scale of the vertical axis began at 0, the fall would not appear to be as dramatic.

   End-of-Quarter Sales 2005

   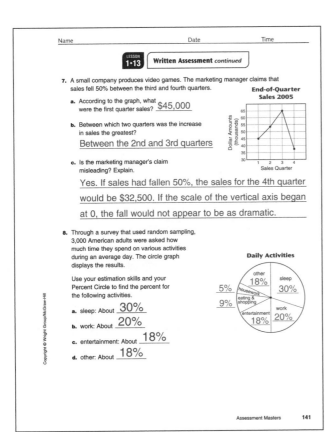

8. Through a survey that used random sampling, 3,000 American adults were asked how much time they spend on various activities during an average day. The circle graph displays the results.

   Use your estimation skills and your Percent Circle to find the percent for the following activities.

   a. sleep: About **30%**

   b. work: About **20%**

   c. entertainment: About **18%**

   d. other: About **18%**

   Daily Activities

Name   Date   Time

LESSON 1·13   **Written Assessment** *continued*

Part B

9. The length of a rectangle is 6 cm and the width is 9 cm.

   a. Write a number sentence for the perimeter of the rectangle.
   Sample answers: $2 * (6 + 9)$ or $6 + 6 + 9 + 9$

   b. What is the area of the rectangle? Area = **54** cm²

10. Write four expressions for 25. Each must use a 7 and a 9. Sample answers:

   $9 * 2 + 7$ $7 + 9 + 9$

   $9 + (7 * 2) + 2$ $(9 * 5) - (7 * 2) - 6$

11. Use the step graph to answer the following questions.

   a. How much would it cost to rent a canoe for
   1½ hours? **$15**   3 hours? **$20**
   3 hours 5 minutes? **$25**

   b. Dimitri and his friends rent a canoe at 3:15 P.M. They don't want to pay more than $20. By what time do they need to return the canoe? **6:15 P.M.**

   Canoe Rental Rates

   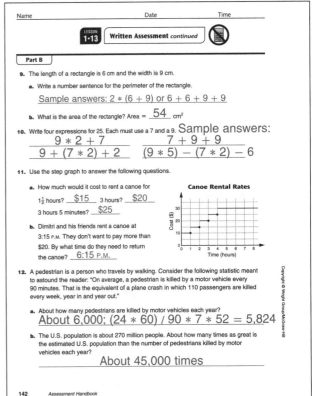

12. A pedestrian is a person who travels by walking. Consider the following statistic meant to astound the reader: "On average, a pedestrian is killed by a motor vehicle every 90 minutes. That is the equivalent of a plane crash in which 110 passengers are killed every week, year in and year out."

   a. About how many pedestrians are killed by motor vehicles each year?
   About 6,000; $(24 * 60) / 90 * 7 * 52 = 5,824$

   b. The U.S. population is about 270 million people. About how many times as great is the estimated U.S. population than the number of pedestrians killed by motor vehicles each year?
   About 45,000 times

LESSON 2·12 **Written Assessment** — Progress Check 2

Part A

1. Write the digit in each place of the number below.

5,146,702,897,352.6138

a. ten billions __4__   b. hundredths __1__   c. hundred millions __7__

d. thousandths __3__   e. trillions __5__   f. tenths __6__

2. Write the following numbers in standard notation.

a. 4.6 million __4,600,000__   b. 32.1 trillion __32,100,000,000,000__

3. Write each number in number-and-word notation.

a. 5,600,000,000 __5.6 billion__

b. 462,800,000,000,000 __462.8 trillion__

4. Write the exponent for each of the following numbers.

a. $0.001 = 10^{\boxed{-3}}$ b. $1 \text{ billion} = 10^{\boxed{9}}$

c. $10 * 10 * 10 * 10 = 10^{\boxed{4}}$ d. $\frac{1}{10} = 10^{\boxed{-1}}$

5. Complete.

a. $76,541 * 0.0001 = $ __7.6541__   b. $0.421 * 10,000 = $ __4,210__

c. $45.7 * 10^{-3} = $ __0.0457__   d. $85 = 0.0085 * $ __10,000, or 10^4__

e. $2.9 * 10^5 = $ __290,000__   f. $0.7 = 0.007 * $ __100, or 10^2__

LESSON 2·12 **Written Assessment** *continued*

6. Suppose that Pluto is about $2.8 * 10^9$ miles from the sun. Write $2.8 * 10^9$ in standard notation. __2,800,000,000__

7. Suppose that Earth travels about 600,000,000 miles in its orbit around the sun every year. Write 600,000,000 in scientific notation. __$6 * 10^8$__

Add or subtract.

8. $9.394 + 5.67 = $ __15.064__   9. $4.4 - 3.82 = $ __0.58__

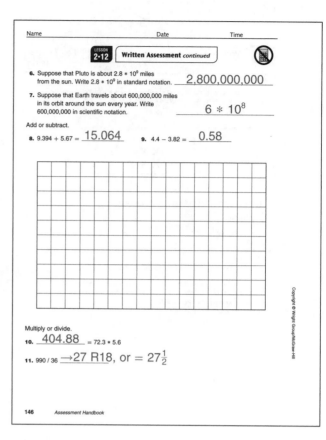

Multiply or divide.

10. __404.88__ $= 72.3 * 5.6$

11. $990 / 36 \rightarrow$ __27 R18, or $= 27\frac{1}{2}$__

LESSON 2·12 **Written Assessment** *continued*

Part B

12. Write each of the following numbers in expanded notation.

Example: $23.89 = (2 * 10) + (3 * 1) + (8 * 0.1) + (9 * 0.01)$

a. 67,051 __$(6 * 10,000) + (7 * 1,000) + (5 * 10) + (1 * 1)$__

b. 2.904 __$(2 * 1) + (9 * 0.1) + (4 * 0.001)$__

13. Use a calculator to help you convert the numbers written in exponential notation to standard notation.

a. $13^5 = $ __371,293__   b. $8^{-6} = $ __0.0000038__

Metric Measurements		
Length	**Capacity**	**Mass**
1 meter (m) = 100 centimeters (cm)	1 liter (L) = 1,000 milliliters (mL)	1 kilogram (kg) = 1,000 grams (g)
1 centimeter (cm) = 10 millimeters (mm)	1 kiloliter (kL) = 1,000 liters (L)	1 gram (g) = 1,000 milligrams (mg)

14. Use the table of metric measurements above to complete the following.

a. 245 cm = __2.45__ m   b. 3.6 L = __3,600__ mL

c. 19,200 g = __19.2__ kg   d. 591 mL = __0.591__ L

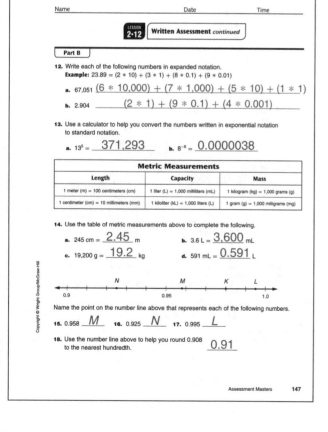

Name the point on the number line above that represents each of the following numbers.

15. 0.958 __M__   16. 0.925 __N__   17. 0.995 __L__

18. Use the number line above to help you round 0.908 to the nearest hundredth. __0.91__

LESSON 2·12 **Written Assessment** *continued*

19. The scores for a math quiz appear in the table at the right.

Math Quiz Scores									
83	91	88	91	95	66	91	81	85	71
98	91	41	63	49	74	85	80	75	

a. Make a stem-and-leaf plot for the quiz data.

Math Quiz Scores

Stems (10s)	Leaves (1s)
4	1 9
6	3 6
7	1 4 5
8	0 1 3 5 5 8
9	1 1 1 1 5 8

b. Use your stem-and-leaf plot to find the following landmarks.

median __83__   mean (round to nearest tenth) __78.8__

c. Which landmark, mean or median, is the better indicator of students' overall performance on the math quiz? Explain.
__Sample answer: median; Because the majority of__
__scores are above 80, the median is a better__
__indicator of student performance.__

20. Gabriella is trying to convince her boss that she deserves a salary increase. She claims that over the past 8 weeks, her number of working hours has greatly increased. She uses the broken-line graph at the right to support her claim.

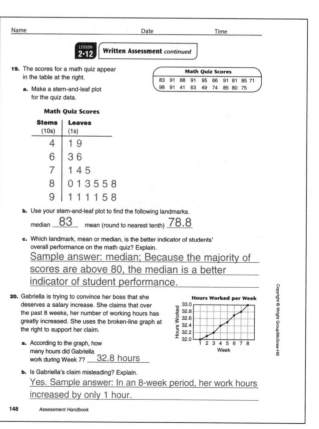

a. According to the graph, how many hours did Gabriella work during Week 7? __32.8 hours__

b. Is Gabriella's claim misleading? Explain.
__Yes. Sample answer: In an 8-week period, her work hours__
__increased by only 1 hour.__

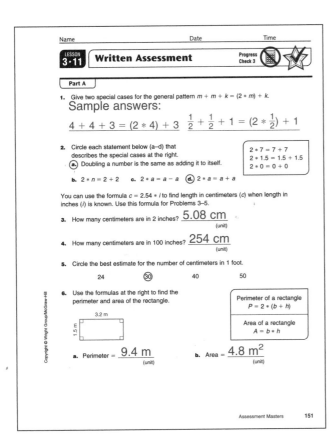

Name _____ Date _____ Time _____

LESSON 3·11 Written Assessment Progress Check 3

Part A

1. Give two special cases for the general pattern $m + m + k = (2 * m) + k$.

Sample answers:

$$4 + 4 + 3 = (2 * 4) + 3 \qquad \frac{1}{2} + \frac{1}{2} + 1 = (2 * \frac{1}{2}) + 1$$

2. Circle each statement below (a–d) that describes the special cases at the right.

$2 * 7 = 7 + 7$
$2 * 1.5 = 1.5 + 1.5$
$2 * 0 = 0 + 0$

(a.) Doubling a number is the same as adding it to itself.

b. $2 * n = 2 + 2$ c. $2 * a = a - a$ (d.) $2 * a = a + a$

You can use the formula $c = 2.54 * i$ to find length in centimeters (c) when length in inches (i) is known. Use this formula for Problems 3–5.

3. How many centimeters are in 2 inches? __5.08 cm__ (unit)

4. How many centimeters are in 100 inches? __254 cm__ (unit)

5. Circle the best estimate for the number of centimeters in 1 foot.

24   (30)   40   50

6. Use the formulas at the right to find the perimeter and area of the rectangle.

Perimeter of a rectangle
$P = 2 * (b + h)$

Area of a rectangle
$A = b * h$

3.2 m
1.5 m

a. Perimeter = __9.4 m__ (unit)
b. Area = __4.8 m²__ (unit)

Assessment Masters 151

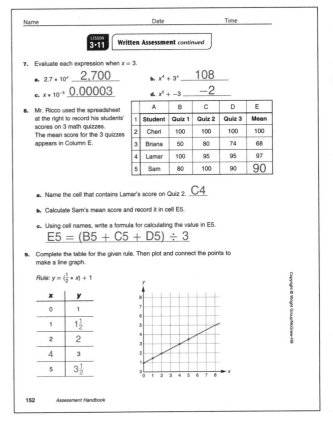

Name _____ Date _____ Time _____

LESSON 3·11 Written Assessment *continued*

7. Evaluate each expression when $x = 3$.

a. $2.7 * 10^x$ __2,700__
b. $x^4 + 3^x$ __108__
c. $x * 10^{-5}$ __0.00003__
d. $x^0 + -3$ __−2__

8. Mr. Ricco used the spreadsheet at the right to record his students' scores on 3 math quizzes. The mean score for the 3 quizzes appears in Column E.

	A	B	C	D	E
1	Student	Quiz 1	Quiz 2	Quiz 3	Mean
2	Cheri	100	100	100	100
3	Briana	50	80	74	68
4	Lamar	100	95	95	97
5	Sam	80	100	90	90

a. Name the cell that contains Lamar's score on Quiz 2. __C4__

b. Calculate Sam's mean score and record it in cell E5.

c. Using cell names, write a formula for calculating the value in E5.
__E5 = (B5 + C5 + D5) ÷ 3__

9. Complete the table for the given rule. Then plot and connect the points to make a line graph.

Rule: $y = (\frac{1}{2} * x) + 1$

x	y
0	1
1	$1\frac{1}{2}$
2	2
4	3
5	$3\frac{1}{2}$

152 Assessment Handbook

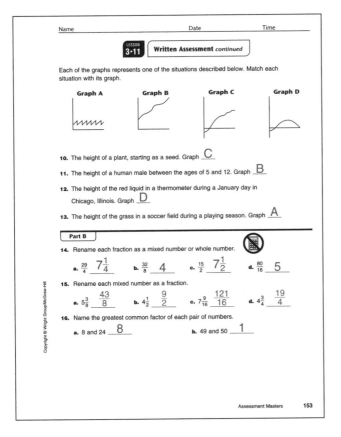

Name _____ Date _____ Time _____

LESSON 3·11 Written Assessment *continued*

Each of the graphs represents one of the situations described below. Match each situation with its graph.

Graph A   **Graph B**   **Graph C**   **Graph D**

10. The height of a plant, starting as a seed. Graph __C__

11. The height of a human male between the ages of 5 and 12. Graph __B__

12. The height of the red liquid in a thermometer during a January day in Chicago, Illinois. Graph __D__

13. The height of the grass in a soccer field during a playing season. Graph __A__

Part B

14. Rename each fraction as a mixed number or whole number.

a. $\frac{29}{4}$ $7\frac{1}{4}$
b. $\frac{32}{8}$ 4
c. $\frac{15}{2}$ $7\frac{1}{2}$
d. $\frac{80}{16}$ 5

15. Rename each mixed number as a fraction.

a. $5\frac{3}{8}$ $\frac{43}{8}$
b. $4\frac{1}{2}$ $\frac{9}{2}$
c. $7\frac{9}{16}$ $\frac{121}{16}$
d. $4\frac{3}{4}$ $\frac{19}{4}$

16. Name the greatest common factor of each pair of numbers.

a. 8 and 24 __8__
b. 49 and 50 __1__

Assessment Masters 153

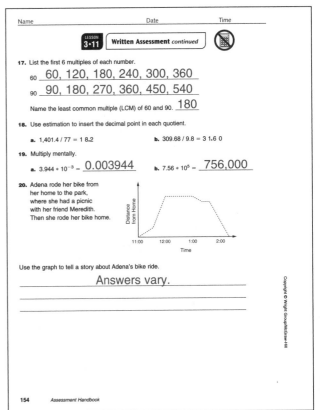

Name _____ Date _____ Time _____

LESSON 3·11 Written Assessment *continued*

17. List the first 6 multiples of each number.

60 __60, 120, 180, 240, 300, 360__
90 __90, 180, 270, 360, 450, 540__

Name the least common multiple (LCM) of 60 and 90. __180__

18. Use estimation to insert the decimal point in each quotient.

a. $1,401.4 / 77 = 1\ 8.2$
b. $309.68 / 9.8 = 3\ 1.6\ 0$

19. Multiply mentally.

a. $3.944 * 10^{-3}$ = __0.003944__
b. $7.56 * 10^5$ = __756,000__

20. Adena rode her bike from her home to the park, where she had a picnic with her friend Meredith. Then she rode her bike home.

Use the graph to tell a story about Adena's bike ride.

__Answers vary.__

154 Assessment Handbook

LESSON 4·12 **Written Assessment**

Part A

1. Write each of the following fractions in simplest form.

   a. $\frac{6}{8}$　$\frac{3}{4}$　　b. $\frac{9}{12}$　$\frac{3}{4}$　　c. $\frac{45}{100}$　$\frac{9}{20}$　　d. $\frac{63}{108}$　$\frac{7}{12}$

2. Complete the table below. Simplify all fractions.

	Fraction	Decimal	Percent		Fraction	Decimal	Percent
a.	$\frac{9}{25}$	0.36	36%	e.	$\frac{97}{100}$	0.97	97%
b.	$\frac{22}{25}$	0.88	88%	f.	$\frac{3}{20}$	0.15	15%
c.	$\frac{1}{50}$	0.02	2%	g.	$\frac{13}{40}$	0.325	32.5%
d.	$\frac{3}{5}$	0.60	60%	h.	$1\frac{3}{5}$	1.60	160%

3. Compare using < or >.

   a. $\frac{1}{2}$ > $\frac{4}{9}$　　b. $2\frac{3}{8}$ < $2\frac{5}{12}$　　c. $1\frac{1}{3}$ > $\frac{7}{6}$　　d. 3.57 < $3\frac{3}{5}$

4. When Monica began first grade, she was $45\frac{3}{4}$ in. tall. At the end of the year, she was $47\frac{3}{8}$ in. tall. How much had Monica grown? $1\frac{5}{8}$ in. (unit)

5. Evan uses a pencil to do his math work. He started the week with a new pencil, which measured 18.5 cm in length. At the end of 2 weeks, the pencil measured 10.8 cm in length. Find the difference between the 2 pencil lengths. Express your answer as a mixed number. $7\frac{7}{10}$ cm

6. Add. Write all answers greater than 1 as mixed numbers. Write all fractions in simplest form.

   a. $3\frac{5}{6} + 2\frac{1}{4} =$ $6\frac{1}{12}$　　　　b. $2\frac{4}{5} + 1\frac{1}{3} =$ $4\frac{2}{15}$

   c. $2\frac{1}{8} + 1\frac{1}{6} + 1\frac{7}{8} =$ $5\frac{1}{6}$　　d. $\frac{4}{9} + \frac{2}{3} =$ $1\frac{1}{9}$

LESSON 4·12 **Written Assessment** *continued*

7. Use the diagram to solve the problems below. Write your answers in simplest form.

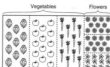

Vegetables　　　　Flowers

Mr. Dahli plants $\frac{3}{4}$ of his garden with vegetables and $\frac{1}{4}$ of it with flowers. He plants $\frac{2}{3}$ of the flower section with daisies and the rest of the flower section with lilies.

   a. What fraction of the entire garden is lilies? $\frac{1}{12}$

   b. Write a number model for the fraction of the entire garden that is daisies. $\frac{1}{4} * \frac{2}{3} = \frac{1}{6}$

   c. Suppose Mr. Dahli's garden has an area of 1,408 ft². How many square feet are planted in vegetables? 1,056 ft²

Part B

8. Sixth graders were asked the following question: *If you could use only one of the following forms of entertainment, which would you choose?*

   Complete the table below.

	Form of Entertainment	Number of Students	Percent of Students
a.	Computer with Internet access	120	25%
b.	TV or DVDs	168	35%
c.	Video games	96	20%
d.	Books or magazines	24	5%
e.	Music CDs	72	15%
f.	Total	480	100%

LESSON 4·12 **Written Assessment** *continued*

9. Use the Percent Circle on the Geometry Template to make a circle graph of the data in Problem 8.

Forms of Entertainment

Internet / Music / Books / TV/DVD / Video games

10. Find the perimeter and area of the rectangle shown below.

8 in.　　$4\frac{5}{16}$ in.

Perimeter $24\frac{5}{8}$ in.　　　　　Area $34\frac{1}{2}$ in.²

11. Evaluate each expression when $x = 5$.

   a. $0.0035 * 10^x$ 350　　　　b. $2^x + 3^3$ 59

   c. $-(x) + -18$ -23　　　　d. $x^0 + -8$ -7

12. Estimate the quotient $928.8 \div 36$. Then divide. Estimate Sample estimate: 30

   $36 \overline{)928.8}$

   $928.8 \div 36 =$ 25.8

LESSON 5·11 | **Written Assessment** | Progress Check 5

Part A

Measure each angle to the nearest degree.

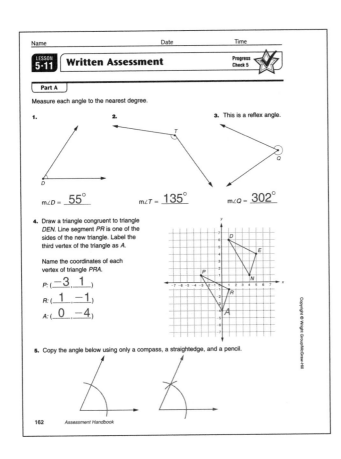

1.

2.

3. This is a reflex angle.

m∠D = $55°$

m∠T = $135°$

m∠Q = $302°$

4. Draw a triangle congruent to triangle DEN. Line segment PR is one of the sides of the new triangle. Label the third vertex of the triangle as A.

Name the coordinates of each vertex of triangle PRA.

P: (-3 , 1)

R: (1 , -1)

A: (0 , -4)

5. Copy the angle below using only a compass, a straightedge, and a pencil.

162   Assessment Handbook

LESSON 5·11 | **Written Assessment** continued

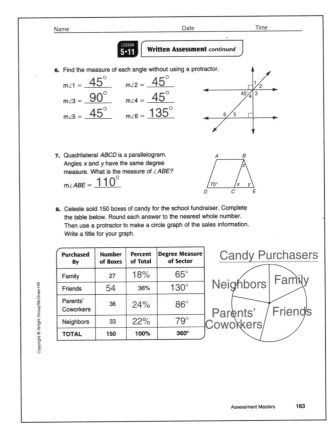

6. Find the measure of each angle without using a protractor.

m∠1 = $45°$ m∠2 = $45°$

m∠3 = $90°$ m∠4 = $45°$

m∠5 = $45°$ m∠6 = $135°$

7. Quadrilateral ABCD is a parallelogram. Angles x and y have the same degree measure. What is the measure of ∠ABE?

m∠ABE = $110°$

8. Celeste sold 150 boxes of candy for the school fundraiser. Complete the table below. Round each answer to the nearest whole number. Then use a protractor to make a circle graph of the sales information. Write a title for your graph.

Purchased By	Number of Boxes	Percent of Total	Degree Measure of Sector
Family	27	18%	65°
Friends	54	36%	130°
Parents' Coworkers	36	24%	86°
Neighbors	33	22%	79°
TOTAL	150	100%	360°

Candy Purchasers

Neighbors Family

Parents' Coworkers Friends

Assessment Masters   163

LESSON 5·11 | **Written Assessment** continued

Part B

Estimate each sum, difference, or product. Then solve. Write each answer in simplest form.

Sample estimates are given.

9. $8\frac{1}{6} - \frac{5}{6}$ Estimate 7

$8\frac{1}{6} - \frac{5}{6} = 7\frac{1}{3}$

10. $6\frac{2}{5} + 3\frac{1}{4}$ Estimate $9\frac{1}{2}$

$6\frac{2}{5} + 3\frac{1}{4} = 9\frac{13}{20}$

11. $2\frac{7}{10} * 4\frac{4}{9}$ Estimate 12

$2\frac{7}{10} * 4\frac{4}{9} = 12$

Find each sum.

12. $34 + (12 + -18) = 28$ 13. $-75 + 50 + 40 = 15$

Divide to rename each fraction as a decimal rounded to the nearest hundredth.

14. $\frac{11}{16} = 0.69$ 15. $\frac{5}{9} = 0.56$

164   Assessment Handbook

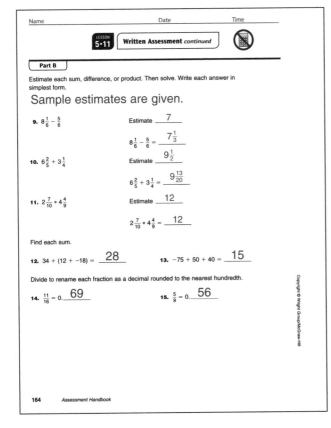

LESSON 6·13 **Written Assessment**   Progress Check 6

Part A

Divide. Show your work. Write your answers in simplest form.

1. $\frac{2}{3} \div \frac{1}{3} =$ __2__

2. $1\frac{5}{6} \div \frac{2}{3} =$ __$2\frac{3}{4}$__

3. $5 \div \frac{2}{3} =$ __$7\frac{1}{2}$__

4. $1\frac{3}{4} \div 3\frac{1}{2} =$ __$\frac{1}{2}$__

Solve.

5. $50 + (-42) =$ __8__

6. __32.7__ $= -32.5 + 65.2$

7. $-(\frac{3}{4}) - (\frac{1}{4}) =$ __-1__

8. $-8 - (-8) =$ __0__

9. __-360__ $= 12 * (-30)$

10. $(-3 * 8) * (-3) =$ __72__

11. $\frac{28}{(-7)} =$ __-4__

12. __21__ $= -42 \div (-2)$

Tell whether each number sentence is true or false.

13. $(6 * 8) + 10 = 6 * (8 + 10)$ __false__

14. $-14 * (3 - 4) > 10$ __true__

15. $(-2)^3 < (-2)^2$ __true__

16. $4 \div (2 + 2) \leq 1 + \frac{3}{4}$ __true__

17. Explain how you can decide whether $9 - 14 \neq 14 - 9$ is true or false without performing any computations.
Sample answer: Subtraction is not commutative, so $9 - 14$ cannot equal $14 - 9$.

Use order of operations to evaluate each expression.

18. $12 + 9 * 3 - 28$ __11__

19. $36 \div 3 + 4 * 5 - 3$ __29__

20. $-4 * 10^2 + 6 / 2 + 9$ __-388__

21. $(\frac{4}{2} + 5)^2 + (\frac{6}{2} - 3)^3$ __49__

LESSON 6·13 **Written Assessment** *continued*

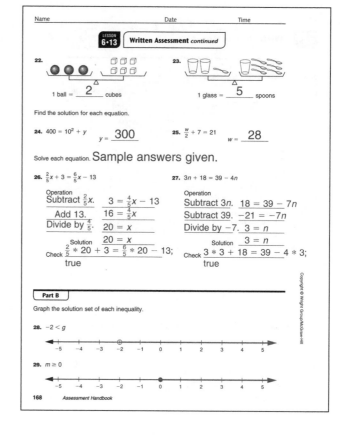

22. 1 ball = __2__ cubes

23. 1 glass = __5__ spoons

Find the solution for each equation.

24. $400 = 10^2 + y$ $y =$ __300__

25. $\frac{w}{2} + 7 = 21$ $w =$ __28__

Solve each equation. **Sample answers given.**

26. $\frac{2}{5}x + 3 = \frac{6}{5}x - 13$

Operation
Subtract $\frac{2}{5}x$. $3 = \frac{4}{5}x - 13$
Add 13. $16 = \frac{4}{5}x$
Divide by $\frac{4}{5}$. $20 = x$
$20 = x$
Check $\frac{2}{5} * 20 + 3 = \frac{6}{5} * 20 - 13$; true

27. $3n + 18 = 39 - 4n$

Operation
Subtract $3n$. $18 = 39 - 7n$
Subtract 39. $-21 = -7n$
Divide by -7. $3 = n$
$3 = n$
Check $3 * 3 + 18 = 39 - 4 * 3$; true

Part B

Graph the solution set of each inequality.

28. $-2 < g$

-5 -4 -3 -2 -1 0 1 2 3 4 5

29. $m \geq 0$

-5 -4 -3 -2 -1 0 1 2 3 4 5

LESSON 6·13 **Written Assessment** *continued*

30. General admission to the county fair is $10. Each ride ticket costs an additional $2.50. The general pattern $y = 10 + 2.50x$ represents the total amount of money someone can spend on admission and ride tickets.

a. Use the formula to complete the table. Then graph the data and connect the points.

Rule: Total Spent = 10 + (2.50 * Number of Ride Tickets)
Formula: $y = 10 + 2.50x$

x	y
0	10
2	15
4	20
5	22.50

Admission and Rides

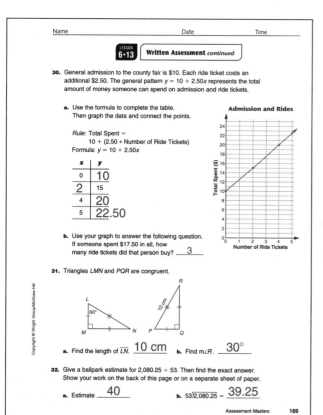

b. Use your graph to answer the following question. If someone spent $17.50 in all, how many ride tickets did that person buy? __3__

31. Triangles *LMN* and *PQR* are congruent.

a. Find the length of $\overline{LN}$. __10 cm__

b. Find m∠R. __30°__

32. Give a ballpark estimate for $2,080.25 \div 53$. Then find the exact answer. Show your work on the back of this page or on a separate sheet of paper.

a. Estimate __40__

b. $53\overline{)2,080.25}$ __39.25__

LESSON 7·9 | **Written Assessment** | Progress Check 7 ✓

Part A

Refer to the spinner at the right. Name the color that fits each of the following statements.

1. The spinner will land on this color about as often as it lands on white. _blue_

2. The probability of getting this color is $\frac{1}{6}$. _red_

3. The probability of landing on this color is greater than 30%. _green_

4. In 20 spins, the spinner lands on blue 12 times. Explain how this is possible if the spinner should only land on blue 1 out of every 4 times.
   Sample answer: The actual results in a small sample
   of trials are often very different from the expected
   probability. The more trials that are done, the closer
   the results will be to the expected probability.

Answer the following questions about random draws from a deck of 5 cards numbered 1, 2, 3, 4, and 5. Express each probability as a fraction, decimal, and percent.

1 2 3 4 5

5. What is the probability of drawing the number 1?
   $\frac{1}{5}$ fraction   0.2 decimal   20% percent

6. What is the probability of *not* drawing the number 3?
   $\frac{4}{5}$ fraction   0.8 decimal   80% percent

7. Suppose you draw the number 2. If you replace the card and then shuffle the deck, what is the probability that 2 will come up on the next draw?
   $\frac{1}{5}$ fraction   0.2 decimal   20% percent

8. Suppose you draw a card from the deck 60 times, replacing the card and shuffling the deck after each draw. About how many times would you expect to draw the number 4? _12 times_

LESSON 7·9 | **Written Assessment** *continued*

9. Sixty small marbles are dropped, one at a time, into the maze shown below at the left. Each time the maze divides, the marble has an equal chance of going down any of the new paths. Complete the tree diagram at the right by writing the number of marbles you expect to go down each branch of the maze.

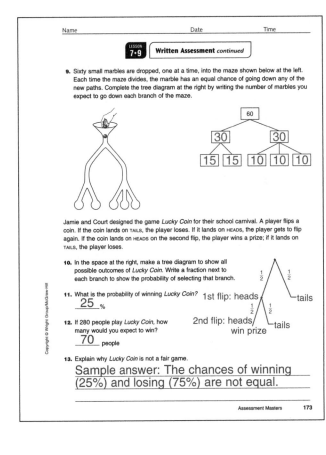

Jamie and Court designed the game *Lucky Coin* for their school carnival. A player flips a coin. If the coin lands on TAILS, the player loses. If it lands on HEADS, the player gets to flip again. If the coin lands on HEADS on the second flip, the player wins a prize; if it lands on TAILS, the player loses.

10. In the space at the right, make a tree diagram to show all possible outcomes of *Lucky Coin*. Write a fraction next to each branch to show the probability of selecting that branch.

11. What is the probability of winning *Lucky Coin*? _25_ %

12. If 280 people play *Lucky Coin*, how many would you expect to win? _70_ people

13. Explain why *Lucky Coin* is not a fair game.
    Sample answer: The chances of winning
    (25%) and losing (75%) are not equal.

LESSON 7·9 | **Written Assessment** *continued*

Part B

The Venn diagram below shows the number of sixth-grade students at Conley Middle School who participate in Science Olympiad and the regional science fair.

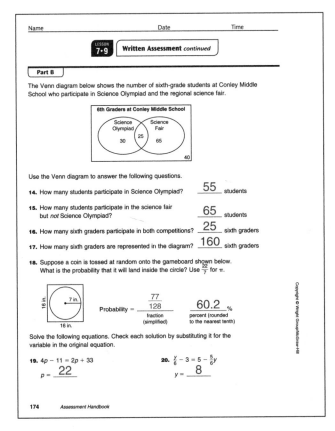

Use the Venn diagram to answer the following questions.

14. How many students participate in Science Olympiad? _55_ students

15. How many students participate in the science fair but *not* Science Olympiad? _65_ students

16. How many sixth graders participate in both competitions? _25_ sixth graders

17. How many sixth graders are represented in the diagram? _160_ sixth graders

18. Suppose a coin is tossed at random onto the gameboard shown below. What is the probability that it will land inside the circle? Use $\frac{22}{7}$ for π.

    Probability = $\frac{77}{128}$ fraction (simplified)   60.2 % percent (rounded to the nearest tenth)

Solve the following equations. Check each solution by substituting it for the variable in the original equation.

19. $4p - 11 = 2p + 33$
    $p =$ _22_

20. $\frac{y}{6} - 3 = 5 - \frac{5}{6}y$
    $y =$ _8_

LESSON 8·13 Written Assessment Progress Check 8

Part A

Use the advertisement at the right to solve Problems 1–4.

☞ **Feed 12 people for $18!**

You can, when you buy a **3-foot** cold-cut party submarine sandwich.

1. Complete the rate table below.

inches	3	9	36	12	1
people	1	3	12	4	$\frac{1}{3}$

2. Nine inches of sandwich feed 3 people. At this rate, how many feet of sandwich are needed to feed 20 people? _____5_____ ft

3. If 12 people share a sandwich equally, how many inches will each person get? _____3_____ in.

4. What is the cost per person? **$1.50**

5. Explain how you found the cost per person.
I divided the total cost ($18) by the number of people (12).

Find the missing value in each proportion.

6. $\frac{4}{10} = \frac{10}{m}$ m = _____25_____

7. $\frac{4}{6} = \frac{k}{15}$ k = _____10_____

8. $\frac{w}{20} = \frac{4}{16}$ w = _____5_____

9. $\frac{12}{f} = \frac{8}{12}$ f = _____18_____

For Problem 10, complete the rate table. Use the table to write an open proportion. Then solve the proportion.

10. A species of bamboo grows at a rate of 3 inches every 6 hours. About how many hours does this species take to grow 4 inches?

_____8_____ hours

inches	1	3	4	6	$\frac{1}{2}$
hours	2	6	8	12	1

$\frac{\text{(inches)}}{\text{(hours)}}$ $\frac{3}{6} = \frac{4}{h}$

LESSON 8·13 Written Assessment continued

For Problem 11, complete the rate table. Then use the table to write an open proportion. Solve the proportion.

11. Mr. Marconi rode his motorcycle 120 miles on 3 gallons of gasoline. How far can he ride on 4.5 gallons of gasoline?

miles	1	120	40	180
gallons	0.025	3	1	4.5

$\frac{\text{(miles)}}{\text{(gallons)}}$ $\frac{120}{3} = \frac{m}{4.5}$

_____180_____ miles

Write proportions to solve each problem below.

12. Jennie bought 6 boxes of pencils for $4. How many boxes of pencils can she buy for $6?

$\frac{\text{(boxes)}}{\text{(dollars)}}$ $\frac{6}{4} = \frac{b}{6}$

_____9_____ boxes of pencils

13. George was reading a mystery story. He read 42 pages in 1 hour. At this rate, how many pages can he read in 40 minutes?

$\frac{\text{(pages)}}{\text{(minutes)}}$ $\frac{42}{60} = \frac{p}{40}$

_____28_____ pages

14. An astronaut standing on the Moon would weigh about 16% of her weight on Earth. If an astronaut weighs 150 lb on Earth, about how much would she weigh on the Moon?

$\frac{\text{(Moon weight)}}{\text{(Earth weight)}}$ $\frac{16}{100} = \frac{m}{150}$

_____24_____ lb

15. 15% of what number is 9?

$\frac{\text{(part)}}{\text{(whole)}}$ $\frac{15}{100} = \frac{9}{x}$

15% of _____60_____ is 9.

LESSON 8·13 Written Assessment continued

16. The table below shows the calorie and fat content in 1 cup of two kinds of yogurt. Complete the table. Round the calculated fat percent to the nearest whole percent.

Food Label	Food	Calories from Fat / Total Calories	Calculated Fat Percent
Nutrition Facts Serving Size 1 cup (225 g) Servings Per Container 1 — Amount Per Serving — Calories 260 Calories from Fat 73	Strawberry yogurt	$\frac{73}{260}$	About 28%
Nutrition Facts Serving Size 1 cup (225 g) Servings Per Container 1 — Amount Per Serving — Calories 220 Calories from Fat 42	Vanilla yogurt	$\frac{42}{220}$	About 19%

Solve each problem.

17. Three out of every 5 cards are faceup. If 20 cards are facedown, how many cards are there in all?

There are _____50_____ cards in all.

18. The ratio of facedown to faceup cards is 2 to 3. If there are 25 cards altogether, how many cards are facedown?

_____10_____ cards are facedown.

19. Shade $\frac{4}{5}$ of the circles below.

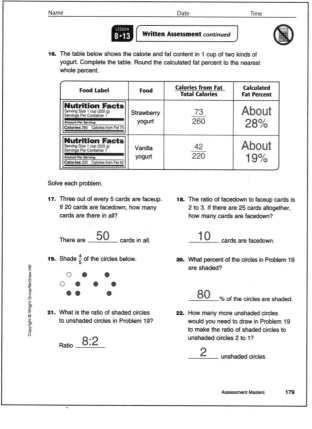

20. What percent of the circles in Problem 19 are shaded?

_____80_____ % of the circles are shaded.

21. What is the ratio of shaded circles to unshaded circles in Problem 19?

Ratio _____8:2_____

22. How many more unshaded circles would you need to draw in Problem 19 to make the ratio of shaded circles to unshaded circles 2 to 1?

_____2_____ unshaded circles

LESSON 8·13 Written Assessment continued

23. Triangles MNO and PQR are similar.

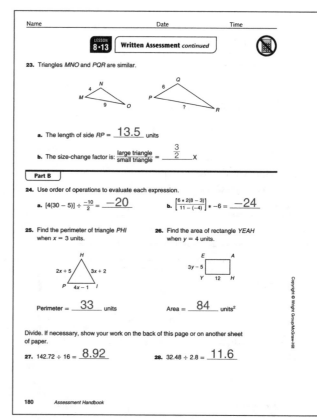

a. The length of side RP = _____13.5_____ units

b. The size-change factor is: $\frac{\text{large triangle}}{\text{small triangle}}$ = $\frac{3}{2}$ X

Part B

24. Use order of operations to evaluate each expression.

a. $[4(30 - 5)] \div \frac{-10}{2}$ = _____−20_____

b. $\left[\frac{6 \cdot 2(8 - 3)}{11 - (-4)}\right] * -6$ = _____−24_____

25. Find the perimeter of triangle PHI when x = 3 units.

Perimeter = _____33_____ units

26. Find the area of rectangle YEAH when y = 4 units.

Area = _____84_____ units²

Divide. If necessary, show your work on the back of this page or on another sheet of paper.

27. 142.72 ÷ 16 = _____8.92_____

28. 32.48 ÷ 2.8 = _____11.6_____

Name _____ Date _____ Time _____

LESSON 9·14 **Written Assessment** Progress Check 9

Part A

1. Write 2 number sentences for finding the area of the shaded part of the rectangle.

Sentence 1: (__11__ – __6__) * __4__ = 20

Sentence 2: (__4__ * __11__) – (__4__ * __6__) = 20

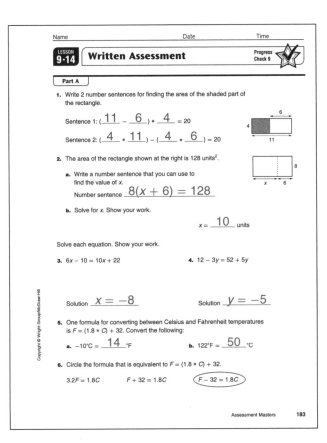

2. The area of the rectangle shown at the right is 128 units².

   a. Write a number sentence that you can use to find the value of x.

   Number sentence __$8(x + 6) = 128$__

   b. Solve for x. Show your work.

   $x = $ __10__ units

Solve each equation. Show your work.

3. $6x - 10 = 10x + 22$

4. $12 - 3y = 52 + 5y$

Solution __$x = -8$__

Solution __$y = -5$__

5. One formula for converting between Celsius and Fahrenheit temperatures is $F = (1.8 * C) + 32$. Convert the following:

   a. $-10°C = $ __14__ °F

   b. $122°F = $ __50__ °C

6. Circle the formula that is equivalent to $F = (1.8 * C) + 32$.

   $3.2F = 1.8C$ $F + 32 = 1.8C$ ⟨$F - 32 = 1.8C$⟩

Name _____ Date _____ Time _____

LESSON 9·14 **Written Assessment** *continued*

7. The mobile shown at the right is in balance. The fulcrum of the mobile is the center point of the rod.

   Formula:
   $(W * D) = (w * d)$

   What is the weight of the object to the right of the fulcrum? __6__ units

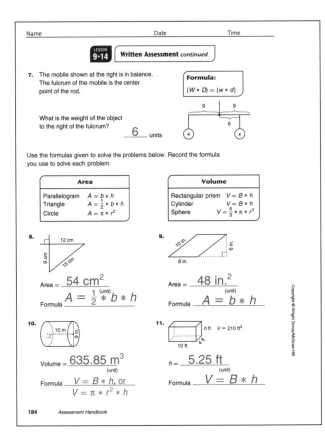

Use the formulas given to solve the problems below. Record the formula you use to solve each problem.

Area		Volume	
Parallelogram	$A = b * h$	Rectangular prism	$V = B * h$
Triangle	$A = \frac{1}{2} * b * h$	Cylinder	$V = B * h$
Circle	$A = \pi * r^2$	Sphere	$V = \frac{4}{3} * \pi * r^3$

8. (12 cm, 9 cm, 15 cm triangle)

   Area = __54 cm²__ (unit)

   Formula __$A = \frac{1}{2} * b * h$__

9. (10 in., 6 in., 8 in. parallelogram)

   Area = __48 in.²__ (unit)

   Formula __$A = b * h$__

10. (10 m cylinder, E/9, 10 ft)

    Volume = __635.85 m³__ (unit)

    Formula __$V = B * h$, or $V = \pi * r^2 * h$__

11. (h ft, $V = 210$ ft³, 4 ft)

    $h = $ __5.25 ft__ (unit)

    Formula __$V = B * h$__

Name _____ Date _____ Time _____

LESSON 9·14 **Written Assessment** *continued*

12. Figures $ABCD$ and $LMJK$ are similar. Figure $ABCD$ is an enlargement of $LMJK$.

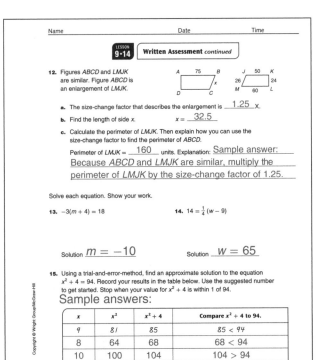

   a. The size-change factor that describes the enlargement is __1.25__ x.

   b. Find the length of side x. $x = $ __32.5__

   c. Calculate the perimeter of $LMJK$. Then explain how you can use the size-change factor to find the perimeter of $ABCD$.

   Perimeter of $LMJK = $ __160__ units. Explanation: Sample answer: Because $ABCD$ and $LMJK$ are similar, multiply the perimeter of $LMJK$ by the size-change factor of 1.25.

Solve each equation. Show your work.

13. $-3(m + 4) = 18$

14. $14 = \frac{1}{4}(w - 9)$

Solution __$m = -10$__

Solution __$w = 65$__

15. Using a trial-and-error-method, find an approximate solution to the equation $x^2 + 4 = 94$. Record your results in the table below. Use the suggested number to get started. Stop when your value for $x^2 + 4$ is within 1 of 94.

Sample answers:

x	x^2	$x^2 + 4$	Compare $x^2 + 4$ to 94.
9	81	85	$85 < 94$
8	64	68	$68 < 94$
10	100	104	$104 > 94$
9.5	90.25	94.25	$x = 9.5$ is slightly too large.

Name _____ Date _____ Time _____

LESSON 9·14 **Written Assessment** *continued*

Part B

16. There are 24 members on the school's track team. Two out of every 3 members were on the team last year. How many members were on the team?

   There were __16__ members last year.

17. Without using a protractor, find the measure of each numbered angle.

   Lines b and d are parallel.

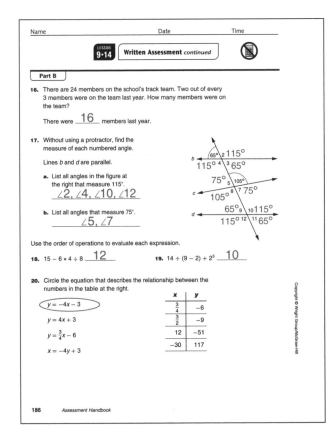

   a. List all angles in the figure at the right that measure 115°.

   __$\angle 2, \angle 4, \angle 10, \angle 12$__

   b. List all angles that measure 75°.

   __$\angle 5, \angle 7$__

Use the order of operations to evaluate each expression.

18. $15 - 6 * 4 \div 8$ __12__

19. $14 \div (9 - 2) + 2^3$ __10__

20. Circle the equation that describes the relationship between the numbers in the table at the right.

   ⟨$y = -4x - 3$⟩

   $y = 4x + 3$

   $y = \frac{3}{4}x - 6$

   $x = -4y + 3$

x	y
$\frac{3}{4}$	-6
$\frac{3}{2}$	-9
12	-51
-30	117

LESSON 10·6 | **Written Assessment** | Progress Check 10

Part A

1. Find the measure of ∠E without using a protractor.

m∠A = 160°
m∠B = 50°
m∠C = 140°
m∠D = 150°

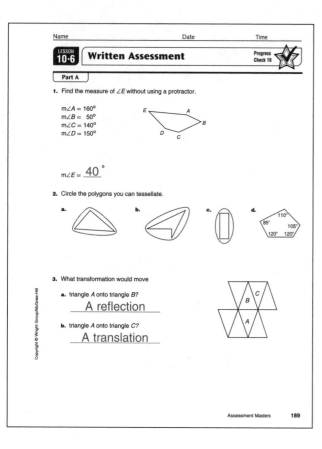

m∠E = _40_ °

2. Circle the polygons you can tessellate.

a.   b.   c.   d.

110°
85°   105°
120°   120°

3. What transformation would move

a. triangle A onto triangle B?

    A reflection

b. triangle A onto triangle C?

    A translation

LESSON 10·6 | **Written Assessment** *continued*

4. Lines *a* and *b* are parallel.

a. Write an equation you can use to find the value of *x*.

Equation $(x + 30)° + (2x + 30)° = 180°$

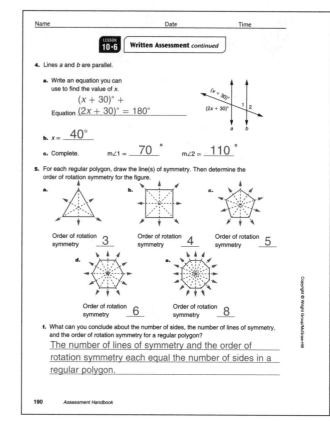

b. $x =$ _40°_

c. Complete.   m∠1 = _70_ °   m∠2 = _110_ °

5. For each regular polygon, draw the line(s) of symmetry. Then determine the order of rotation symmetry for the figure.

a.   b.   c.

Order of rotation symmetry _3_   Order of rotation symmetry _4_   Order of rotation symmetry _5_

d.   e.

Order of rotation symmetry _6_   Order of rotation symmetry _8_

f. What can you conclude about the number of sides, the number of lines of symmetry, and the order of rotation symmetry for a regular polygon?

The number of lines of symmetry and the order of rotation symmetry each equal the number of sides in a regular polygon.

LESSON 10·6 | **Written Assessment** *continued*

6. Circle the objects that are topologically equivalent to the bowl.

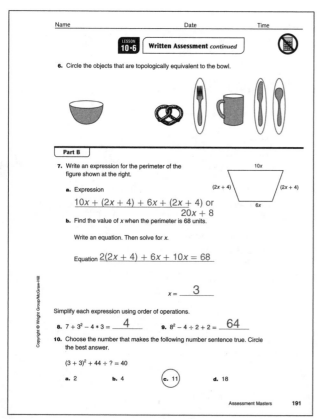

Part B

7. Write an expression for the perimeter of the figure shown at the right.

10x
(2x + 4)   (2x + 4)
6x

a. Expression

$10x + (2x + 4) + 6x + (2x + 4)$ or $20x + 8$

b. Find the value of *x* when the perimeter is 68 units.

Write an equation. Then solve for *x*.

Equation $2(2x + 4) + 6x + 10x = 68$

$x = $ _3_

Simplify each expression using order of operations.

8. $7 + 3^2 - 4 * 3 = $ _4_   9. $8^2 - 4 ÷ 2 + 2 = $ _64_

10. Choose the number that makes the following number sentence true. Circle the best answer.

$(3 + 3)^2 + 44 ÷ ? = 40$

a. 2   b. 4   (c. 11)   d. 18

Beginning-of-Year Assessment

1. Write the value of the 7 in each of the numbers below.

   a. 7,629 _____

   b. 872,019 _____

   c. 24.078 _____

   d. 7,000,194 _____

   e. 0.7912 _____

   f. 1,854,623,072 _____

2. Write the following numbers in expanded notation.

   a. 1,683 _____

   _____

   b. 47.29 _____

   _____

Solve. Show your work

3. 614 * 72 = _____   **4.** 48.6 * 3.8 = _____

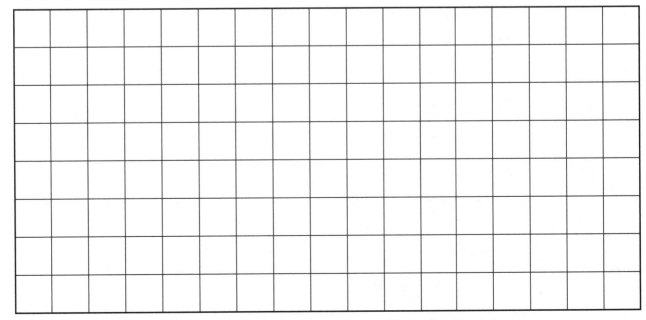

Beginning-of-Year Assessment *continued*

5. Write the rule. Then, complete the "What's My Rule?" table.

Rule: _____

in	out
9	45
15	75
6	
	100
	60
15	

6. Write the 9-digit number that has

9 in the hundred thousands place,

8 in the hundredths place,

2 in the hundreds place,

7 in the thousands place,

0 in the tens place,

6 in the thousandths place, and

1 in every other place.

_____ _____ _____, _____ _____ _____. _____ _____ _____

7. Angelica solved the problem 18 * 62. Her work is shown below.
Is she correct? Explain.

```
   18    _____
 * 62    _____
   60    _____
   48    _____
    2    _____
   16    _____
  126
```

Beginning-of-Year Assessment *continued*

8. Robert is *N* years old. Robert's brother is 6 years younger than Robert.

a. Write an expression that shows how old Robert's brother is.

_____

b. Write an expression that shows how old Robert will be in 12 years.

_____

9. Complete the table.

Standard Notation	Number-and-Word Notation	Exponential Notation
	6 thousand	
		$9 * 10^6$
210,000,000		
		$7.4 * 10^9$

Solve. Show your work.

10. $864 \div 27 =$ _____

11. $74.4 \div 6 =$ _____

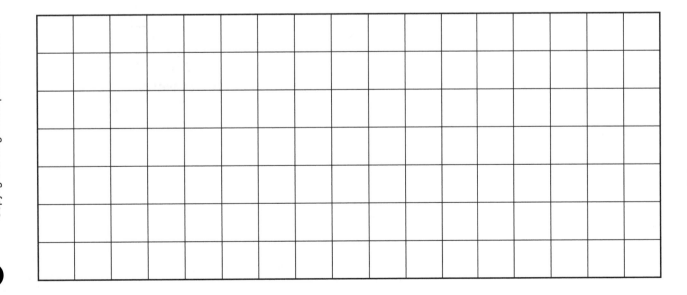

Beginning-of-Year Assessment *continued*

12. In the number 4,735,691,786.1027, which digit is in the:

a. millions place? _____

b. hundredths place? _____

c. ten-thousands place? _____

d. billions place? _____

e. thousandths place? _____

f. hundred-millions place? _____

13. Complete the table. Then graph the data. Connect the points with line segments.

Sasha earns $15 per hour.

Rule: Earnings = 15 ∗ Number of Hours

Hours	Earnings ($)
3	
5	
	135
7	
	60

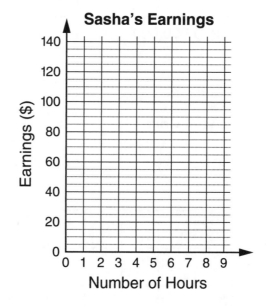

Sasha's Earnings

LESSON 5·11

Mid-Year Assessment

1. The ages of the teachers at Composite Middle School are represented by the following data set:

   56, 32, 34, 29, 24, 43, 26, 39, 45, 37, 50, 34, 55, 62, 29, 34, 47, 52, 49

   a. Construct a stem-and-leaf plot to represent the age data.

   **Ages of Teachers at
   Composite Middle School**

Stems (10s)	Leaves (1s)

   b. Use your stem-and-leaf plot to find the following landmarks:

   Range   _____

   Mode(s)   _____

   Median   _____

2. George's math test scores are 82, 59, 91, and 88.

   a. Find the median and the mean score.   Median _____   Mean _____

   b. Is the median or the mean the better representation of George's overall performance, or are they about the same? Explain your reasoning.

   _____

   _____

   c. Suppose George needs a mean score of 83 to earn a B in his math class and there is only one test left to take. What is the least score George can receive on this last test to get a B for the class?

   _____ Explain how you got your answer.

   _____

   _____

   _____

LESSON
5·11

Mid-Year Assessment *continued*

3. A clothing designer surveyed adult women and men on the color of pants they preferred to wear for formal occasions. The stacked bar graph below displays the results of that survey.

   a. How many men preferred blue pants?

   _____

   b. Which pant color did the majority of men prefer?

   _____

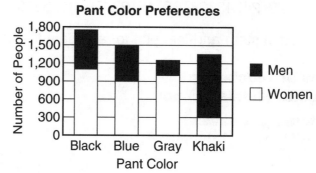

   c. The owner of The Men's and Women's Formalwear Store can carry 3 colors of pants. Based on the survey data, which 3 colors should the owner select? Why?

   _____

   _____

   _____

4. Write each of the following numbers using digits.

   a. one hundred ninety six and sixty-four hundredths _____

   b. four hundred six thousandths _____

   c. three billion, two hundred million, six hundred twenty-three thousand, nine hundred nine and six hundredths

   _____

5. In the number 3,984,520,116,392.7683, which digit is in the:

   a. hundred-billions place? _____   **b.** millions place? _____

   c. ten-thousandths place? _____   **d.** hundred-thousands place? _____

   e. hundredths place? _____   **f.** ten-millions place? _____

6. The Mouawad Splendour diamond sold for 12.76 million dollars in 1990. Write 12.76 million in

   a. standard notation. _____

   b. scientific notation. _____

Mid-Year Assessment *continued*

7. The moon orbits at an average distance from Earth of about 384,400 kilometers. Write 384,400 in

   a. number-and-word notation. _____

   b. expanded notation. (___ * 10⁻) + (___ * 10⁻) + (___ * 10⁻) + (___ * 10⁻)

8. An angstrom (Å) is a unit of length.
   It is equivalent to 0.0000001 millimeter.
   Write 0.0000001 as a power of 10. _____

9. Complete the following table.

Standard Notation	Scientific Notation	Number-and-Word Notation
6,240,000		
	$3.6 * 10^9$	
		81.3 trillion

10. Write the value of the 2 in each of the numbers below.

   a. 2,593,017 _____

   b. 54.028 _____

   c. 364,095,826,115 _____

   d. 664,198.8502 _____

11. A rabbit named Nipper's Geronimo has ears that measure 31.125 inches in length. Write 31.125 in expanded notation.

_____

LESSON 5·11 Mid-Year Assessment *continued*

Solve. Express any remainders as fractions. Show your work.

12. $93.701 + 115.39 =$ _____   **13.** $96.8 - 15.92 =$ _____

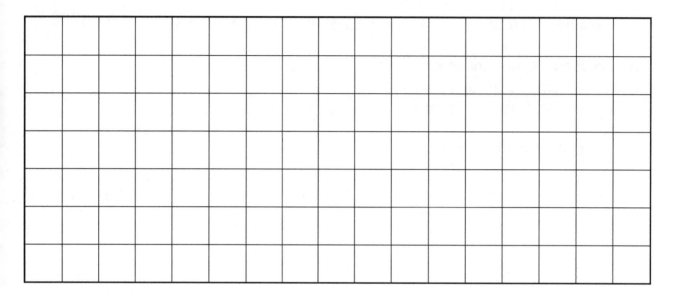

14. $672 * 84 =$ _____   **15.** $762 \div 24 =$ _____

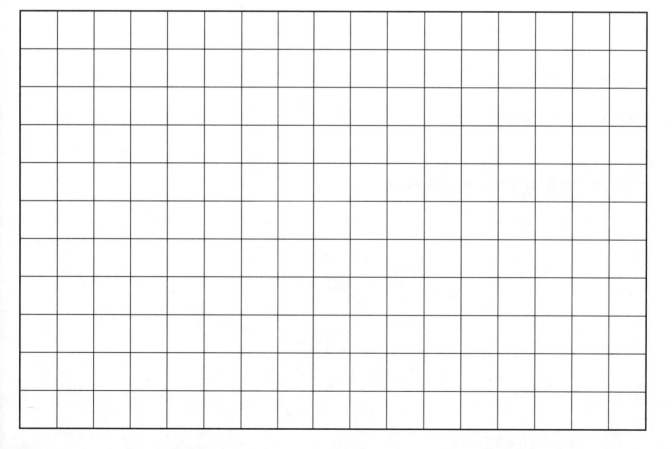

LESSON 5·11 | **Mid-Year Assessment** *continued*

16. Janice went to the art store to purchase supplies for a school project. She bought a canvas for $36.99, paints for $23.71, and brushes for $16.42. There was no tax. She paid with a $100 bill. How much change did she receive? Show your work.

$ _____

17. Suppose you want to share $175.68 equally among 32 people. How much money should each person get? Show your work.

$ _____

Solve. Express any remainders as fractions. Show your work.

18. $52.8 * 3.64 =$ _____   **19.** $63,509 \div 328 =$ _____

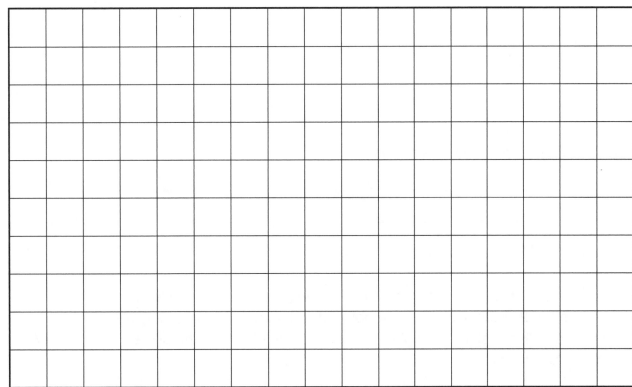

LESSON 5·11 | **Mid-Year Assessment** *continued*

20. **a.** Write a data set that fits the following description.

There are at least 12 numbers in the data set.

The maximum is 100.

The minimum is 62.

The median is 84.

The mode is 70.

_____

b. Make a bar graph of your data. Write labels for the title and the axes.

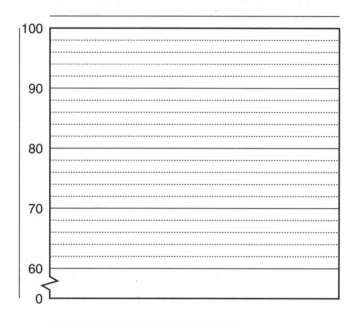

c. Explain why your title makes sense.

_____

_____

_____

21. Mrs. Bren's class is planning a pizza party. The local pizzeria is running a special offer: 2 slices of pizza and a bottle of water for $3.57, including tax. How much will it cost for the entire class of 32 students to get the pizza special? Show your work.

$ _____

LESSON 5·11 Mid-Year Assessment *continued*

22. The Lions played 12 basketball games this year. Each of the following graphs shows the number of points that the team scored in each game.

Points Scored in Basketball Games

(line graph: x-axis labeled "Game Number" 1–12; y-axis labeled "Number of Points" from 40 to 60)

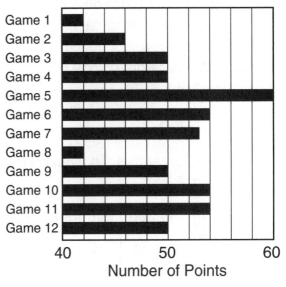

Points Scored in Basketball Games

(horizontal bar graph: Game 1 through Game 12; x-axis labeled "Number of Points" 40, 50, 60)

Points Scored in Basketball Games

Stems (10s)	Leaves (1s)
4	2 2 6
5	0 0 0 0 3 4 4 4
6	0

Points Scored in Basketball Games

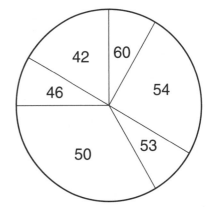

The local newspaper wants to publish an article about the Lions. Which graph best shows how many points the team scored in their games? Explain your choice.

_____

_____

_____

_____

LESSON 5·11 | **Mid-Year Assessment** *continued*

23. Suppose that the thickness of the wall of a capillary in a human heart is $0.5 * 10^{-6}$ meters. Write $0.5 * 10^{-6}$ in standard notation. _____

24. An Asian elephant eats about 330 pounds of food each day. A gorilla eats about 40 pounds of food each day, and a giant panda eats about 84 pounds of food each day. About how much food would a zoo need to buy in order to feed one Asian elephant, one gorilla, and one giant panda for one week? Show your work.

Answer: _____

25. The table below shows the average high temperature in Washington, D.C., each month.

Month	Jan	Feb	Mar	Apr	May	Jun	Jul	Aug	Sep	Oct	Nov	Dec
Avg. High Temp. (°F)	42	46	55	66	75	83	88	86	79	68	57	46

a. Use the data table to complete the line graph below.

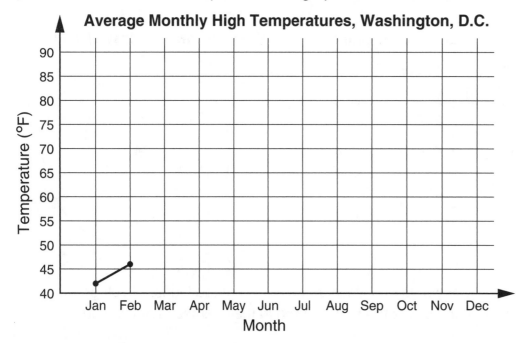

Average Monthly High Temperatures, Washington, D.C.

b. Based on this data, during what month would you choose to visit Washington, D.C.? Explain your answer.

_____

_____

LESSON 10·6 | **End-of-Year Assessment**

1. Compare using >, <, or =.

   a. 0.95_____ $\frac{39}{40}$ **b.** 0.07_____70%

2. Identify the value of the following digits in the number 4,598,722,061.053.

   a. 9 _____   **b.** 3 _____

   c. 7 _____   **d.** 4 _____

3. Use order of operations to evaluate each expression.

   a. $3 * 5 + 16 \div 4 =$ _____   **b.** $5 + 3 * 9 \div 3 - (-7) =$ _____

4. Solve.

   a. $64 + (-16) =$ _____   **b.** _____ $= 12 * (-16)$

   c. _____ $= -84 \div (-3)$ **d.** $-23 - (-16) =$ _____

5. Complete the table for the given rule. Then plot the points and connect them to make a line graph.

Rule: $y = 2x + 3$

x	y
−2	
	1
0	
1	
	7

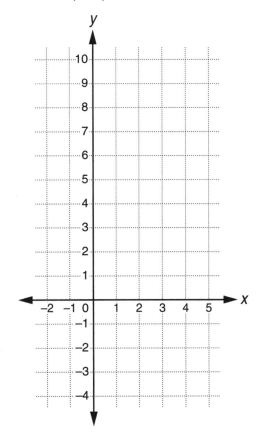

End-of-Year Assessment *continued*

6. Is each number sentence true or false?

a. $(9 * 60) + 20 = 9 * (60 + 20)$ _____

b. $-12 * (10 - 20) < 100$ _____

c. $(-4)^3 > (-4)^2$ _____

d. $16 * (8 \div (-8)) \leq -8 \div \frac{3}{4}$ _____

Solve each equation. Show your work.

7. $3c + 12 = 36$

8. $5y + 2 + 3y = 18$

$c =$ _____

$y =$ _____

9. $\frac{3}{8}x + 16 = \frac{9}{8}x - 20$

10. $18n - 20 = 36 - 10n$

$x =$ _____

$n =$ _____

11. Graph the solution set for each inequality.

a. $p \leq 3 - 4$

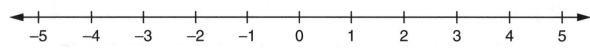

b. $0 > t$

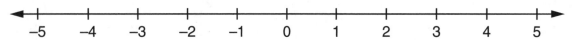

LESSON 10·6 | **End-of-Year Assessment** *continued*

12. Corbin flips a coin three times.

   a. Make an organized list or a tree diagram to display all possible outcomes.

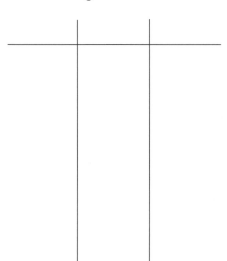

   b. What is the probability Corbin will get 3 HEADS? Express
this probability as a percent. _____

13. Marni rolled a fair die 5 times
and recorded the result of each
roll in the table at the right.

roll	1st	2nd	3rd	4th	5th
number rolled	6	5	6	2	6

   a. What is the probability that the die will land on 6 when
Marni rolls again? Express the probability as a fraction. _____

   b. About how many times would you expect Marni to
get a 3 if she rolls the same fair die 648 times? _____ times

14. A 16-oz box of *Sweety Pi* breakfast cereal costs $3.68.
A 20-oz box costs $4.79. Which box is the better buy?

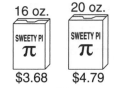

   a. The _____-oz box of cereal is the better buy.

   b. Explain how you determined which box is the better buy.

_____

_____

_____

LESSON 10·6 **End-of-Year Assessment** *continued*

Estimate. Then solve. Write each answer in simplest form.

15. $274.8 + 94.67$

16. $36.25 \div 0.5$

Estimate: _____

Solution: _____

Estimate: _____

Solution: _____

17. $3\frac{2}{5} * 4\frac{2}{3}$

18. $62.04 - 8.627$

Estimate: _____

Solution: _____

Estimate: _____

Solution: _____

19. $7\frac{1}{8} \div 2\frac{2}{9}$

20. $316.2 * 6.8$

Estimate: _____

Solution: _____

Estimate: _____

Solution: _____

21. $16\frac{1}{2} - 4\frac{8}{9}$

22. $14\frac{5}{6} + 8\frac{3}{8}$

Estimate: _____

Solution: _____

Estimate: _____

Solution: _____

LESSON 10·6

End-of-Year Assessment *continued*

23. Triangles *MAY* and *JUL* are similar.

a. Measure the sides of each triangle to the nearest millimeter. Write the measurements next to the sides.

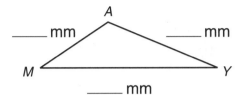

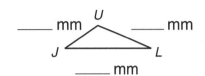

_____ mm

b. What is the size-change ratio between the two triangles? _____

24. Lines *p* and *q* are parallel and intersect the *x*- and *y*-axes to form similar right triangles.

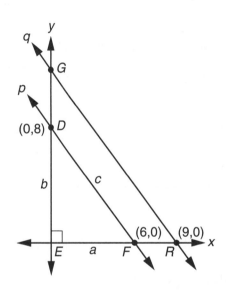

a. What are the coordinates of point *G*?

(_____,_____)

b. Find the area of triangle *DEF*.

Area = _____ units²

c. Use the Pythagorean theorem to find the length of $\overline{DF}$.

$\overline{DF}$ = _____ units

> **Pythagorean theorem**
> $a^2 + b^2 = c^2$

d. Explain how you can use the dimensions of triangle *DEF* to find the perimeter of triangle *GER*.

_____

_____

_____

_____

_____

LESSON 10·6 **End-of-Year Assessment** *continued*

25. Rewrite each of the following numbers in standard notation.
Then, compare using >, <, or =.

Example: 2 thousand; 3^5

2,000 > 243

a. 5.2 million; $5.4 * 10^6$

_____ _____ _____

b. 72 hundredths;
$(7 * 0.10) + (2 * 0.01) + (3 * 0.001)$

_____ _____ _____

c. 3^3; $2.4 * 10^{-3}$

_____ _____ _____

d. $3.4 * 10^{-2}$; $5 * 10^{-3}$

_____ _____ _____

26. Complete the tables. Write each fraction in simplest form.

Fraction	Decimal	Percent
$\frac{7}{8}$		
		72%

Fraction	Decimal	Percent
	0.06	
	0.005	

Solve Problems 27–29 using any method. Show your work.

27. Find 56% of 75.

28. 120 is 15% of what number?

56% of 75 is _____.

120 is 15% of _____.

29. Software for a personal digital assistant (PDA) that regularly
sells for $60 is on sale for 15% off. Find the sale price.

Sale price _____

30. Identify the greatest common factor of 56 and 60. _____

31. Identify the least common multiple of 56 and 60. _____

LESSON 10·6

End-of-Year Assessment *continued*

32. Cross out the names that do not belong
in the name collection box.
Then add 3 more names.

48
$(3^2 + 6) * 2 + (36 * 0.5)$
$((2 + 3) * 6) + (2^3 + 10)$
$16 \div 2 + 40 * \frac{1}{2}$
$32\frac{1}{2} * 2 \div 2\frac{1}{2}$
$100 * (\frac{1}{2} * \frac{1}{2}) * 2 - 2$

33. Using only a compass and a straightedge,
draw a figure congruent to the figure below.

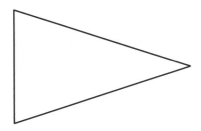

Explain how you know the two figures are congruent.

_____

_____

_____

34. Write an equation to solve for *x*.
Find any missing dimensions.
You may use a calculator.

Volume: 1,078 units^3
Use $\pi = \frac{22}{7}$

Formulas		
Area		
Circle		πr^2
Volume		
Cylinder		$B * h$

a. Equation _____

b. $x =$ _____ units

LESSON 10·6

End-of-Year Assessment *continued*

35. Find the measure of each angle without using a protractor. Lines *m* and *n* are parallel.

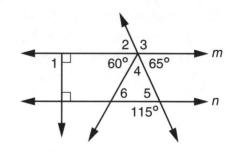

a. m∠1 = _____

b. m∠2 = _____

c. m∠3 = _____

d. m∠4 = _____

e. m∠5 = _____

f. m∠6 = _____

Use triangle *ABC* with vertices at (5,4), (7,8), and (3,8) to complete Problem 36.

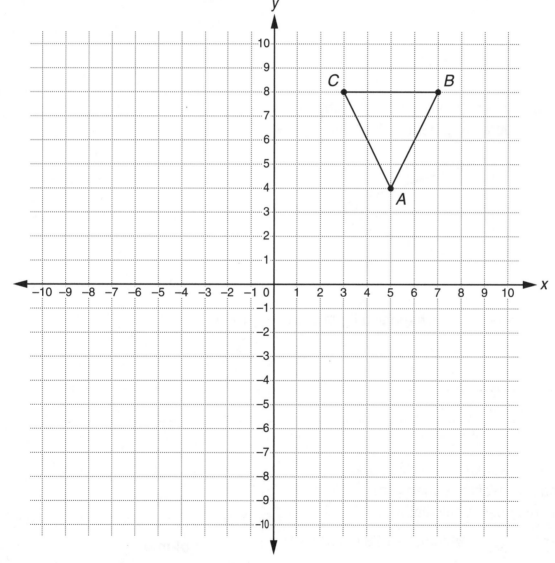

36. Draw and label the image of triangle *ABC* after

    a. a reflection over the *y*-axis.   *A'*(____,____); *B'*(____,____); *C'*(____,____)

    b. a translation 10 units down.   *A''*(____,____); *B''*(____,____); *C''*(____,____)

LESSON 10·6

End-of-Year Assessment *continued*

37. Carl runs the 100 meter dash for his school's track team. His 10 most recent times are listed below, to the nearest 0.1 second.

| 13.4 seconds | 14.0 seconds | 13.4 seconds | 12.9 seconds | 13.0 seconds |
| 13.4 seconds | 13.6 seconds | 19.1 seconds | 12.9 seconds | 13.5 seconds |

a. Construct a stem-and-leaf plot to represent the data.

Carl's 100 Meter Dash Times

Stems (10s and 1s)	Leaves (0.1s)

b. Use your stem-and-leaf plot to find the following landmarks. Round to the nearest 0.1 second.

Range: _____ seconds

Median: _____ seconds

Mode: _____ seconds

Mean: _____ seconds

c. Should a reporter for the school paper use the mean or the median to more accurately represent Carl's time in the 100 meter dash? Explain.

_____

_____

_____

38. Match each sentence with the property that it illustrates.

A. $a + b = b + a$ _____ Multiplication Property of One

B. $a * (b + c) = (a * b) + (a * c)$ _____ Distributive Property

C. $a * \frac{1}{a} = 1$ _____ Commutative Property

D. $a * 1 = a$ _____ Multiplication of Reciprocals Property

39. Suppose you were playing *Angle Tangle* and your partner drew this angle:

Estimate the measure of your partner's angle: _____

Use a protractor to measure your partner's angle: _____

Beginning-of-Year Assessment

1. Write the value of the 7 in each of the numbers below.

a. 7,629   7,000 or 7 thousand

b. 872,019   70,000 or 70 thousand

c. 24.078   0.07 or 7 hundredths

d. 7,000,194   7,000,000 or 7 million

e. 0.7912   0.7 or 7 tenths

f. 1,854,623,072   70

2. Write the following numbers in expanded notation.

a. 1,683   1,000 + 600 + 80 + 3 or
(1 * 1000) + (6 * 100) + (8 * 10) + (3 * 1)

b. 47.29   40 + 7 + 0.2 + 0.09 or
(4 * 10) + (7 * 1) + (2 * 0.1) + (9 * 0.01)

Solve. Show your work

3. 614 * 72 =   44,208   **4.** 48.6 * 3.8 =   184.68

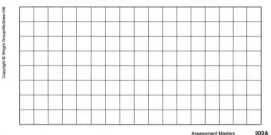

Beginning-of-Year Assessment *continued*

5. Write the rule. Then, complete the "What's My Rule?" table.

Rule: multiply by 5

in	out
9	45
15	75
6	30
20	100
12	60
15	75

6. Write the 9-digit number that has
9 in the hundred thousands place,
8 in the hundredths place,
2 in the hundreds place,
7 in the thousands place,
0 in the tens place,
6 in the thousandths place, and
1 in every other place.

9   1   7   2   0   1   1   8   6

7. Angelica solved the problem 18 * 62. Her work is shown below.
Is she correct? Explain.

18
* 62
60
48
2
16
126

Sample: No, Angelica is not correct. She multiplied 6 * 10 instead of 60 * 10, 8 * 6 instead of 80 * 60, and 2 * 1 instead of 2 * 10. The product should be 1,116.

Beginning-of-Year Assessment *continued*

8. Robert is N years old. Robert's brother is 6 years younger than Robert.

a. Write an expression that shows how old Robert's brother is.

$N - 6$

b. Write an expression that shows how old Robert will be in 12 years.

$N + 12$

9. Complete the table.

Standard Notation	Number-and-Word Notation	Exponential Notation
6,000	6 thousand	$6 * 10^3$
9,000,000	9 million	$9 * 10^6$
210,000,000	210 million	$2.1 * 10^8$
7,400,000,000	7.4 billion	$7.4 * 10^9$

Solve. Show your work.

10. 864 ÷ 27 =   32   **11.** 74.4 ÷ 6 =   12.4

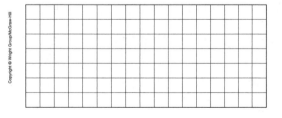

Beginning-of-Year Assessment *continued*

12. In the number 4,735,691,786.1027, which digit is in the:

a. millions place?   5   **b.** hundredths place?   0

c. ten-thousands place?   9   **d.** billions place?   4

e. thousandths place?   2   **f.** hundred-millions place?   7

13. Complete the table. Then graph the data. Connect the points
with line segments.

Sasha earns $15 per hour.

Rule: Earnings = 15 * Number of Hours

Hours	Earnings ($)
3	45
5	75
9	135
7	105
4	60

Sasha's Earnings

LESSON 5·11 **Mid-Year Assessment**

1. The ages of the teachers at Composite Middle School are represented by the following data set:

   56, 32, 34, 29, 24, 43, 26, 39, 45, 37, 50, 34, 55, 62, 29, 34, 47, 52, 49

   a. Construct a stem-and-leaf plot to represent the age data.

   Ages of Teachers at Composite Middle School

Stems (10s)	Leaves (1s)
6	2
5	0 2 5 6
4	3 5 7 9
3	2 4 4 4 7 9
2	4 6 9 9

   b. Use your stem-and-leaf plot to find the following landmarks:

   Range __38__

   Mode(s) __34__

   Median __39__

2. George's math test scores are 82, 59, 91, and 88.

   a. Find the median and the mean score.   Median __85__   Mean __80__

   b. Is the median or the mean the better representation of George's overall performance, or are they about the same? Explain your reasoning.

   Sample answer: Because 4 test scores are at or above 82, the median score is a better indicator of George's overall performance.

   c. Suppose George needs a mean score of 83 to earn a B in his math class and there is only one test left to take. What is the least score George can receive on this last test to get a B for the class?

   __95__ Explain how you got your answer.
   Sample answer: Five test scores will determine his average. Because
   $(x + 82 + 59 + 91 + 88) \div 5 = 83$, $x = 95$.

LESSON 5·11 **Mid-Year Assessment** *continued*

3. A clothing designer surveyed adult women and men on the color of pants they preferred to wear for formal occasions. The stacked bar graph below displays the results of that survey.

   a. How many men preferred blue pants?

   __600__

   b. Which pant color did the majority of men prefer?

   khaki

   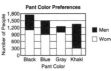

   c. The owner of The Men's and Women's Formalwear Store can carry 3 colors of pants. Based on the survey data, which 3 colors should the owner select? Why?

   Sample answer: The owner should select black, blue, and khaki because those are the three colors that the greatest number of men and women selected.

4. Write each of the following numbers using digits.

   a. one hundred ninety six and sixty-four hundredths __196.64__

   b. four hundred six thousandths __0.406__

   c. three billion, two hundred million, six hundred twenty-three thousand, nine hundred nine and six hundredths

   __3,200,623,909.06__

5. In the number 3,984,520,116,392.7683, which digit is in the:

   a. hundred-billions place? __9__   **b.** millions place? __0__

   c. ten-thousandths place? __3__   **d.** hundred-thousands place? __1__

   e. hundredths place? __6__   **f.** ten-millions place? __2__

6. The Mouawad Splendour diamond sold for 12.76 million dollars in 1990. Write 12.76 million in

   a. standard notation. __12,760,000__

   b. scientific notation. __$1.276 * 10^7$__

LESSON 5·11 **Mid-Year Assessment** *continued*

7. The moon orbits at an average distance from Earth of about 384,400 kilometers. Write 384,400 in

   a. number-and-word notation. __384.4 thousand__

   b. expanded notation. $(\underline{3} * 10^5) + (\underline{8} * 10^4) + (\underline{4} * 10^3) + (\underline{4} * 10^2)$

8. An angstrom (Å) is a unit of length. It is equivalent to 0.0000001 millimeter. Write 0.0000001 as a power of 10.

   __$1 * 10^{-7}$__

9. Complete the following table.

Standard Notation	Scientific Notation	Number-and-Word Notation
6,240,000	$6.24 * 10^6$	6.24 million
3,600,000,000	$3.6 * 10^9$	3.6 billion
81,300,000,000,000	$8.13 * 10^{13}$	81.3 trillion

10. Write the value of the 2 in each of the numbers below.

    a. 2,593,017   2,000,000 or 2 million

    b. 54.028   0.02 or 2 hundredths

    c. 364,095,826,115   20,000 or 20 thousand

    d. 664,198.8502   0.0002 or 2 ten-thousandths

11. A rabbit named Nipper's Geronimo has ears that measure 31.125 inches in length. Write 31.125 in expanded notation.

    $(3 * 10) + (1 * 1) + (1 * 0.1) + (2 * 0.01) + (5 * 0.001)$

LESSON 5·11 **Mid-Year Assessment** *continued*

Solve. Express any remainders as fractions. Show your work.

12. 93.701 + 115.39 = __209.091__   13. 96.8 − 15.92 = __80.88__

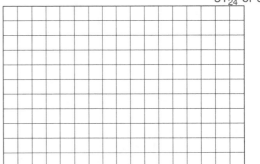

14. 672 * 84 = __56,448__   15. 762 ÷ 24 = Sample answer: __$31\frac{18}{24}$ or $31\frac{3}{4}$__

Page 1 (top left)

LESSON 5·11   Mid-Year Assessment *continued*

16. Janice went to the art store to purchase supplies for a school project. She bought a canvas for $36.99, paints for $23.71, and brushes for $16.42. There was no tax. She paid with a $100 bill. How much change did she receive? Show your work.

$ __22.88__

17. Suppose you want to share $175.68 equally among 32 people. How much money should each person get? Show your work.

$ __5.49__

Solve. Express any remainders as fractions. Show your work.

Sample answer:

18. 52.8 * 3.64 = __192.192__   19. 63,509 ÷ 328 = __$193\frac{205}{328}$ or $193\frac{5}{8}$__

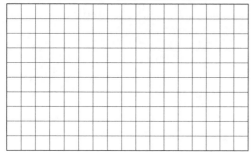

Page 2 (top right)

Name   Date   Time

LESSON 5·11   Mid-Year Assessment *continued*

20. **a.** Write a data set that fits the following description.
   There are at least 12 numbers in the data set.
   The maximum is 100.
   The minimum is 62.
   The median is 84.
   The mode is 70.

Sample answer: 62, 65, 70, 70, 70, 84, 84, 85, 89, 90, 92, 100

b. Make a bar graph of your data. Write labels for the title and the axes.

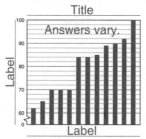

Title

Answers vary.

Label

Label

c. Explain why your title makes sense.
Answers vary.

21. Mrs. Bren's class is planning a pizza party. The local pizzeria is running a special offer: 2 slices of pizza and a bottle of water for $3.57, including tax. How much will it cost for the entire class of 32 students to get the pizza special? Show your work.

$ __114.24__

Page 3 (bottom left)

Name   Date   Time

LESSON 5·11   Mid-Year Assessment *continued*

22. The Lions played 12 basketball games this year. Each of the following graphs shows the number of points that the team scored in each game.

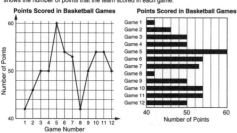

The local newspaper wants to publish an article about the Lions. Which graph best shows how many points the team scored in their games? Explain your choice.

Sample answers: The bar graph; it shows the points scored in each game. It is easy to compare the points in any two games by comparing the heights of the bars. The stem-and-leaf graph; it lists each game and it is easy to compare the scores.

Page 4 (bottom right)

Name   Date   Time

LESSON 5·11   Mid-Year Assessment *continued*

23. Suppose that the thickness of the wall of a capillary in a human heart is $0.5 * 10^{-6}$ meters. Write $0.5 * 10^{-6}$ in standard notation. __0.0000005__

24. An Asian elephant eats about 330 pounds of food each day. A gorilla eats about 40 pounds of food each day, and a giant panda eats about 84 pounds of food each day. About how much food would a zoo need to buy in order to feed one Asian elephant, one gorilla, and one giant panda for one week? Show your work.

Answer: __3,178 pounds__

25. The table below shows the average high temperature in Washington, D.C., each month.

Month	Jan	Feb	Mar	Apr	May	Jun	Jul	Aug	Sep	Oct	Nov	Dec
Avg. High Temp. (°F)	42	46	55	66	75	83	88	86	79	68	57	46

a. Use the data table to complete the line graph below.

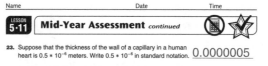

Average Monthly High Temperatures, Washington, D.C.

b. Based on this data, during what month would you choose to visit Washington, D.C.? Explain your answer.

Sample answer: I would visit Washington, D.C., during the month of June because the weather would be warm, but not too hot.

Panel 1 (page 211)

Name _____ Date _____ Time _____

LESSON 10·6 — **End-of-Year Assessment**

1. Compare using >, <, or =.

a. $0.95 \underset{<}{} \frac{39}{40}$ b. $0.07 \underset{<}{} 70\%$

2. Identify the value of the following digits in the number 4,598,722,061.053.

a. 9 _90,000,000 or 90 million_   b. 3 _0.003 or 3 thousandths_

c. 7 _700,000 or 700 thousand_   d. 4 _4,000,000,000 or 4 billion_

3. Use order of operations to evaluate each expression.

a. $3 * 5 + 16 \div 4 =$ _19_   b. $5 + 3 * 9 \div 3 - (-7) =$ _21_

4. Solve.

a. $64 + (-16) =$ _48_   b. _−192_ $= 12 * (-16)$

c. _28_ $= -84 \div (-3)$ d. $-23 - (-16) =$ _−7_

5. Complete the table for the given rule. Then plot the points and connect them to make a line graph.

Rule: $y = 2x + 3$

x	y
−2	−1
−1	1
0	3
1	5
2	7

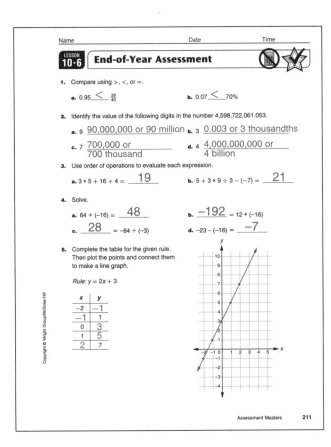

Panel 2 (page 212)

Name _____ Date _____ Time _____

LESSON 10·6 — **End-of-Year Assessment** continued

6. Is each number sentence true or false?

a. $(9 * 60) + 20 = 9 * (60 + 20)$ _false_   b. $-12 * (10 - 20) < 100$ _false_

c. $(-4)^3 > (-4)^2$ _false_   d. $16 * (8 \div (-8)) \le -8 * \frac{3}{4}$ _true_

Solve each equation. Show your work.

7. $3c + 12 = 36$ **8.** $5y + 2 + 3y = 18$

$c =$ _8_ $y =$ _2_

9. $\frac{3}{8}x + 16 = \frac{9}{8}x - 20$ **10.** $18n - 20 = 36 - 10n$

$x =$ _48_ $n =$ _2_

11. Graph the solution set for each inequality.

a. $p \le 3 - 4$

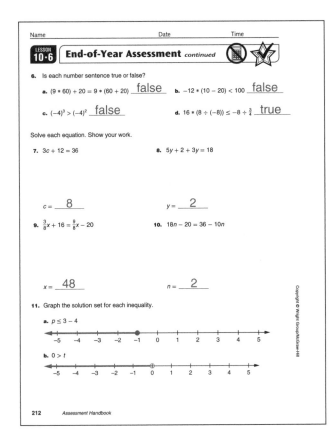

b. $0 > t$

Panel 3 (page 213)

Name _____ Date _____ Time _____

LESSON 10·6 — **End-of-Year Assessment** continued

12. Corbin flips a coin three times.

a. Make an organized list or a tree diagram to display all possible outcomes.

Flip 1	Flip 2	Flip 3
H	H	H
H	H	T
H	T	H
H	T	T
T	H	H
T	H	T
T	T	H
T	T	T

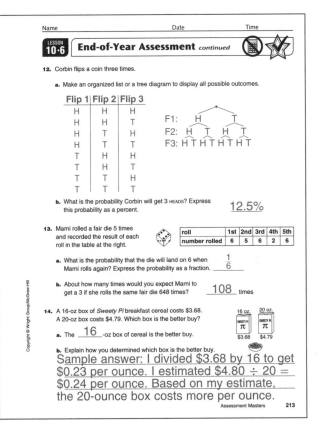

b. What is the probability Corbin will get 3 HEADS? Express this probability as a percent. _12.5%_

13. Marni rolled a fair die 5 times and recorded the result of each roll in the table at the right.

roll	1st	2nd	3rd	4th	5th
number rolled	6	5	6	2	6

a. What is the probability that the die will land on 6 when Marni rolls again? Express the probability as a fraction. $\frac{1}{6}$

b. About how many times would you expect Marni to get a 3 if she rolls the same fair die 648 times? _108_ times

14. A 16-oz box of *Sweety Pi* breakfast cereal costs $3.68. A 20-oz box costs $4.79. Which box is the better buy?

16 oz. SWEETY PI π $3.68   20 oz. SWEETY PI π $4.79

a. The _16_ -oz box of cereal is the better buy.

b. Explain how you determined which box is the better buy.

Sample answer: I divided $3.68 by 16 to get $0.23 per ounce. I estimated $4.80 ÷ 20 = $0.24 per ounce. Based on my estimate, the 20-ounce box costs more per ounce.

Panel 4 (page 214)

Name _____ Date _____ Time _____

LESSON 10·6 — **End-of-Year Assessment** continued

Estimate. Then solve. Write each answer in simplest form.
All estimates are sample answers.

15. $274.8 + 94.67$ **16.** $36.25 \div 0.5$

Estimate: _375_   Estimate: _72_
Solution: _369.47_   Solution: _72.5_

17. $3\frac{2}{5} * 4\frac{2}{3}$ **18.** $62.04 - 8.627$

Estimate: _15_   Estimate: _51_
Solution: _$15\frac{13}{15}$_   Solution: _53.413_

19. $7\frac{1}{8} \div 2\frac{2}{9}$ **20.** $316.2 * 6.8$

Estimate: _$3\frac{1}{2}$_   Estimate: _2,275_
Solution: _$3\frac{33}{160}$_   Solution: _2,150.16_

21. $16\frac{1}{2} - 4\frac{8}{9}$ **22.** $14\frac{5}{6} + 8\frac{3}{8}$

Estimate: _$11\frac{1}{2}$_   Estimate: _$23\frac{1}{2}$_
Solution: _$11\frac{11}{18}$_   Solution: _$23\frac{5}{24}$_

LESSON 10·6 **End-of-Year Assessment** *continued*

23. Triangles *MAY* and *JUL* are similar.

　　a. Measure the sides of each triangle to the nearest millimeter. Write the measurements next to the sides.

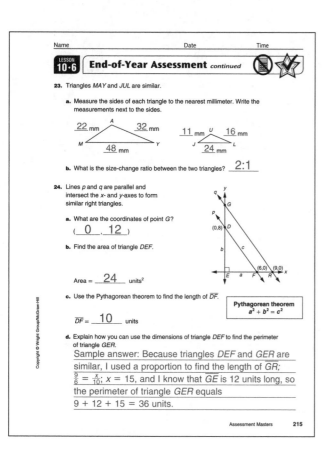

22 mm　32 mm　48 mm　11 mm　16 mm　24 mm

　　b. What is the size-change ratio between the two triangles?　**2:1**

24. Lines *p* and *q* are parallel and intersect the *x*- and *y*-axes to form similar right triangles.

　　a. What are the coordinates of point *G*?

　　(__0__ , __12__)

　　b. Find the area of triangle *DEF*.

　　Area = __24__ units²

　　c. Use the Pythagorean theorem to find the length of $\overline{DF}$.

| Pythagorean theorem |
| $a^2 + b^2 = c^2$ |

　　$\overline{DF} = $ __10__ units

　　d. Explain how you can use the dimensions of triangle *DEF* to find the perimeter of triangle *GER*.

　　Sample answer: Because triangles *DEF* and *GER* are similar, I used a proportion to find the length of $\overline{GR}$; $\frac{9}{6} = \frac{x}{10}$; $x = 15$, and I know that $\overline{GE}$ is 12 units long, so the perimeter of triangle *GER* equals $9 + 12 + 15 = 36$ units.

Assessment Masters　**215**

LESSON 10·6 **End-of-Year Assessment** *continued*

25. Rewrite each of the following numbers in standard notation. Then, compare using >, <, or =.

　　Example: 2 thousand; 3⁵
　　　　　　2,000 > 243

　　a. 5.2 million; $5.4 * 10^6$

　　5,200,000 __<__ 5,400,000

　　b. 72 hundredths;
　　　$(7 * 0.10) + (2 * 0.01) + (3 * 0.001)$

　　0.72 __<__ 0.723

　　c. 3³; $2.4 * 10^{-3}$

　　27 __>__ 0.0024

　　d. $3.4 * 10^{-2}$; $5 * 10^{-3}$

　　0.034 __>__ 0.005

26. Complete the tables. Write each fraction in simplest form.

Fraction	Decimal	Percent
$\frac{7}{8}$	0.875	87.5%
$\frac{18}{25}$	0.72	72%

Fraction	Decimal	Percent
$\frac{3}{50}$	0.06	6%
$\frac{1}{200}$	0.005	0.5%

Solve Problems 27–29 using any method. Show your work.

27. Find 56% of 75.

28. 120 is 15% of what number?

56% of 75 is __42__.

120 is 15% of __800__.

29. Software for a personal digital assistant (PDA) that regularly sells for $60 is on sale for 15% off. Find the sale price.

Sale price __$51__

30. Identify the greatest common factor of 56 and 60. __4__

31. Identify the least common multiple of 56 and 60. __840__

216　Assessment Handbook

LESSON 10·6 **End-of-Year Assessment** *continued*

32. Cross out the names that do not belong in the name collection box. Then add 3 more names.

48
$(3^2 + 6) * 2 + (36 * 0.5)$
$((2 + 3) * 6) + (2^3 + 10)$
~~$16 ÷ 2 + 40 * \frac{1}{2}$~~
~~$32\frac{1}{2} ÷ 2 ÷ 2\frac{1}{2}$~~
$100 * (\frac{1}{2} * \frac{1}{2}) * 2 - 2$

Answers vary.

33. Using only a compass and a straightedge, draw a figure congruent to the figure below.

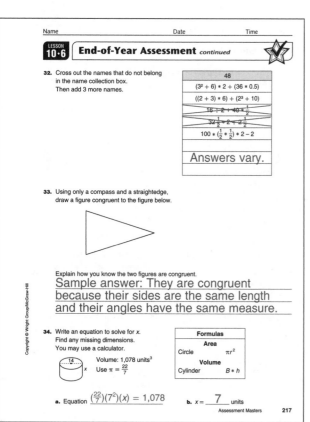

Explain how you know the two figures are congruent.

Sample answer: They are congruent because their sides are the same length and their angles have the same measure.

34. Write an equation to solve for *x*. Find any missing dimensions. You may use a calculator.

Formulas
Area
Circle　　πr^2
Volume
Cylinder　　$B * h$

Volume: 1,078 units³
Use $\pi = \frac{22}{7}$

　　a. Equation $(\frac{22}{7})(7^2)(x) = 1,078$

　　b. $x = $ __7__ units

Assessment Masters　**217**

LESSON 10·6 **End-of-Year Assessment** *continued*

35. Find the measure of each angle without using a protractor. Lines *m* and *n* are parallel.

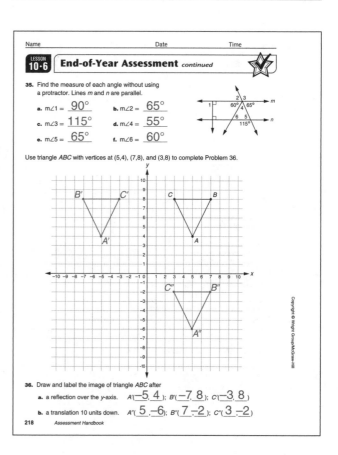

　　a. m∠1 = __90°__　　**b.** m∠2 = __65°__

　　c. m∠3 = __115°__　　**d.** m∠4 = __55°__

　　e. m∠5 = __65°__　　**f.** m∠6 = __60°__

Use triangle *ABC* with vertices at (5,4), (7,8), and (3,8) to complete Problem 36.

36. Draw and label the image of triangle *ABC* after

　　a. a reflection over the *y*-axis. A′(__-5__, __4__); B′(__-7__, __8__); C′(__-3__, __8__)

　　b. a translation 10 units down. A″(__5__, __-6__); B″(__7__, __-2__); C″(__3__, __-2__)

218　Assessment Handbook

LESSON 10·6 **End-of-Year Assessment** *continued*

37. Carl runs the 100 meter dash for his school's track team. His 10 most recent times are listed below, to the nearest 0.1 second.

| 13.4 seconds | 14.0 seconds | 13.4 seconds | 12.9 seconds | 13.0 seconds |
| 13.4 seconds | 13.6 seconds | 19.1 seconds | 12.9 seconds | 13.5 seconds |

a. Construct a stem-and-leaf plot to represent the data.

Carl's 100 Meter Dash Times

Stems (10s and 1s)	Leaves (0.1s)
12	9 9
13	0 4 4 4 5 6
14	0
19	1

b. Use your stem-and-leaf plot to find the following landmarks. Round to the nearest 0.1 second.

Range: __6.2__ seconds

Median: __13.4__ seconds

Mode: __13.4__ seconds

Mean: __13.9__ seconds

c. Should a reporter for the school paper use the mean or the median to more accurately represent Carl's time in the 100 meter dash? Explain.

Sample answer: Median; it is more representative than the mean because the mean is affected by the outlier, 19.1.

38. Match each sentence with the property that it illustrates.

A. $a + b = b + a$ __D__ Multiplication Property of One

B. $a * (b + c) = (a * b) + (a * c)$ __B__ Distributive Property

C. $a * \frac{1}{a} = 1$ __A__ Commutative Property

D. $a * 1 = a$ __C__ Multiplication of Reciprocals Property

39. Suppose you were playing *Angle Tangle* and your partner drew this angle:

Estimate the measure of your partner's angle: __Answers vary.__

Use a protractor to measure your partner's angle: __137°__

Individual Profile of Progress

Name _____   Date _____

Lesson	Recognizing Student Achievement	A.P.*	Comments
1•1	**Multiply 2-digit whole numbers.** [Operations and Computation Goal 2]		
1•2	**Demonstrate knowledge of landmark terms.** [Data and Chance Goal 2]		
1•3	**Find the minimum, maximum, range, and mode of data displayed in a stem-and-leaf plot.** [Data and Chance Goal 2]		
1•4	**Acknowledge the difference between median and mean.** [Data and Chance Goal 2]		
1•5	**Construct a line plot and calculate the mean of a data set.** [Data and Chance Goals 1 and 2]		
1•5a	**Calculate the interquartile range of a data set.** [Data and Chance Goal 2]		
1•6	**Read data values from a broken-line graph.** [Data and Chance Goal 1]		
1•7	**Construct a bar graph from a description of data.** [Data and Chance Goal 1]		
1•8	**Draw a broken-line graph from a table of data values.** [Data and Chance Goal 1]		
1•9	**Estimate and measure sector sizes using the Percent Circle.** [Measurement and Reference Frames Goal 1]		
1•10	**Explain how data landmarks change as data values change.** [Data and Chance Goal 2]		
1•11	**Read and interpret a broken-line graph.** [Data and Chance Goal 2]		
1•12	**Read and interpret side-by-side bar graphs.** [Data and Chance Goal 2]		

*Assess Progress: **A** = adequate progress **N** = not adequate progress **N/A** = not assessed

Copyright © Wright Group/McGraw-Hill

Individual Profile of Progress

Name _____   Date _____

Problem(s)	Progress Check 1	A.P.*	Comments
Oral/Slate Assessment			
1	**Solve problems using mean and median.** [Data and Chance Goal 2]		
2	**Identify perimeter and area of a rectangle.** [Measurement and Reference Frames Goal 2]		
3	**Convert between metric units of measure.** [Operations and Computation Goal 2]		
4	**Solve problems using perimeter and area.** [Measurement and Reference Frames Goal 2]		
5	**Round whole numbers to the nearest ten thousand and round decimals to the nearest tenth.** [Number and Numeration Goal 1]		
Written Assessment Part A			
1–4	**Analyze and compare data landmarks.** [Data and Chance Goal 2]		
5	**Use algorithms to add, subtract, multiply, and divide whole numbers.** [Operations and Computation Goal 2]		
1, 2, 5–7	**Construct and interpret a graph.** [Data and Chance Goal 1]		
8	**Use the Percent Circle to measure sectors ± 2%.** [Measurement and Reference Frames Goal 1]		
Written Assessment Part B			
9	**Calculate perimeter and area of a rectangle.** [Measurement and Reference Frames Goal 2]		
10	**Represent equivalent names for numbers.** [Number and Numeration Goal 4]		
11	**Interpret a step graph.** [Data and Chance Goal 1]		
12	**Apply multiplication and extended facts; estimate products of whole numbers.** [Operations and Computation Goal 2]		

*Assess Progress: **A** = adequate progress   **N** = not adequate progress   **N/A** = not assessed   Formative Assessments

Class Checklist:
Recognizing Student Achievement

Class _____

Date _____

Names	1·1	1·2	1·3	1·4	1·5	1·5a	1·6	1·7	1·8	1·9	1·10	1·11	1·12
1.													
2.													
3.													
4.													
5.													
6.													
7.													
8.													
9.													
10.													
11.													
12.													
13.													
14.													
15.													
16.													
17.													
18.													
19.													
20.													
21.													
22.													
23.													
24.													
25.													

Column headers:
- 1·1 **Multiply 2-digit whole numbers.** [Operations and Computation Goal 2]
- 1·2 **Demonstrate knowledge of landmark terms.** [Data and Chance Goal 2]
- 1·3 **Find the minimum, maximum, range, and mode of data displayed in a stem-and-leaf plot.** [Data and Chance Goal 2]
- 1·4 **Acknowledge the difference between median and mean.** [Data and Chance Goal 2]
- 1·5 **Construct a line plot and calculate the mean of a data set.** [Data and Chance Goals 1 and 2]
- 1·5a **Calculate the interquartile range of a data set.** [Data and Chance Goal 2]
- 1·6 **Read data values from a broken-line graph.** [Data and Chance Goal 1]
- 1·7 **Construct a bar graph from a description of data.** [Data and Chance Goal 1]
- 1·8 **Draw a broken-line graph from a table of data values.** [Data and Chance Goal 1]
- 1·9 **Estimate and measure sector sizes using the Percent Circle.** [Measurement and Reference Frames Goal 1]
- 1·10 **Explain how data landmarks change as data values change.** [Data and Chance Goal 2]
- 1·11 **Read and interpret a broken-line graph.** [Data and Chance Goal 2]
- 1·12 **Read and interpret side-by-side bar graphs.** [Data and Chance Goal 2]

Assess Progress: **A** = adequate progress **N** = not adequate progress **N/A** = not assessed

Class _____

Date _____

Names	Oral/Slate					Written Part A				Part B			
	1. Solve problems using mean and median. [Data and Chance Goal 2]	2. Identify perimeter and area of a rectangle. [Measurement and Reference Frames Goal 2]	3. Convert between metric units of measure. [Operations and Computation Goal 2]	4. Solve problems using perimeter and area. [Measurement and Reference Frames Goal 2]	5. Round whole numbers to the nearest ten thousand and round decimals to the nearest tenth. [Number and Numeration Goal 1]	1–4. Analyze and compare data landmarks. [Data and Chance Goal 2]	5. Use algorithms to add, subtract, multiply, and divide whole numbers. [Operations and Computation Goal 2]	1, 2, 5–7. Construct and interpret a graph. [Data and Chance Goal 1]	8. Use the Percent Circle to measure sectors ± 2%. [Measurement and Reference Frames Goal 1]	9. Calculate perimeter and area of a rectangle. [Measurement and Reference Frames Goal 2]	10. Represent equivalent names for numbers. [Number and Numeration Goal 4]	11. Interpret a step graph. [Data and Chance Goal 1]	12. Apply multiplication and extended facts; estimate products of whole numbers. [Operations and Computation Goal 2]
1.													
2.													
3.													
4.													
5.													
6.													
7.													
8.													
9.													
10.													
11.													
12.													
13.													
14.													
15.													
16.													
17.													
18.													
19.													
20.													
21.													
22.													
23.													
24.													
25.													

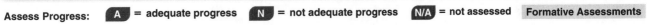

Assess Progress: **A** = adequate progress **N** = not adequate progress **N/A** = not assessed **Formative Assessments**

Go to *www.everydaymathonline.com* for digital checklists.

Name _____ Date _____

Lesson	Recognizing Student Achievement	A.P.*	Comments
2◆1	**Write whole numbers to billions.** [Number and Numeration Goal 1]		
2◆2	**Compare decimals through thousandths.** [Number and Numeration Goal 6]		
2◆3	**Align the digits of whole and decimal numbers by place value.** [Number and Numeration Goal 1]		
2◆4	**Write decimals to thousandths.** [Number and Numeration Goal 1]		
2◆5	**Estimate products of decimals.** [Operations and Computation Goal 5]		
2◆6	**Multiply decimals.** [Operations and Computation Goal 2]		
2◆7	**Divide whole numbers by 2-digit divisors.** [Operations and Computation Goal 2]		
2◆8	**Solve a division problem.** [Operations and Computation Goal 2]		
2◆9	**Determine the power of 10 needed to move the decimal point in the other factor to the right or left.** [Number and Numeration Goal 1]		
2◆10	**Interpret exponential notation and use the power key on the calculator.** [Number and Numeration Goal 1]		
2◆11	**Translate from scientific notation to standard notation.** [Number and Numeration Goal 1]		

*Assess Progress: 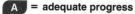 **A** = adequate progress **N** = not adequate progress **N/A** = not assessed

Individual Profile of Progress

Name _____ Date _____

Problem(s)	Progress Check 2	A.P.*	Comments
Oral/Slate Assessment			
1	**Translate between standard and scientific notation.** [Number and Numeration Goal 1]		
2	**Compare numbers using <, >, or =.** [Number and Numeration Goal 6]		
3	**Estimate products and quotients by using "close" numbers and record a number sentence.** [Operations and Computation Goal 5]		
4	**Mentally calculate sums and differences of decimal numbers.** [Operations and Computation Goal 1]		
Written Assessment Part A			
1	**Identify place value in whole and decimal numbers.** [Number and Numeration Goal 1]		
2, 3	**Translate between standard and number-and-word notations.** [Number and Numeration Goal 1]		
4, 6, 7	**Translate between standard, exponential, and scientific notations.** [Number and Numeration Goal 1]		
5	**Multiply by positive and negative powers of 10.** [Operations and Computation Goal 2]		
8–11	**Add, subtract, multiply, and divide decimals.** [Operations and Computation Goals 1 and 2]		
Written Assessment Part B			
12	**Write numbers in expanded notation.** [Number and Numeration Goal 1]		
13	**Translate between exponential and standard notations.** [Number and Numeration Goal 1]		
14	**Convert between metric units of linear measure.** [Operations and Computation Goal 2]		
15–18	**Order and round decimals.** [Number and Numeration Goal 6]		
19, 20	**Construct and interpret a graph.** [Data and Chance Goals 1 and 2]		

*Assess Progress:  **A** = adequate progress   **N** = not adequate progress   **N/A** = not assessed   **Formative Assessments**

Class _____

Date _____

Names	2·1 Write whole numbers to billions. [Number and Numeration Goal 1]	2·2 Compare decimals through thousandths. [Number and Numeration Goal 6]	2·3 Align the digits of whole and decimal numbers by place value. [Number and Numeration Goal 1]	2·4 Write decimals to thousandths. [Number and Numeration Goal 1]	2·5 Estimate products of decimals. [Operations and Computation Goal 5]	2·6 Multiply decimals. [Operations and Computation Goal 2]	2·7 Divide whole numbers by 2-digit divisors. [Operations and Computation Goal 2]	2·8 Solve a division problem. [Operations and Computation Goal 2]	2·9 Determine the power of 10 needed to move the decimal point in the other factor to the right or left. [Number and Numeration Goal 1]	2·10 Interpret exponential notation and use the power key on the calculator. [Number and Numeration Goal 1]	2·11 Translate from scientific notation to standard notation. [Number and Numeration Goal 1]
1.											
2.											
3.											
4.											
5.											
6.											
7.											
8.											
9.											
10.											
11.											
12.											
13.											
14.											
15.											
16.											
17.											
18.											
19.											
20.											
21.											
22.											
23.											
24.											
25.											

Assess Progress: **A** = adequate progress   **N** = not adequate progress   **N/A** = not assessed

Go to *www.everydaymathonline.com* for digital checklists.

Class _____

Date _____

Names	Oral/Slate				Written — Part A					Written — Part B				
	1. Translate between standard and scientific notation. [Numbers and Numeration Goal 1]	2. Compare numbers using <, >, or =. [Number and Numeration Goal 6]	3. Estimate products and quotients by using "close" numbers and record a number sentence. [Operations and Computation Goal 5]	4. Mentally calculate sums and differences of decimal numbers. [Operations and Computation Goal 1]	1. Identify place value in whole and decimal numbers. [Number and Numeration Goal 1]	2, 3. Translate between standard and number-and-word notations. [Number and Numeration Goal 1]	4, 6, 7. Translate between standard, exponential, and scientific notations. [Number and Numeration Goal 1]	5. Multiply by positive and negative powers of 10. [Operations and Computation Goal 2]	8–11. Add, subtract, multiply, and divide decimals. [Operations and Computation Goals 1 and 2]	12. Write numbers in expanded notation. [Number and Numeration Goal 1]	13. Translate between exponential and standard notations. [Number and Numeration Goal 1]	14. Convert between metric units of linear measure. [Operations and Computation Goal 2]	15–18. Order and round decimals. [Number and Numeration Goal 6]	19, 20. Construct and interpret a graph. [Data and Chance Goals 1 and 2]
1.														
2.														
3.														
4.														
5.														
6.														
7.														
8.														
9.														
10.														
11.														
12.														
13.														
14.														
15.														
16.														
17.														
18.														
19.														
20.														
21.														
22.														
23.														
24.														
25.														

Assess Progress: **A** = adequate progress **N** = not adequate progress **N/A** = not assessed **Formative Assessments**

Individual Profile of Progress

Name _____   Date _____

Lesson	Recognizing Student Achievement	A.P.*	Comments
3•1	**Write special cases for a general pattern.** [Patterns, Functions, and Algebra Goal 1]		
3•2	**Write a general pattern with two variables to represent a special case.** [Patterns, Functions, and Algebra Goal 1]		
3•3	**Find decimal solutions to whole-number division problems.** [Operations and Computation Goal 2]		
3•4	**Use algebraic notation to describe general patterns.** [Patterns, Functions, and Algebra Goal 1]		
3•5	**Complete a table from a formula and graph the data.** [Patterns, Functions, and Algebra Goal 1]		
3•6	**Complete a table from a formula and graph the data.** [Patterns, Functions, and Algebra Goal 1]		
3•7	**Add positive and negative numbers.** [Operations and Computation Goal 1]		
3•8	**Solve open number sentences involving signed numbers.** [Operations and Computation Goal 1]		
3•9	**Analyze the shape of a graph and draw conclusions about data trends.** [Data and Chance Goal 2]		
3•10	**Name a spreadsheet cell and identify a spreadsheet formula for calculating a total.** [Patterns, Functions, and Algebra Goal 1]		

*Assess Progress: **A** = adequate progress   **N** = not adequate progress   **N/A** = not assessed

    Go to *www.everydaymathonline.com* for digital checklists.

Name   Date

Problem(s)	Progress Check 3	A.P.*	Comments
Oral/Slate Assessment			
1	**Give an algebraic expression to represent the situation in a number problem.** [Patterns, Functions, and Algebra Goal 1]		
2	**Use close numbers to estimate.** [Operations and Computation Goal 5]		
3	**Add positive and negative numbers mentally.** [Operations and Computation Goal 1]		
4	**Find equivalent names for numbers.** [Number and Numeration Goal 4]		
Written Assessment Part A			
1, 2	**Relate general patterns and special cases.** [Patterns, Functions, and Algebra Goal 1]		
3–8	**Multiply and divide whole numbers and decimals.** [Operations and Computation Goal 2]		
5	**Estimate products.** [Operations and Computation Goal 5]		
3–6	**Use formulas.** [Measurement and Reference Frames Goal 2]		
7, 9	**Evaluate expressions.** [Patterns, Functions, and Algebra Goal 3]		
8, 9	**Represent fuctions with formulas, tables, and graphs.** [Patterns, Functions, and Algebra Goal 1]		
8, 10–13	**Use and interpret graphs and data landmarks.** [Data and Chance Goal 2]		
Written Assessment Part B			
14, 15	**Find equivalent names for numbers.** [Number and Numeration Goal 4]		
16, 17	**Find the GCF and LCM of a set of numbers.** [Number and Numeration Goal 3]		
18	**Use estimation to insert the decimal point in a quotient.** [Operations and Computation Goal 5]		
19	**Multiply decimals by powers of 10.** [Operations and Computation Goal 2]		
20	**Write a time story based on a graph.** [Data and Chance Goal 2]		

Assess Progress: **A** = adequate progress   **N** = not adequate progress   **N/A** = not assessed   **Formative Assessments**

Class _____

Date _____

Names	3·1	3·2	3·3	3·4	3·5	3·6	3·7	3·8	3·9	3·10
	Write special cases for a general pattern. [Patterns, Functions, and Algebra Goal 1]	Write a general pattern with two variables to represent a special case. [Patterns, Functions, and Algebra Goal 1]	Find decimal solutions to whole-number division problems. [Operations and Computation Goal 2]	Use algebraic notation to describe general patterns. [Patterns, Functions, and Algebra Goal 1]	Complete a table from a formula and graph the data. [Patterns, Functions, and Algebra Goal 1]	Complete a table from a formula and graph the data. [Patterns, Functions, and Algebra Goal 1]	Add positive and negative numbers. [Operations and Computation Goal 1]	Solve open number sentences involving signed numbers. [Operations and Computation Goal 1]	Analyze the shape of a graph and draw conclusions about data trends. [Data and Chance Goal 2]	Name a spreadsheet cell and identify a spreadsheet formula for calculating a total. [Patterns, Functions, and Algebra Goal 1]
1.										
2.										
3.										
4.										
5.										
6.										
7.										
8.										
9.										
10.										
11.										
12.										
13.										
14.										
15.										
16.										
17.										
18.										
19.										
20.										
21.										
22.										
23.										
24.										
25.										

Assess Progress: **A** = adequate progress **N** = not adequate progress **N/A** = not assessed

Class Checklist:
Progress Check 3

Class _____

Date _____

	Oral/Slate					Written Part A									Part B				
Names	1. Give an algebraic expression to represent the situation in a number problem. [Patterns, Functions, and Algebra Goal 1]	2. Use close numbers to estimate. [Operations and Computation Goal 5]	3. Add positive and negative numbers mentally. [Operations and Computation Goal 1]	4. Find equivalent names for numbers. [Number and Numeration Goal 4]		1, 2. Relate general patterns and special cases. [Patterns, Functions, and Algebra Goal 1]	3–8. Multiply and divide whole numbers and decimals. [Operations and Computation Goal 2]	5. Estimate products. [Operations and Computation Goal 5]	3–6. Use formulas. [Measurement and Reference Frames Goal 2]	7, 9. Evaluate expressions. [Patterns, Functions, and Algebra Goal 3]	8, 9. Represent functions with formulas, tables, and graphs. [Patterns, Functions, and Algebra Goal 1]	8, 10–13. Use and interpret graphs and data landmarks. [Data and Chance Goal 2]		14, 15. Find equivalent names for numbers. [Number and Numeration Goal 4]	16, 17. Find the GCF and LCM of a set of numbers. [Number and Numeration Goal 3]	18. Use estimation to insert the decimal point in a quotient. [Operations and Computation Goal 5]	19. Multiply decimals by powers of 10. [Operations and Computation Goal 2]	20. Write a time story based on a graph. [Data and Chance Goal 2]
1.																		
2.																		
3.																		
4.																		
5.																		
6.																		
7.																		
8.																		
9.																		
10.																		
11.																		
12.																		
13.																		
14.																		
15.																		
16.																		
17.																		
18.																		
19.																		
20.																		
21.																		
22.																		
23.																		
24.																		
25.																		

Assess Progress: = adequate progress 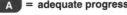 = not adequate progress 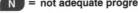 = not assessed **Formative Assessments**

Individual Profile of Progress

Name _____ Date _____

Lesson	Recognizing Student Achievement	A.P.*	Comments
4•1	**Rename fractions in simplest form.** [Number and Numeration Goal 5]		
4•2	**Name the least common multiple (LCM) for a number pair.** [Number and Numeration Goal 3]		
4•3	**Add and subtract fractions with unlike denominators.** [Operations and Computation Goal 3]		
4•4	**Add mixed numbers with like denominators.** [Operations and Computation Goal 3]		
4•5	**Subtract mixed numbers.** [Operations and Computation Goal 3]		
4•6	**Add and subtract fractions with unlike denominators.** [Operations and Computation Goal 3]		
4•7	**Multiply fractions.** [Operations and Computation Goal 4]		
4•8	**Convert between fractions, decimals, and percents.** [Number and Numeration Goal 5]		
4•9	**Multiply a whole number by a fraction to find a fractional part of the number.** [Operations and Computation Goal 4]		
4•10	**Rename fractions as decimals and percents.** [Number and Numeration Goal 5]		
4•11	**Convert between fractions, decimals, and percents.** [Number and Numeration Goal 5]		

***Assess Progress:** **A** = adequate progress   **N** = not adequate progress   **N/A** = not assessed

Go to *www.everydaymathonline.com* for digital checklists.

Individual Profile of Progress

Name _____ Date _____

Problem(s)	Progress Check 4	A.P.*	Comments
Oral/Slate Assessment			
1	**Compare estimated sums of fractions to 1.** [Number and Numeration Goal 6; Operations and Computation Goal 5]		
2	**Decide which product is larger without computing.** [Operations and Computation Goal 5]		
3	**List fractions from least to greatest.** [Number and Numeration Goal 6]		
4	**Calculate percents of numbers.** [Number and Numeration Goal 2]		
Written Assessment Part A			
1, 6	**Write fractions in simplest form.** [Number and Numeration Goal 5]		
2, 5	**Convert between fractions, decimals, and percents.** [Number and Numeration Goal 5]		
3	**Compare fractions with unlike denominators.** [Number and Numeration Goal 6]		
4, 6	**Add and subtract fractions and mixed numbers with unlike denominators.** [Operations and Computation Goal 3]		
7	**Use a diagram to find fractional parts of a region. Find products of fractions and mixed numbers.** [Number and Numeration Goal 2; Operations and Computation Goal 4]		
Written Assessment Part B			
8	**Calculate the percent of a number.** [Number and Numeration Goal 2]		
9	**Use the Percent Circle to construct a circle graph.** [Data and Chance Goal 1]		
10	**Find the perimeter and area of a rectangle.** [Operations and Computation Goals 3 and 4; Measurement and Reference Frames Goal 2]		
11	**Evaluate expressions involving exponents and integers.** [Patterns, Functions, and Algebra Goal 3]		
12	**Divide a decimal number by a whole number.** [Operations and Computation Goal 2]		

*Assess Progress: **A** = adequate progress   **N** = not adequate progress   **N/A** = not assessed   **Formative Assessments**

Go to *www.everydaymathonline.com* for digital checklists.

Class Checklist:
Recognizing Student Achievement

Class _____

Date _____

Names	Rename fractions in simplest form. [Number and Numeration Goal 5] 4•1	Name the least common multiple (LCM) for a number pair. [Number and Numeration Goal 3] 4•2	Add and subtract fractions with unlike denominators. [Operations and Computation Goal 3] 4•3	Add mixed numbers with like denominators. [Operations and Computation Goal 3] 4•4	Subtract mixed numbers. [Operations and Computation Goal 3] 4•5	Add and subtract fractions with unlike denominators. [Operations and Computation Goal 3] 4•6	Multiply fractions. [Operations and Computation Goal 4] 4•7	Convert between fractions, decimals, and percents. [Number and Numeration Goal 5] 4•8	Multiply a whole number by a fraction to find a fractional part of the number. [Operations and Computation Goal 4] 4•9	Rename fractions as decimals and percents. [Number and Numeration Goal 5] 4•10	Convert between fractions, decimals, and percents. [Number and Numeration Goal 5] 4•11
1.											
2.											
3.											
4.											
5.											
6.											
7.											
8.											
9.											
10.											
11.											
12.											
13.											
14.											
15.											
16.											
17.											
18.											
19.											
20.											
21.											
22.											
23.											
24.											
25.											

Assess Progress: **A** = adequate progress   **N** = not adequate progress   **N/A** = not assessed

Class _____

Date _____

Names	Oral/Slate				Written — Part A					Written — Part B				
	1. Compare estimated sums of fractions to 1. [Number and Numeration Goal 6; Operation and Computation Goal 5]	2. Decide which product is larger without computing. [Operations and Computation Goal 5]	3. List fractions from least to greatest. [Number and Numeration Goal 6]	4. Calculate percents of numbers. [Number and Numeration Goal 2]	1, 6. Write fractions in simplest form. [Number and Numeration Goal 5]	2, 5. Convert between fractions, decimals, and percents. [Number and Numeration Goal 5]	3. Compare fractions with unlike denominators. [Number and Numeration Goal 6]	4, 6. Add and subtract fractions and mixed numbers with unlike denominators. [Operations and Computation Goal 3]	7. Use a diagram to find fractional parts of a region. Find products of fractions and mixed numbers. [Number and Numeration Goal 2; Operations and Computation Goal 4]	8. Calculate the percent of a number. [Number and Numeration Goal 2]	9. Use the Percent Circle to construct a circle graph. [Data and Chance Goal 1]	10. Find the perimeter and area of a rectangle. [Operations and Computation Goals 3 and 4; Measurement and Reference Frames Goal 2]	11. Evaluate expressions involving exponents and integers. [Patterns, Functions, and Algebra Goal 3]	12. Divide a decimal number by a whole number. [Operations and Computation Goal 2]
1.														
2.														
3.														
4.														
5.														
6.														
7.														
8.														
9.														
10.														
11.														
12.														
13.														
14.														
15.														
16.														
17.														
18.														
19.														
20.														
21.														
22.														
23.														
24.														
25.														

Assess Progress: **A** = adequate progress **N** = not adequate progress **N/A** = not assessed **Formative Assessments**

Name _____ Date _____

Lesson	Recognizing Student Achievement	A.P.*	Comments
5•1	**Use a half-circle protractor to measure an angle.** [Measurement and Reference Frames Goal 1]		
5•2	**Name, label, and measure angles.** [Measurement and Reference Frames Goal 1; Geometry Goal 1]		
5•3	**Find the measures of supplementary and vertical angles using angle relationships.** [Geometry Goal 1]		
5•4	**Use a strategy for solving problems involving percents and discounts.** [Number and Numeration Goal 2]		
5•5	**Name ordered pairs in the third quadrant of a coordinate grid.** [Measurement and Reference Frames Goal 3]		
5•6	**Rotate a figure and name points on a coordinate grid.** [Measurement and Reference Frames Goal 3; Geometry Goal 3]		
5•7	**Convert between fraction and decimal equivalents.** [Number and Numeration Goal 5]		
5•8	**Add, subtract, and multiply fractions and mixed numbers.** [Operations and Computation Goals 3 and 4]		
5•9	**Determine angle measures by applying the properties of adjacent angles, supplementary angles, and sums of angle measures in triangles and quadrangles.** [Geometry Goal 1]		
5•10	**Calculate the degree measures of the sectors of a circle graph.** [Number and Numeration Goal 2; Measurement and Reference Frames Goal 1]		

*Assess Progress: **A** = adequate progress   **N** = not adequate progress   **N/A** = not assessed

Individual Profile of Progress

Name _____ Date _____

Problem(s)	Progress Check 5	A.P.*	Comments
Oral/Slate Assessment			
1	**Mentally calculate the missing angle measure in triangles and quadrangles.** [Operations and Computation Goal 1; Geometry Goal 1]		
2	**Mentally solve percent problems.** [Number and Numeration Goal 2]		
3	**Draw and label acute, obtuse, right, reflex, straight, adjacent, supplementary, and vertical angles.** [Geometry Goal 1]		
4	**Write decimal and percent equivalencies for fractions.** [Number and Numeration Goal 5]		
Written Assessment Part A			
1–3	**Measure angles to the nearest degree.** [Measurement and Reference Frames Goal 1]		
4	**Translate a figure. Name points on a coordinate grid.** [Measurement and Reference Frames Goal 3; Geometry Goal 3]		
5	**Copy a figure using a compass and straightedge.** [Geometry Goal 2]		
6, 7	**Apply definitions and properties of angles and other figures.** [Operations and Computation Goal 1; Geometry Goal 1]		
8	**Calculate the percent of a number. Create circle graphs.** [Number and Numeration Goal 2; Data and Chance Goal 1]		
Written Assessment Part B			
9–11	**Perform operations with fractions.** [Operations and Computation Goals 3–5]		
12, 13	**Add integers.** [Operations and Computation Goal 1]		
14, 15	**Rename fractions and decimals.** [Number and Numeration Goal 5]		

Copyright © Wright Group/McGraw-Hill

*Assess Progress:  = adequate progress    = not adequate progress    = not assessed   **Formative Assessments**

Go to *www.everydaymathonline.com* for digital checklists.

Class _____

Date _____

Names	5·1	5·2	5·3	5·4	5·5	5·6	5·7	5·8	5·9	5·10
	Use a half-circle protractor to measure an angle. [Measurement and Reference Frames Goal 1]	Name, label, and measure angles. [Measurement and Reference Frames Goal 1; Geometry Goal 1]	Find the measures of supplementary and vertical angles using angle relationships. [Geometry Goal 1]	Use a strategy for solving problems involving percents and discounts. [Numbers and Numeration Goal 2]	Name ordered pairs in the third quadrant of a coordinate grid. [Measurement and Reference Frames Goal 3]	Rotate a figure and name points on a coordinate grid. [Measurement and Reference Frames Goal 3; Geometry Goal 3]	Convert between fraction and decimal equivalents. [Number and Numeration Goal 5]	Add, subtract, and multiply fractions and mixed numbers. [Operations and Computation Goals 3 and 4]	Determine angle measures by applying the properties of adjacent angles, supplementary angles, and sums of angle measures in triangles and quadrangles. [Geometry Goal 1]	Calculate the degree measures of the sectors of a circle graph. [Number and Numeration Goal 2; Measurement and Reference Frames Goal 1]
1.										
2.										
3.										
4.										
5.										
6.										
7.										
8.										
9.										
10.										
11.										
12.										
13.										
14.										
15.										
16.										
17.										
18.										
19.										
20.										
21.										
22.										
23.										
24.										
25.										

Assess Progress: **A** = adequate progress   **N** = not adequate progress   **N/A** = not assessed

Go to *www.everydaymathonline.com* for digital checklists.

Class Checklist:
Progress Check 5

Class _____

Date _____

Names	Oral/Slate				Written Part A					Part B		
	1. Mentally calculate the missing angle measure in triangles and quadrangles. [Operations and Computation Goal 1; Geometry Goal 1]	**2. Mentally solve percent problems.** [Number and Numeration Goal 2]	**3. Draw and label acute, obtuse, right, reflex, straight, adjacent, supplementary, and vertical angles.** [Geometry Goal 1]	**4. Write decimal and percent equivalencies for fractions.** [Number and Numeration Goal 5]	**1–3. Measure angles to the nearest degree.** [Measurement and Reference Frames Goal 1]	**4. Translate a figure. Name points on a coordinate grid.** [Measurement and Reference Frames Goal 3; Geometry Goal 3]	**5. Copy a figure using a compass and straightedge.** [Geometry Goal 2]	**6, 7. Apply definitions and properties of angles and other figures.** [Operations and Computation Goal 1; Geometry Goal 1]	**8. Calculate the percent of a number. Create circle graphs.** [Number and Numeration Goal 2; Data and Chance Goal 1]	**9–11. Perform operations with fractions.** [Operations and Computation Goals 3–5]	**12, 13. Add integers.** [Operations and Computation Goal 1]	**14, 15. Rename fractions and decimals.** [Number and Numeration Goal 5]
1.												
2.												
3.												
4.												
5.												
6.												
7.												
8.												
9.												
10.												
11.												
12.												
13.												
14.												
15.												
16.												
17.												
18.												
19.												
20.												
21.												
22.												
23.												
24.												
25.												

Assess Progress: = adequate progress = not adequate progress **N/A** = not assessed **Formative Assessments**

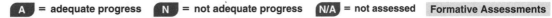

Go to *www.everydaymathonline.com* for digital checklists.

Individual Profile of Progress

Name _____   Date _____

Lesson	Recognizing Student Achievement	A.P.*	Comments
6◆1	**Name and identify the reciprocal of a number.** [Patterns, Functions, and Algebra Goal 4]		
6◆2	**Solve fraction division problems.** [Operations and Computation Goal 4]		
6◆3	**Understand the inverse relationship between addition and subtraction.** [Patterns, Functions, and Algebra Goal 4]		
6◆4	**Calculate and compare sums and differences of signed numbers.** [Operations and Computation Goal 1]		
6◆4a	**Use a formula to find the volume of a rectangular prism.** [Measurement and Reference Frames Goal 2]		
6◆5	**Divide fractions and mixed numbers.** [Operations and Computation Goal 4]		
6◆6	**Evaluate numeric expressions.** [Patterns, Functions, and Algebra Goal 3]		
6◆7	**Apply the order of operations to evaluate numeric expressions.** [Patterns, Functions, and Algebra Goal 3]		
6◆8	**Use trial-and-error or cover-up method to solve equations.** [Patterns, Functions, and Algebra Goal 2]		
6◆9	**Solve equations and check the solutions.** [Patterns, Functions, and Algebra Goal 2]		
6◆10	**Use a pan-balance model to solve an equation.** [Patterns, Functions, and Algebra Goal 2]		
6◆11	**Solve equations and check the solutions.** [Patterns, Functions, and Algebra Goal 2]		
6◆12	**Determine whether inequalities are true or false.** [Patterns, Functions, and Algebra Goal 2]		

*Assess Progress: **A** = adequate progress   **N** = not adequate progress   **N/A** = not assessed

Name _____ Date _____

Problem(s)	Progress Check 6	A.P.*	Comments
Oral/Slate Assessment			
1	**Estimate products and quotients.** [Operations and Computation Goal 5]		
2	**Identify properties of addition and multiplication.** [Patterns, Functions, and Algebra Goal 4]		
3	**Find reciprocals.** [Patterns, Functions, and Algebra Goal 4]		
4	**Mentally solve "percent-of" problems.** [Operations and Computation Goal 2]		
Written Assessment Part A			
1–4	**Divide fractions and mixed numbers.** [Operations and Computation Goal 4]		
5–8	**Add or subtract signed numbers.** [Operations and Computation Goal 1]		
9–12	**Multiply or divide signed numbers.** [Operations and Computation Goal 2]		
13–16	**Compare signed numbers.** [Numbers and Numeration Goal 6]		
13–17, 22–27	**Tell whether inequalities are true or false. Solve equations.** [Patterns, Functions, and Algebra Goal 2]		
13, 15, 17	**Apply properties of arithmetic.** [Patterns, Functions, and Algebra Goal 4]		
18–21	**Apply order of operations.** [Patterns, Functions, and Algebra Goal 3]		
Written Assessment Part B			
28, 29	**Graph the solution set of an inequality.** [Patterns, Functions, and Algebra Goal 2]		
30	**Complete a table for a given rule and graph the results.** [Patterns, Functions, and Algebra Goal 1]		
31	**Identify corresponding sides and angles.** [Geometry Goal 2]		
32	**Estimate and find quotients.** [Operations and Computation Goals 2 and 5]		

*Assess Progress: **A** = adequate progress   **N** = not adequate progress   **N/A** = not assessed Formative Assessments

Go to *www.everydaymathonline.com* for digital checklists.

Class Checklist:
Recognizing Student Achievement

Class _____

Date _____

Names	Name and identify the reciprocal of a number. [Patterns, Functions, and Algebra Goal 4] 6•1	Solve fraction division problems. [Operations and Computation Goal 4] 6•2	Understand the inverse relationship between addition and subtraction. [Patterns, Functions, and Algebra Goal 4] 6•3	Calculate and compare sums and differences of signed numbers. [Operations and Computation Goal 1] 6•4	Use a formula to find the volume of a rectangular prism. [Measurement and Reference Frames Goal 2] 6•4a	Divide fractions and mixed numbers. [Operations and Computation Goal 4] 6•5	Evaluate numeric expressions. [Patterns, Functions, and Algebra Goal 4] 6•6	Apply the order of operations to evaluate numeric expressions. [Patterns, Functions, and Algebra Goal 3] 6•7	Use trial-and-error or cover-up method to solve equations. [Patterns, Functions, and Algebra Goal 3] 6•8	Solve equations and check the solutions. [Patterns, Functions, and Algebra Goal 2] 6•9	Use a pan-balance model to solve an equation. [Patterns, Functions, and Algebra Goal 2] 6•10	Solve equations and check the solutions. [Patterns, Functions, and Algebra Goal 2] 6•11	Determine whether inequalities are true or false. [Patterns, Functions, and Algebra Goal 2] 6•12
1.													
2.													
3.													
4.													
5.													
6.													
7.													
8.													
9.													
10.													
11.													
12.													
13.													
14.													
15.													
16.													
17.													
18.													
19.													
20.													
21.													
22.													
23.													
24.													
25.													

Assess Progress: **A** = adequate progress   **N** = not adequate progress   **N/A** = not assessed

Go to *www.everydaymathonline.com* for digital checklists.

Names	Oral/Slate				Written Part A								Part B			
	1. Estimate products and quotients. [Operations and Computation Goal 5]	2. Identify properties of addition and multiplication. [Patterns, Functions, and Algebra Goal 4]	3. Find reciprocals. [Patterns, Functions, and Algebra Goal 4]	4. Mentally solve "percent-of" problems. [Operations and Computation Goal 2]	1–4. Divide fractions and mixed numbers. [Operations and Computation Goal 4]	5–8. Add or subtract signed numbers. [Operations and Computation Goal 1]	9–12. Multiply or divide signed numbers. [Operations and Computation Goal 2]	13–16. Compare signed numbers. [Number and Numeration Goal 6]	13–17, 22–27. Tell whether inequalities are true or false. Solve equations. [Patterns, Functions, and Algebra Goal 2]	13, 15, 17. Apply properties of arithmetic. [Patterns, Functions, and Algebra Goal 4]	18–21. Apply order of operations. [Patterns, Functions, and Algebra Goal 3]	28, 29. Graph the solution set of an inequality. [Patterns, Functions, and Algebra Goal 2]	30. Complete a table for a given rule and graph the results. [Patterns, Functions, and Algebra Goal 1]	31. Identify corresponding sides and angles. [Geometry Goal 2]	32. Estimate and find quotients. [Operations and Computation Goals 2 and 5]
1.															
2.															
3.															
4.															
5.															
6.															
7.															
8.															
9.															
10.															
11.															
12.															
13.															
14.															
15.															
16.															
17.															
18.															
19.															
20.															
21.															
22.															
23.															
24.															
25.															

Class _____

Date _____

Assess Progress: **A** = adequate progress   **N** = not adequate progress   **N/A** = not assessed   **Formative Assessments**

Copyright © Wright Group/McGraw-Hill

Lesson	Recognizing Student Achievement	A.P.*	Comments
7•1	**Identify outcomes and calculate probabilities.** [Data and Chance Goal 3]		
7•2	**Understand how sample size affects outcomes.** [Data and Chance Goal 3]		
7•3	**Solve equations using a trial and error method.** [Patterns, Functions, and Algebra Goal 2]		
7•4	**Calculate probabilities.** [Data and Chance Goal 3]		
7•5	**Determine expected outcomes and use a tree diagram to calculate probabilities of chance events.** [Data and Chance Goal 3]		
7•6	**Calculate probabilities, and use a tree diagram to find the probability of a compound event.** [Data and Chance Goal 3]		
7•7	**Use a tree diagram to calculate probabilities.** [Data and Chance Goal 3]		
7•8	**Calculate probabilities and determine expected outcomes for chance events.** [Data and Chance Goal 3]		

*Assess Progress: **A** = adequate progress **N** = not adequate progress **N/A** = not assessed

Name _____ Date _____

Problem(s)	Progress Check 7	A.P.	Comments
Oral/Slate Assessment			
1	**Determine whether inequalities are true or false.** [Patterns, Functions, and Algebra Goal 2]		
2	**Mentally calculate products of fractions and whole numbers.** [Operations and Computation Goal 4]		
3	**Rename fractions as decimals and percents.** [Number and Numeration Goal 5]		
4	**Translate between number-and-word and standard notation.** [Number and Numeration Goal 1]		
Written Assessment Part A			
1–3, 5–7, 11	**Calculate probabilities of outcomes.** [Data and Chance Goal 3]		
3, 5–7	**Convert between fractions, decimals, and percents.** [Number and Numeration Goal 5]		
4	**Distinguish between expected outcomes and actual results.** [Data and Chance Goal 3]		
9, 10	**Make and use probability tree diagrams.** [Data and Chance Goal 3]		
9, 11	**Multiply fractions and whole numbers.** [Operations and Computation Goal 4]		
8, 12	**Determine expected outcomes.** [Operations and Computation Goal 2; Data and Chance Goal 3]		
13	**Determine fairness in games.** [Data and Chance Goal 3]		
Written Assessment Part B			
14–17	**Interpret Venn diagrams.** [Data and Chance Goal 1]		
18	**Find the area of squares and circles.** [Operations and Computation Goal 2; Data and Chance Goal 3]		
19, 20	**Solve equations and check solutions.** [Patterns, Functions, and Algebra Goal 2]		

Copyright © Wright Group/McGraw-Hill

*Assess Progress: **A** = adequate progress **N** = not adequate progress **N/A** = not assessed **Formative Assessments**

Class _____

Date _____

Names	Identify outcomes and calculate probabilities. [Data and Chance Goal 3] 7•1	Understand how sample size affects outcomes. [Data and Chance Goal 3] 7•2	Solve equations using a trial and error method. [Patterns, Functions, and Algebra Goal 2] 7•3	Calculate probabilities. [Data and Chance Goal 3] 7•4	Determine expected outcomes and use a tree diagram to calculate probabilities of chance events. [Data and Chance Goal 3] 7•5	Calculate probabilities and use a tree diagram to find the probability of a compound event. [Data and Chance Goal 3] 7•6	Use a tree diagram to calculate probabilities. [Data and Chance Goal 3] 7•7	Caculate probabilities for chance events and determine expected outcomes [Data and Chance Goal 3] 7•8
1.								
2.								
3.								
4.								
5.								
6.								
7.								
8.								
9.								
10.								
11.								
12.								
13.								
14.								
15.								
16.								
17.								
18.								
19.								
20.								
21.								
22.								
23.								
24.								
25.								

Assess Progress: **A** = adequate progress   **N** = not adequate progress   **N/A** = not assessed

Class _____

Date _____

Names	Oral/Slate				Written Part A							Part B		
	1. Determine whether inequalities are true or false. [Patterns, Functions, and Algebra Goal 2]	2. Mentally calculate products of fractions and whole numbers. [Operations and Computation Goal 4]	3. Rename fractions as decimals and percents. [Number and Numeration Goal 5]	4. Translate between number-and-word and standard notation. [Number and Numeration Goal 1]	1–3, 5–7, 11. Calculate probabilities of outcomes. [Data and Chance Goal 3]	3, 5–7. Convert between fractions, decimals, and percents. [Number and Numeration Goal 5]	4. Distinguish between expected outcomes and actual results. [Data and Chance Goal 3]	9, 10. Make and use probability tree diagrams. [Data and Chance Goal 3]	9, 11. Multiply fractions and whole numbers. [Operations and Computation Goal 4]	8, 12. Determine expected outcomes. [Operations and Computation Goal 2; Data and Chance Goal 3]	13. Determine fairness in games. [Data and Chance Goal 3]	14–17. Interpret Venn diagrams. [Data and Chance Goal 1]	18. Find the area of squares and circles. [Operations and Computation Goal 2; Data and Chance Goal 3]	19, 20. Solve equations and check solutions. [Patterns, Functions, and Algebra Goal 2]
1.														
2.														
3.														
4.														
5.														
6.														
7.														
8.														
9.														
10.														
11.														
12.														
13.														
14.														
15.														
16.														
17.														
18.														
19.														
20.														
21.														
22.														
23.														
24.														
25.														

Copyright © Wright Group/McGraw-Hill

Assess Progress: 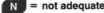 **A** = adequate progress **N** = not adequate progress **N/A** = not assessed **Formative Assessments**

Individual Profile of Progress

Name _____ Date _____

Lesson	Recognizing Student Achievement	A.P.*	Comments
8◆1	**Apply the per-unit-rate and rate-table methods to solve problems.** [Patterns, Functions, and Algebra Goal 1]		
8◆2	**Use proportions to model, summarize, and solve rate problems.** [Operations and Computation Goal 6]		
8◆3	**Use cross products to write an open number sentence.** [Operations and Computation Goal 6]		
8◆4	**Use unit rates, rate tables, or proportions to solve simple rate problems.** [Operations and Computation Goal 6]		
8◆5	**Use proportions to model and solve rate problems.** [Operations and Computation Goal 6]		
8◆6	**Use proportions to model and solve ratio problems.** [Operations and Computation Goal 6]		
8◆7	**Use open proportions to solve percent problems.** [Operations and Computation Goal 6]		
8◆8	**Express ratios as fractions and percents.** [Number and Numeration Goal 5]		
8◆9	**Measure line segments to the nearest $\frac{1}{16}$ inch.** [Measurement and Reference Frames Goal 1]		
8◆10	**Use ratios to solve problems involving similar polygons.** [Operations and Computation Goal 6]		
8◆11	**Use fraction equivalents or proportions to solve "percent-of" problems.** [Number and Numeration Goal 2]		
8◆12	**Find corresponding side lengths of similar polygons and use proportions to find the length of the unknown side.** [Operations and Computation Goal 6]		

*Assess Progress: **A** = adequate progress   **N** = not adequate progress   **N/A** = not assessed

Name _____ Date _____

Problem(s)	Progress Check 8	A.P.*	Comments
Oral/Slate Assessment			
1	**Estimate equivalent percents for fractions.** [Number and Numeration Goal 5]		
2	**Name the reciprocal of numbers.** [Patterns, Functions, and Algebra Goal 4]		
3	**Use <, >, or = to compare ratios.** [Number and Numeration Goal 6]		
4	**Find the unit whole when a fractional part is given.** [Number and Numeration Goal 2]		
Written Assessment Part A			
1–5	**Use rate tables and unit rates to solve problems.** [Patterns, Functions, and Algebra Goal 1]		
6–15	**Write and solve open proportions.** [Operations and Computation Goal 6]		
14–16, 19–20	**Solve percent problems.** [Number and Numeration Goal 2]		
17–18, 21–23	**Set up and solve ratio problems.** [Operations and Computation Goal 6]		
23	**Apply properties of similar figures.** [Geometry Goal 2]		
23	**Use a size-change factor to solve problems.** [Operations and Computation Goal 6]		
Written Assessment Part B			
24–26	**Evaluate expressions using order of operations.** [Patterns, Functions, and Algebra Goal 3]		
25–26	**Solve perimeter and area problems.** [Measurement and Reference Frames Goal 2]		
27–28	**Divide with decimals.** [Operations and Computation Goal 2]		

*Assess Progress: **A** = adequate progress **N** = not adequate progress **N/A** = not assessed Formative Assessments

Class Checklist:
Recognizing Student Achievement

Class _____

Date _____

Names	Apply the per-unit-rate and rate-table methods to solve problems. [Patterns, Functions, and Algebra Goal 1]	Use proportions to model, summarize, and solve rate problems. [Operations and Computation Goal 6]	Use cross products to write an open number sentence. [Operations and Computation Goal 6]	Use unit rates, rate tables, or proportions to solve simple rate problems. [Operations and Computation Goal 6]	Use proportions to solve [Operations and Computation Goal 6]	Use proportions to model and solve rate problems. [Operations and Computation Goal 6]	Use open proportions to model and solve ratio problems. [Operations and Computation Goal 6]	Use open proportions to solve percent problems. [Operations and Computation Goal 6]	Express ratios as fractions and percents. [Number and Numeration Goal 5]	Measure line segments to the nearest $\frac{1}{16}$ inch. [Measurement and Reference Frames Goal 1]	Use ratios to solve problems involving similar polygons. [Operations and Computation Goal 6]	Use fraction equivalents or proportions to solve "percent-of" problems. [Number and Numeration Goal 2]	Find corresponding side lengths of similar polygons and use proportions to find the length of the unknown sides. [Operations and Computation Goal 6]
	8•1	8•2	8•3	8•4	8•5	8•6	8•7	8•8	8•9	8•10	8•11	8•12	
1.													
2.													
3.													
4.													
5.													
6.													
7.													
8.													
9.													
10.													
11.													
12.													
13.													
14.													
15.													
16.													
17.													
18.													
19.													
20.													
21.													
22.													
23.													
24.													
25.													

Assess Progress:　**A** = adequate progress　**N** = not adequate progress　**N/A** = not assessed

Class Checklist:
Progress Check 8

Class _____

Date _____

Names	Oral/Slate				Written Part A						Part B		
	1. Estimate equivalent percents for fractions. [Number and Numeration Goal 5]	2. Name the reciprocal of numbers. [Patterns, Functions, and Algebra Goal 4]	3. Use <, >, or = to compare ratios. [Number and Numeration Goal 6]	4. Find the unit whole when a fractional part is given. [Number and Numeration Goal 2]	1–5. Use rate tables and unit rates to solve problems. [Patterns, Functions, and Algebra Goal 1]	6–15. Write and solve open proportions. [Operations and Computation Goal 6]	14–16, 19–20. Solve percent problems. [Number and Numeration Goal 2]	17–18, 21–23. Set up and solve ratio problems. [Operations and Computation Goal 6]	23. Apply properties of similar figures. [Geometry Goal 2]	23. Use a size-change factor to solve problems. [Operations and Computation Goal 6]	24–26. Evaluate expressions using order of operations. [Patterns, Functions, and Algebra Goal 3]	25–26. Solve perimeter and area problems. [Measurement and Reference Frames Goal 2]	27–28. Divide with decimals. [Operations and Computation Goal 2]
1.													
2.													
3.													
4.													
5.													
6.													
7.													
8.													
9.													
10.													
11.													
12.													
13.													
14.													
15.													
16.													
17.													
18.													
19.													
20.													
21.													
22.													
23.													
24.													
25.													

Assess Progress: **A** = adequate progress   **N** = not adequate progress   **N/A** = not assessed   **Formative Assessments**

Go to *www.everydaymathonline.com* for digital checklists.

Name _____   Date _____

Lesson	Recognizing Student Achievement	A.P.*	Comments
9◆1	**Use a trial-and-error strategy to solve for an unknown value.** [Patterns, Functions, and Algebra Goal 2]		
9◆2	**Find the total number of objects in a set when a fractional part of the set is given.** [Number and Numeration Goal 2]		
9◆3	**Solve equations and check the solution using substitution.** [Patterns, Functions, and Algebra Goal 2]		
9◆4	**Write an expression for an area model and then evaluate that expression for a given value.** [Patterns, Functions, and Algebra Goal 3]		
9◆5	**Simplify equations and recognize equivalent equations.** [Patterns, Functions, and Algebra Goal 2]		
9◆6	**Use a distributive strategy to mentally calculate quotients.** [Operations and Computation Goal 2]		
9◆7	**Evaluate algebraic expressions using order of operations.** [Patterns, Functions, and Algebra Goal 3]		
9◆8	**Apply area formulas.** [Measurement and Reference Frames Goal 2]		
9◆9	**Simplify and solve equations.** [Patterns, Functions, and Algebra Goal 2]		
9◆10	**Use a trial-and-error method to approximate solutions of equations.** [Patterns, Functions, and Algebra Goal 2]		
9◆11	**Substitute known values in appropriate formulas and then solve the resulting equations.** [Patterns, Functions, and Algebra Goal 2]		
9◆12	**Use the appropriate formula to solve an area problem.** [Measurement and Reference Frames Goal 2]		
9◆13	**Apply a size-change factor to find missing lengths of similar figures.** [Operations and Computation Goal 6]		

*Assess Progress: **A** = adequate progress   **N** = not adequate progress   **N/A** = not assessed

Individual Profile of Progress

Name _____ Date _____

Problem(s)	Progress Check 9	A.P.*	Comments
Oral/Slate Assessment			
1	**Apply the distributive property to mentally calculate products.** [Patterns, Functions, and Algebra Goal 4]		
2	**Use calculators to evaluate expressions.** [Patterns, Functions, and Algebra Goal 3]		
3	**Find the whole when a fractional part or a percent is given.** [Number and Numeration Goal 2]		
4	**Simplify expressions by combining like terms.** [Patterns, Functions, and Algebra Goal 3]		
Written Assessment Part A			
1–2, 13, 14	**Apply distributive strategies to solve problems.** [Patterns, Functions, and Algebra Goal 4]		
2–4, 6, 13–15	**Solve equations. Identify equivalent equations.** [Patterns, Functions, and Algebra Goal 2]		
5, 7–11	**Use formulas to solve for an unknown.** [Measurement and Reference Frames Goal 2; Patterns, Functions, and Algebra Goal 3]		
12	**Use a size-change factor to solve problems.** [Operations and Computation Goal 6; Geometry Goal 2; Measurement and Reference Frames Goal 2]		
Written Assessment Part B			
16	**Solve ratio problems.** [Operations and Computation Goal 6]		
17	**Determine angle measures by applying orientation of angles.** [Geometry Goal 1]		
18–19	**Evaluate expressions using order of operations.** [Patterns, Functions, and Algebra Goal 3]		
20	**Translate between function representations.** [Patterns, Functions, and Algebra Goal 1]		

*Assess Progress: **A** = adequate progress   **N** = not adequate progress   **N/A** = not assessed   Formative Assessments

Class Checklist:
Recognizing Student Achievement

Class _____

Date _____

Names	9•1 Use a trial-and-error strategy to solve for an unknown value. [Patterns, Functions, and Algebra Goal 2]	9•2 Find the total number of objects in a set when a part of the set is given. [Number and Numeration Goal 2]	9•3 Solve equations and check the solution using substitution. [Patterns, Functions, and Algebra Goal 2]	9•4 Write an expression for an area model and then evaluate that expression for a given value. [Patterns, Functions, and Algebra Goal 2]	9•5 Simplify equations and recognize equivalent equations. [Patterns, Functions, and Algebra Goal 3]	9•6 Use a distributive strategy to mentally calculate quotients. [Operations and Computation Goal 2]	9•7 Evaluate algebraic expressions using order of operations. [Patterns, Functions, and Algebra Goal 3]	9•8 Apply area formulas. [Measurement and Reference Frames Goal 2]	9•9 Simplify and solve equations. [Patterns, Functions, and Algebra Goal 2]	9•10 Use a trial-and-error method to approximate solutions of equations. [Patterns, Functions, and Algebra Goal 2]	9•11 Substitute known values in appropriate formulas and then solve the resulting equations. [Patterns, Functions, and Algebra Goal 2]	9•12 Use the appropriate formula to solve an area problem. [Measurement and Reference Frames Goal 2]	9•13 Apply a size-change factor to find missing lengths of similar figures. [Operations and Computation Goal 6]
1.													
2.													
3.													
4.													
5.													
6.													
7.													
8.													
9.													
10.													
11.													
12.													
13.													
14.													
15.													
16.													
17.													
18.													
19.													
20.													
21.													
22.													
23.													
24.													
25.													

Assess Progress: **A** = adequate progress **N** = not adequate progress **N/A** = not assessed

Go to *www.everydaymathonline.com* for digital checklists.

Names	Oral/Slate				Written Part A				Part B			
	1. Apply the distributive property to mentally calculate products. [Patterns, Functions, and Algebra Goal 4]	2. Use calculators to evaluate expressions. [Patterns, Functions, and Algebra Goal 3]	3. Find the whole when a fractional part or a percent is given. [Number and Numeration Goal 2]	4. Simplify expressions by combining like terms. [Patterns, Functions, and Algebra Goal 3]	1–2, 13, 14. Apply distributive strategies to solve problems. [Patterns, Functions, and Algebra Goal 4]	2–4, 6, 13–15. Solve equations. Identify equivalent equations. [Patterns, Functions, and Algebra Goal 2]	5, 7–11. Use formulas to solve for an unknown. [Measurement and Reference Frames Goal 2; Patterns, Functions, and Algebra Goal 3]	12. Use a size-change factor to solve problems. [Operations and Computation Goal 6; Geometry Goal 2; Measurement and Reference Frames Goal 2]	16. Solve ratio problems. [Operations and Computation Goal 6]	17. Determine angle measures by applying orientation of angles. [Geometry Goal 1]	18–19. Evaluate expressions using order of operations. [Patterns, Functions, and Algebra Goal 3]	20. Translate between function representations. [Patterns, Functions, and Algebra Goal 1]
1.												
2.												
3.												
4.												
5.												
6.												
7.												
8.												
9.												
10.												
11.												
12.												
13.												
14.												
15.												
16.												
17.												
18.												
19.												
20.												
21.												
22.												
23.												
24.												
25.												

Class _____

Date _____

Assess Progress: **A** = adequate progress **N** = not adequate progress   **N/A** = not assessed   Formative Assessments

Go to *www.everydaymathonline.com* for digital checklists.

Individual Profile of Progress

Name _____ Date _____

Lesson	Recognizing Student Achievement	A.P.*	Comments
10◆1	**Apply the definitions of supplementary and vertical angles.** [Geometry Goal 1]		
10◆2	**Compare rational numbers.** [Number and Numeration Goal 6]		
10◆3	**Apply properties of angle orientations.** [Geometry Goal 1]		
10◆4	**Apply order of operations to write numerical expressions for rational numbers.** [Number and Numeration Goal 4]		
10◆5	**Identify instances of reflection and rotation symmetry.** [Geometry Goal 3]		

Assess Progress: **A** = adequate progress **N** = not adequate progress **N/A** = not assessed

Go to *www.everydaymathonline.com* for digital checklists.

Name _____   Date _____

Problem(s)	Progress Check 10	A.P.*	Comments
Oral/Slate Assessment			
1	Convert numbers dictated in number-and-word notation to standard notation. [Number and Numeration Goal 1]		
2	Use dot paper or geoboards to demonstrate and describe the difference between similar and congruent figures. [Geometry Goal 2]		
3	Convert between scientific and standard notations. [Number and Numeration Goal 1]		
4	Estimate products and quotients of decimal numbers. [Operations and Computation Goal 5]		
Written Assessment Part A			
1, 2, 4	Apply properties of orientations of angles and sums of angle measures in triangles to determine angle measures. [Geometry Goal 1]		
3, 5	Identify and describe instances of translations, reflections, and rotations. [Geometry Goal 3]		
4	Write and solve equations. [Patterns, Functions, and Algebra Goal 2]		
6	Recognize topological equivalence. [Geometry Goal 2]		
Written Assessment Part B			
7a	Write an expression for the perimeter of a figure. [Patterns, Functions, and Algebra Goal 1; Measurement and Reference Frames Goal 2]		
7b	Use a formula to write an expression. [Patterns, Functions, and Algebra Goal 2; Measurement and Reference Frames Goal 2]		
8–10	Apply order of operations to simplify expressions. [Patterns, Functions, and Algebra Goal 3]		

*Assess Progress: = adequate progress    = not adequate progress    = not assessed   **Formative Assessments**

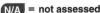

Class Checklist:
Recognizing Student Achievement

Class _____

Date _____

Names	Apply the definitions of supplementary and vertical angles. [Geometry Goal 1]	Compare rational numbers. [Number and Numeration Goal 6]	Apply properties of angle orientations. [Geometry Goal 1]	Apply order of operations to write numerical expressions for rational numbers. [Number and Numeration Goal 4]	Identify instances of reflection and rotation symmetry. [Geometry Goal 3]
	10·1	10·2	10·3	10·4	10·5
1.					
2.					
3.					
4.					
5.					
6.					
7.					
8.					
9.					
10.					
11.					
12.					
13.					
14.					
15.					
16.					
17.					
18.					
19.					
20.					
21.					
22.					
23.					
24.					
25.					

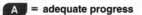 **Assess Progress:** **A** = adequate progress   **N** = not adequate progress   **N/A** = not assessed

 Go to *www.everydaymathonline.com* for digital checklists.

Class _____

Date _____

Names	Oral/Slate				Written Part A				Written Part B		
	1. Convert numbers dictated in number-and-word notation to standard notation. [Number and Numeration Goal 1]	2. Use dot paper or geoboards to demonstrate and describe the difference between similar and congruent figures. [Geometry Goal 2]	3. Convert between scientific and standard notations. [Number and Numeration Goal 1]	4. Estimate products and quotients of decimal numbers. [Operations and Computation Goal 5]	1, 2, 4. Apply properties of orientations of angles and sums of angle measures in triangles to determine angle measures. [Geometry Goal 1]	3, 5. Identify and describe instances of translations, reflections, and rotations. [Geometry Goal 3]	4. Write and solve equations. [Patterns, Functions, and Algebra Goal 2]	6. Recognize topological equivalence. [Geometry Goal 2]	7a. Write an expression for the perimeter of a figure. [Patterns, Functions, and Algebra Goal 1; Measurement and Reference Frames Goal 2]	7b. Use a formula to write an expression. [Patterns, Functions, and Algebra Goal 2; Measurement and Reference Frames Goal 2]	8–10. Apply order of operations to simplify expressions. [Patterns, Functions, and Algebra Goal 3]
1.											
2.											
3.											
4.											
5.											
6.											
7.											
8.											
9.											
10.											
11.											
12.											
13.											
14.											
15.											
16.											
17.											
18.											
19.											
20.											
21.											
22.											
23.											
24.											
25.											

Assess Progress:  **A** = adequate progress **N** = not adequate progress **N/A** = not assessed **Formative Assessments**

Go to *www.everydaymathonline.com* for digital checklists.

Quarterly Checklist: Quarter 1

Section	Number and Numeration							Operations and Computation								Data and Chance						
Goal	1	6	1	1	1	1	1	2	5	2	2	2	2	1	1	2	2	2	1	2	2	1
Lesson	2·1	2·2	2·3	2·4	2·9	2·10	2·11	1·1	2·5	2·6	2·7	2·8	3·3	3·7	3·8	1·2	1·3	1·4	1·5	1·5	1·5a	1·6
Date																						
Names																						
1.																						
2.																						
3.																						
4.																						
5.																						
6.																						
7.																						
8.																						
9.																						
10.																						
11.																						
12.																						
13.																						
14.																						
15.																						
16.																						
17.																						
18.																						
19.																						
20.																						
21.																						
22.																						

Quarterly Checklist: Quarter 1

Names	Data and Chance cont.						Measurement and Reference Frames	Geometry	Patterns, Functions, and Algebra					
Goal	1	1	2	2	2	2	1		1	1	1	1	1	1
Lesson	1·7	1·8	1·10	1·11	1·12	3·9	1·9		3·1	3·2	3·4	3·5	3·6	3·10
Date														
1.														
2.														
3.														
4.														
5.														
6.														
7.														
8.														
9.														
10.														
11.														
12.														
13.														
14.														
15.														
16.														
17.														
18.														
19.														
20.														
21.														
22.														

Quarterly Checklist: Quarter 2

Names	Goal / Lesson / Date																	
		Number and Numeration								**Operations and Computation**								**Data and Chance**
	Goal	5	3	5	5	5	2	5	2	3	3	3	4	4	4	3	4	
	Lesson	4·1	4·2	4·8	4·10	4·11	5·4	5·7	5·10	4·3	4·4	4·5	4·6	4·7	4·9	5·8	5·8	
	Date																	
1.																		
2.																		
3.																		
4.																		
5.																		
6.																		
7.																		
8.																		
9.																		
10.																		
11.																		
12.																		
13.																		
14.																		
15.																		
16.																		
17.																		
18.																		
19.																		
20.																		
21.																		
22.																		

Quarterly Checklist: Quarter 2

Names	Measurement and Reference Frames				Geometry			Patterns, Functions, and Algebra
Goal	1	1	3	3	1	1	3	1	
Lesson	5•1	5•2	5•5	5•6	5•10	5•2	5•3	5•6	5•9	
Date										
1.										
2.										
3.										
4.										
5.										
6.										
7.										
8.										
9.										
10.										
11.										
12.										
13.										
14.										
15.										
16.										
17.										
18.										
19.										
20.										
21.										
22.										

Quarterly Checklist: Quarter 3

Names	Number and Numeration			Operations and Computation			Data and Chance									
Goal				4	1	4	3	3	3	3	3	3	3			
Lesson				6∙2	6∙4	6∙5	7∙1	7∙2	7∙4	7∙5	7∙6	7∙7	7∙8			
Date																
1.																
2.																
3.																
4.																
5.																
6.																
7.																
8.																
9.																
10.																
11.																
12.																
13.																
14.																
15.																
16.																
17.																
18.																
19.																
20.																
21.																
22.																

Quarterly Checklist: Quarter 3

	Measurement and Reference Frames	Geometry	Patterns, Functions, and Algebra									
Goal	2		4	4	3	3	2	2	2	2	2	2
Lesson	6·4a		6·1	6·3	6·6	6·7	6·8	6·9	6·10	6·11	6·12	7·3
Date												
Names												
1.												
2.												
3.												
4.												
5.												
6.												
7.												
8.												
9.												
10.												
11.												
12.												
13.												
14.												
15.												
16.												
17.												
18.												
19.												
20.												
21.												
22.												

Quarterly Checklist: Quarter 4

Names	Goal																
	Number and Numeration					**Operations and Computation**									**Data and Chance**		
	5	2	2	6	4	6	6	6	6	6	6	6	2	6			
Lesson	8·8	8·11	9·2	10·2	10·4	8·2	8·3	8·4	8·5	8·6	8·7	8·10	8·12	9·6	9·13		
Date																	
1.																	
2.																	
3.																	
4.																	
5.																	
6.																	
7.																	
8.																	
9.																	
10.																	
11.																	
12.																	
13.																	
14.																	
15.																	
16.																	
17.																	
18.																	
19.																	
20.																	
21.																	
22.																	

Quarterly Checklist: Quarter 4

Names	Measurement and Reference Frames			Geometry			Patterns, Functions, and Algebra								
Goal	1	2	2	1	1	3	1	2	2	3	2	3	2	2	2
Lesson	8·9	9·8	9·12	10·1	10·3	10·5	8·1	9·1	9·3	9·4	9·5	9·7	9·9	9·10	9·11
Date															
1.															
2.															
3.															
4.															
5.															
6.															
7.															
8.															
9.															
10.															
11.															
12.															
13.															
14.															
15.															
16.															
17.															
18.															
19.															
20.															
21.															
22.															

Individual Profile of Progress

Name _____   Date _____

Lesson	Recognizing Student Achievement	A.P.*	Comments

*Assess Progress:  = adequate progress  = not adequate progress  = not assessed

Class _____

Date _____

Names								
1.								
2.								
3.								
4.								
5.								
6.								
7.								
8.								
9.								
10.								
11.								
12.								
13.								
14.								
15.								
16.								
17.								
18.								
19.								
20.								
21.								
22.								
23.								
24.								
25.								

Assess Progress:  **A** = adequate progress   **N** = not adequate progress   **N/A** = not assessed

Evaluating My Math Class

Interest Inventory

Dislike a Lot 1	Dislike 2	Neither Like nor Dislike 3	Like 4	Like a Lot 5

Use the scale above to describe how you feel about:

1. your math class.   _____

2. working with a partner or in a group.   _____

3. working by yourself.   _____

4. solving problems.   _____

5. making up problems for others to solve.   _____

6. finding new ways to solve problems.   _____

7. challenges in math class.   _____

8. playing mathematical games.   _____

9. working on Study Links.   _____

10. working on projects that take
    more than a day to complete.   _____

11. Which math lesson has been your favorite so far? Why?

_____

_____

_____

_____

_____

_____

_____

My Math Class

Interest Inventory

1. In math class, I am good at _____

   _____

   _____

   _____

2. One thing I like about math is _____

   _____

   _____

   _____

3. One thing I find difficult in mathematics class is _____

   _____

   _____

   _____

4. The most interesting thing I have learned in math so far this year is _____

   _____

   _____

   _____

5. Outside school, I used mathematics when I _____

   _____

   _____

   _____

6. I would like to know more about _____

   _____

   _____

   _____

Weekly Math Log

1. What did you study in math this week?

_____

_____

_____

_____

_____

_____

2. Many ideas in math are related to other ideas within math. Think about how the topic(s) you studied in class this week relate to other topics you learned before.

Your reflection can include what you learned in previous years.

_____

_____

_____

_____

_____

_____

_____

_____

_____

_____

Name _____ Date _____

Math Log

_____
_____
_____
_____
_____
_____
_____
_____
_____
_____
_____
_____

Number-Story Math Log

1. Write an easy number story that uses mathematical ideas that you have studied recently. Solve the problem.

Number Story _____

_____

_____

_____

_____

_____

Solution _____

_____

_____

_____

_____

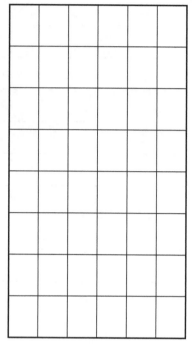

2. Write a difficult number story that uses mathematical ideas that you have studied recently. If you can, solve the number story. If you are not able to solve it, explain what you need to know to solve it.

Number Story _____

_____

_____

_____

_____

_____

Solution _____

_____

_____

_____

_____

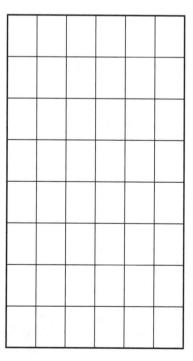

Sample Math Work

Attach a sample of your work to this form.

1. This work is an example of:

_____

_____

_____

_____

_____

_____

2. This work shows that I can:

_____

_____

_____

_____

_____

_____

OPTIONAL

3. This work shows that I still need to improve:

_____

_____

_____

_____

_____

_____

Discussion of My Math Work

Attach a sample of your work to this page. Tell what you think is important about your sample.

_____

_____

_____

_____

_____

_____

_____

_____

_____

_____

_____

_____

_____

_____

_____

_____

_____

_____

_____

_____

_____

_____

Exit Slip

283

✂ -

Exit Slip

Parent Reflections

Use some of the following questions (or your own) and tell us how you see your child progressing in mathematics.

Do you see evidence of your child using mathematics at home?

What do you think are your child's strengths and challenges in mathematics?

Does your child demonstrate responsibility for completing Study Links?

What thoughts do you have about your child's progress in mathematics?

_____

_____

_____

_____

_____

_____

_____

_____

_____

_____

_____

_____

_____

_____

_____

_____

Glossary

Assessment Management Spreadsheets
Digital versions of the Class Checklists and Individual Profiles of Progress that help teachers track student and class progress toward Grade-Level Goals and Common Core State Standards.

Class Checklists Recording tools that can be used to keep track of a class's progress on specific Grade-Level Goals.

Content for Assessment Material that is important for students to learn and is the focus of assessment. *Everyday Mathematics* highlights this content through Grade-Level Goals.

Contexts for Assessment Ongoing, periodic, and external assessments based on products or observations.

Enrichment Activities Optional activities that apply or deepen students' understanding.

Evidence from Assessment Information about student knowledge, skills, and dispositions collected from observations or products.

External Assessments Assessments that are independent of the curriculum, for example, standardized tests.

Formative Assessments Assessments that provide information about students' current knowledge and abilities so that teachers can plan future instruction more effectively and so that students can identify their own areas of weakness or strength.

Grade-Level Goals Mathematical goals organized by content strand and articulated across grade levels from Pre-Kindergarten through Grade 6.

Individual Profile of Progress A recording tool that can be used to keep track of student progress on specific Grade-Level Goals.

Informing Instruction These notes in the *Teacher's Lesson Guide* suggest how to use observations of students' work to adapt instruction by describing common errors and misconceptions in students' thinking and alerting the teacher to multiple solution strategies or unique insights students might offer.

Making Adequate Progress On a trajectory to meet a Grade-Level Goal.

Math Boxes Collections of problems designed to provide distributed practice. Math Boxes revisit content from prior units to build and maintain important concepts and skills. One or two problems on each page preview content from the next unit.

Mental Math and Reflexes Exercises at three levels of difficulty that prepare students for the lesson, build mental-arithmetic skills, and help teachers quickly assess individual strengths and weaknesses.

Observational Assessments Assessments based on observing students during daily activities or periodic assessments.

Ongoing Assessments Assessments based on students' everyday work during regular classroom instruction.

Open Response An extended response assessment included in the Progress Check lesson of each unit.

Periodic Assessments Formal assessments that are built into a curriculum such as the end-of-unit Progress Checks.

Portfolios Collections of student products and observations that provide opportunities for students to reflect on their mathematical growth and for teachers to understand and document that growth.

Product Assessments Assessments based on student work from daily activities or from periodic assessments.

Program Evaluation Assessment intended to reveal how well a program of instruction is working. A school district, for example, might carry out program evaluation to identify schools with strong mathematics programs so that their success can be replicated.

Program Goals The fifteen cross-grade goals in *Everyday Mathematics* that weave the program together across grade levels. They form an organizing framework that supports both curriculum and assessment. Every Grade-Level Goal is linked to a Program Goal.

Progress Check The last lesson in every unit. Progress Check lessons include a student Self Assessment, an Oral and Slate Assessment, a Written Assessment, and an Open Response task.

Purposes for Assessment The reasons for assessment, which include providing information that can be used to plan future instruction, identifying what students have achieved during a period of time, and evaluating the quality of the mathematics program.

Readiness Activities Optional activities in many lessons that preview lesson content or provide alternative routes of access for learning concepts and skills.

Recognizing Student Achievement A feature in many lessons that highlights specific tasks used to monitor students' progress toward Grade-Level Goals. The notes identify the expectations for a student who is making adequate progress and point to skills or strategies that some students might be able to demonstrate.

Rubric A set of suggested guidelines for scoring assessment activities.

Student Self Assessment The individual reflection included in the Progress Check lesson of each unit.

Summative Assessments Assessments that aim to measure student growth and achievement, for example, an assessment to determine whether students have learned certain material by the end of a fixed period of study such as a semester or a course.

Writing/Reasoning Prompt A question linked to a specific Math Boxes problem. Writing/Reasoning Prompts provide students with opportunities to respond to questions that extend and deepen their mathematical thinking.

Written Progress Check The Written Assessment included in the Progress Check lesson of each unit.

Index

Making adequate progress
    based on a rubric, 27
    definition of, 27, 32–33
    in Recognizing Student Achievement notes, 10–14, 27,
        32–33
    in Written Assessments, 19
Math Boxes, 4, 8, 10, 12, 15, 24, 33
Math Logs, 15, 17, 278–280
Mental Math and Reflexes, 4, 8, 10–11, 20
Mid-Year Assessment Answers, 221–222
Mid-Year Assessment Goals, 93
Mid-Year Assessment masters, 203–210
Mid-Year written assessment, 4, 18, 23, 28

Observations, 4, 8, 18, 26, 28
Ongoing Assessment, 3–4, 8–14, 25–26, 28
    by unit, Unit 1: 52–53, Unit 2: 60–61, Unit 3: 68–69,
        Unit 4: 76–77, Unit 5: 84–85, Unit 6: 94–95,
        Unit 7: 102–103, Unit 8: 110–111,
        Unit 9: 118–119, Unit 10: 126–127
Open Response tasks, 4, 18, 21–22, 24, 28
    assessment masters, 143, 149, 155, 160, 165, 170,
        175, 181, 187, 192
    by unit, Unit 1: 55–59, Unit 2: 63–67, Unit 3: 71–75,
        Unit 4: 79–83, Unit 5: 87–91, Unit 6: 97–101,
        Unit 7: 105–109, Unit 8: 113–117,
        Unit 9: 121–125, Unit 10: 129–133
Oral and Slate Assessments, 20
Outside tests, 24

Parent Reflections, 17, 284
Performance-based assessments, 24, 32–33
Periodic Assessment, 3–4, 18–23, 25–26
    by unit, Unit 1: 54–59, Unit 2: 62–67, Unit 3: 70–75,
        Unit 4: 78–83, Unit 5: 86–91, Unit 6: 96–101,
        Unit 7: 104–109, Unit 8: 112–117,
        Unit 9: 120–125, Unit 10: 128–133
Planning tips, 7
Portfolios, 4, 8, 15, 16–17, 26
Product Assessment, 16–17, 26
Products 4, 8, 18
Program Evaluation, 2
Program Goals, 5–6, 28, 32, 37–50
    definition of, 5–6
    table list, 37–50
        Data and Chance, 5, 44–45
        Geometry, 5, 48
        Measurement and Reference Frames, 5, 46–47
        Number and Numeration, 5, 37–39
        Operations and Computation, 5, 40–43
        Patterns, Functions, and Algebra, 5, 49–50
    track progress toward, 32
Progress Check Oral/Slate Assessments, 4, 18, 20, 28
Progress Check Written Assessments, 4, 18, 19, 20, 28,
    138–192, 193–202
Purposes of Assessment, 2

Readiness activities, 12–14, 21
Recognizing Student Achievement notes, 4, 8, 10–14,
    25–28, 32–34
Record Keeping, 25–27, 28, 34
    Assessment Management Spreadsheets, 28–29
    options for recording data on checklists, 27
Rubrics, 22–23, 27, 29

Self Assessment masters, 21, 138, 144, 150, 156, 161, 166,
    171, 176, 182, 188
Student Self Assessment, 4, 21
Sources of Evidence for Assessment, 4
Summative Assessment, 2, 7, 19–20

Written Assessments, 4, 8, 19–20
    masters, Unit 1: 139–142, Unit 2: 145–148,
        Unit 3: 151–154, Unit 4: 157–159,
        Unit 5: 162–164, Unit 6: 167–169,
        Unit 7: 172–174, Unit 8: 177–180,
        Unit 9: 183–186, Unit 10: 189–191
Writing/Reasoning Prompts for Math Boxes, 4, 8, 15